IMMUNOCHEMISTRY
IN PRACTICE

IMMUNOCHEMISTRY IN PRACTICE

ALAN JOHNSTONE

BSc DPhil
Department of Immunology
St George's Hospital Medical School
London SW17 0RE

ROBIN THORPE

BSc PhD
National Institute for Biological
Standards and Control
Hertford EN6 3QG

SECOND EDITION

BLACKWELL SCIENTIFIC PUBLICATIONS

OXFORD LONDON EDINBURGH

BOSTON PALO ALTO MELBOURNE

© 1982, 1987 by
Blackwell Scientific Publications
Editorial offices:
Osney Mead, Oxford OX2 0EL
(Orders: Tel. 0865 240201)
8 John Street, London WC1N 2ES
23 Ainslie Place, Edinburgh EH3 6AJ
3 Cambridge Centre, Suite 208,
  Cambridge, Massachusetts 02142,
  USA
667 Lytton Avenue, Palo Alto
  California 94301, USA
107 Barry Street, Carlton
  Victoria 3053, Australia

First published 1982
Reprinted 1985
Second edition 1987
Reprinted 1988

Set by Oxford Computer Typesetting
Printed and bound in Great Britain by
Richard Clay Ltd, Chichester, Sussex

DISTRIBUTORS

USA
  Year Book Medical Publishers
  200 North LaSalle Street, Chicago,
  Illinois 60601
  (Orders: Tel. 312 726–9733)

Canada
  The C.V. Mosby Company
  5240 Finch Avenue East,
  Scarborough, Ontario
  (Orders: Tel. 416–298–1588)

Australia
  Blackwell Scientific Publications
  (Australia) Pty Ltd
  107 Barry Street,
  Carlton, Victoria 3053
  (Orders: Tel. (03) 347 0300)

British Library
Cataloguing in Publication Data

Johnstone, Alan
  Immunochemistry in practice.—2nd ed.
  1. Immunochemistry
  I. Title   II. Thorpe, Robin
  574.2'9   QR183.6

  ISBN 0-632-01723-6

Contents

v

3 Purification of immunoglobulins, constituent chains and fragments 48

4 Isolation and fractionation of lymphocytes 86

ix

Foreword

Immunology has been important in medicine since Jenner introduced his technique of vaccination to prevent smallpox infection nearly 200 years ago. It is only in recent years, however, that greatly increased understanding of the complex reactions responsible for immunity has given the opportunity to exploit these phenomena, both for the study of immune reactions themselves and also for the investigation of many other problems in biology.

The major feature of immune reactions is their specificity, and antibodies are reagents which can be prepared at will with specificities directed to almost any chemical grouping whether it be in a protein, carbohydrate, nucleic acid or a simpler organic compound. The introduction of monoclonal antibodies produced by fusion of antibody forming cells and transformed cells has made available entirely specific reagents against an apparently infinite range of substances. The application of these reagents to detect, estimate and isolate different molecules in complex biological fluids or on cell surfaces is revolutionizing much biological research. Monoclonal antibodies are becoming major diagnostic reagents and may soon find applications in therapy.

To exploit fully the specific reactions of these substances many techniques have to be mastered. They are often exacting and a thorough understanding is necessary for their effective use. In this book an excellent account is given of these diverse methods and I have no doubt that it will be most valuable for the rapidly increasing number of scientists from different fields who are taking up immunochemical techniques.

R. R. Porter

Preface

TO FIRST EDITION

Rapid progress in recent years has made many scientists increasingly aware of the potential role for immunology in many areas of research. Unfortunately the same progress has tended to widen the psychological gulf between immunology and other biological sciences, all of which would benefit from a freer interchange of experimental expertise. This book seeks to bridge that gulf by describing the preparation, characterization and application of immunoglobulins and antibodies, together with several' analytical and preparative biochemical techniques.

Each procedure is described in detail for one pertinent application (as an illustrative example for research or practical classes), followed by comprehensive explanatory notes including modifications necessary for wider use. A basic knowledge of laboratory practice and a supply of routine laboratory apparatus and chemicals is assumed but beyond this full details are included in the description. The emphasis throughout is on practical aspects but sufficient theory is given to understand the principles of the techniques. A set of references is provided for wider theoretical discussion.

TO SECOND EDITION

Immunochemistry has advanced considerably during the five years since we wrote the first edition. This has been very good for the progress of basic science in the many diverse fields that use immunochemical techniques and also for applied uses in the biotechnology industry. However, the changes have been bad for a couple of lazy authors who thought that their first edition would serve for many years. We have revised and updated all the chapters with advances in handling and applying monoclonal antibodies at the forefront of the changes.

One of the saddest events of the last five years has been the death of Rodney Porter in September 1985. He carried out a large proportion of the basic research on which much of today's applied immunochemistry is based, but, more than that, he inspired many scientists by his incisiveness, integrity and humour combined with a brusque straightforwardness. After dedicating our first edition to one of his students, we would like to dedicate the second to him with many many thanks.

Acknowledgements

TO FIRST EDITION

This book was conceived with a great deal of support from Leslie Hudson. We are grateful to him for his continuing advice and encouragement throughout its progress towards birth.

We wish to thank the numerous colleagues who helped to shape the book with their discussion, advice on methodology or illustrations, in particular: Hansha Bhayani, Maryvonne Brasher, Caroline Bullock, Annette Ford, Jens Jensenius, Alison Mackay, Philip Minor, Sue Peach, Moises Spitz, Alan Williams, Gwyn Williams and John Wood. We are especially grateful to Professor Porter for writing the Foreword.

The completion of the work was due in large part to our wives, Caroline and Sue, who provided mental support and practical help (scientific and editorial) throughout.

Our thanks are also due to Kay Dorelli who completed the arduous task of preparing the typescript in record time.

TO SECOND EDITION

In addition to our colleagues who helped with the preparation of the first edition, we would like to thank all those who contributed to the revision by giving advice on methodology or illustrations, in particular: Chris Bird, Marion Callus, David Darling, Caroline Edmonds, Andy Gearing, Roy Harris, Jan Hawthorn, Leslie Hudson, Susan King, Ruth McNerney, John Murphy, Varsha Patel, Phil Robinson, Edith Sim, Lynne Trickett, Guy Whitley and David Winterbourne. In addition, we are grateful for the encouragement of many reviewers of the first edition and numerous scientists around the world who troubled to write or telephone with helpful comments and suggestions.

Like the first edition, this revision was greatly aided by our wives, Caroline and Sue, who have stayed with us for another five years and provided much editorial and scientific help. Thanks are also due to Elinor Johnstone who, at the age of $3\frac{1}{2}$, has nearly learnt to sleep through the night!

1 Basic techniques

This chapter describes briefly some basic methods central to immunochemistry. They are referred to throughout the book. Some relevant immunological techniques are presented in Chapter 2.

1.1 DETECTION AND MEASUREMENT OF PROTEINS

The simplest method for measuring the concentration of protein in solution is by its absorption of ultra-violet (UV) light (Section 1.1.1). If the protein is pure its absolute concentration can be calculated from the value obtained. If the protein is not pure (e.g. in the eluant from column chromatography) the absorbance will give an approximate estimate of the total protein concentration. The method cannot be used at low protein concentrations (below about 0.05–0.1 mg/ml), in the presence of many substances which also absorb in the UV range (e.g. some buffers, nucleic acids and some lipids) or if the protein is in suspension, not solution (e.g. in membranes or large complexes). Colourimetric methods are more complicated and the samples taken are not recoverable (Section 1.1.2). However, they are usually more sensitive and the solutions used solubilize most proteins.

1.1.1 Ultra-violet absorption

Proteins absorb UV light with a maximum at approximately 280 nm, caused by tryptophan, tyrosine and (to a lesser extent) phenylalanine residues, and at lower wavelengths (215–230 nm) because of the polypeptide chain backbone. Absorbance at 280 nm varies for each protein, but the recorded extinction coefficients (i.e. the absorbance of a 1% solution of the protein in a 1 cm light path) for individual proteins (Table 1.1) allow the concentration of a pure protein to be calculated. The absorbance at lower wavelengths is directly related to the weight of polypeptide material and is usually considerably more sensitive than at 280 nm. However, many buffers and other molecules also absorb at these lower wavelengths (phosphate and tris buffers are acceptable but the preservative sodium azide absorbs strongly). Absorbance at 215 or 230 nm is useful for monitoring peptides that may not contain tryptophan or tyrosine.

Materials and equipment

Protein solution to be measured

1

Table 1.1 Extinction coefficients of immunochemically relevant proteins. The values for $E_{280}^{1\%}$ (i.e. the absorbance of a 10 mg/ml solution at 280 nm) are averages of the heterogeneous proteins

	IgG	13.6
	IgM	11.8
	IgA	13.2
secretory	IgA	13.1
	IgD	17.0
	IgE	15.3
	γ chain	13.7
	μ chain	13.9
	α chain	15.5
	light chain	12.3
	J chain	6.8
secretory	component	12.7
	Fab	15.0
	Fc	12.0
	Fd	16.0
	V_H	27.0
	Concanavalin A	12.0
	Lens culinaris lectin	12.5
	Bovine serum albumin	6.7

Values for other proteins are listed in Fasman (1976).

Buffer in which the protein is dissolved
UV spectrophotometer
Quartz cells — 1 cm light path

Procedure

1 If necessary, centrifuge the sample to remove any particles or complexes in suspension.
2 Set the wavelength of the spectrophotometer to 280 nm and zero the absorbance with the buffer in one cell.
3 Read the absorbance of the sample either in the same cell or its matched twin. If the value obtained is greater than 2.0 dilute an aliquot of the sample (e.g. 1/5 or 1/10) or use shorter light path cells (e.g. 2 mm) until the reading falls between 0.1 and 1.5.
4 Repeat steps 2 and 3 at 260 nm.
5 Calculate the ratio of absorbance 260:280 nm. This should be below 0.6; high ratios indicate that the protein is contaminated with interfering substances, notably nucleic acids.

$$\frac{\text{concentration}}{\text{of sample}} = \frac{\text{absorbance at 280 nm}}{\text{extinction coefficient at 280 nm}} \times 10 \text{ mg/ml}$$

6 For mixtures of proteins or for any protein with unknown extinction coefficient:

$$\text{protein concentration} = 1.55 \times \text{absorbance at 280 nm} - 0.77 \times \text{absorbance at 260 nm}$$

Remember to calculate the absorbance for the *original* solution in a 1 cm light path if it was diluted or measured in thinner cells.

1.1.2 Folin phenol method (modified from Lowry *et al.*, 1951)

This method is used widely when UV absorbance cannot be measured (see above). Several substances interfere with this assay and so a buffer blank should always be included. Non-ionic detergents form precipitates but the supernatant will usually give a valid result (see also note 3 and Section 1.1.3). Many modifications exist for circumventing these problems (Peterson, 1979).

Materials and equipment

Protein solution to be measured
Buffer in which the protein is dissolved
Any standard protein with known extinction coefficient (see step 1 below)
2% (w/v) copper sulphate, hydrated ($5H_2O$)
4% (w/v) sodium potassium tartrate
3% (w/v) sodium carbonate in 0.2 M sodium hydroxide
Folin and Ciocalteu's phenol reagent (BDH — Appendix 3)
Visible light spectrophotometer

Procedure

1 Make a 1 mg/ml solution of the standard protein and calculate the exact concentration from its absorbance at 280 nm (Section 1.1.1).
2 Pipette an aliquot of the unknown solution containing 5–50 μg of protein, the same volume of the buffer blank, and 0, 2, 5, 10, 20, 35, and 50 μl of the standard solution (the zero tube is the water blank) into separate tubes.
3 Add water to bring the contents of each tube to the same volume (ideally less than 200 μl but the assay will cope with up to 1 ml).
4 Mix 1 ml of copper sulphate solution and 1 ml of tartrate solution with 48 ml of carbonate solution (this mixture should be freshly prepared). Add 1 ml of this to each tube, mix and incubate for 10 min at room temperature.
5 Add 50 μl of phenol reagent to each tube, mix again and incubate for 25 min.
6 Mix again and 5 min later read the absorbance of each tube at 640 nm using the water blank to zero the spectrophotometer.
7 Plot the absorbance against protein content for the standard solution (this is not quite linear) and from this read off the amount of protein in the unknown. Subtract any absorbance of the buffer blank and calculate the protein concentration in the original solution from the volume taken for assay in step 2.

3

1   The standard protein should be structurally similar to that in the unknown solution if possible, because proteins vary somewhat in their colour yield. The standard solution can be aliquoted and stored frozen.

2   The lower limits of detection are about 2 μg in 200 μl and 5 μg in 1 ml; 50 μg in 200 μl has an absorbance of approximately 0.4.

3   Pierce (Appendix 3) have introduced an alternative reagent to Folin-Ciocalteu for detecting the Cu^+ produced by the protein — bicinchonic acid (BCA). This reagent is more stable and does not form precipitates with detergents (see above); the assay is simpler and is claimed to be more sensitive with a broader working range.

1.1.3   Dye-binding assays

Bradford (1976) introduced a protein assay based on the shift in absorbance maximum of Coomassie Brilliant Blue G, from 465 to 595 nm, when it binds to protein. It is simpler and less susceptible to interference by many substances than the Folin phenol method but it does not solubilize filamentous or membrane proteins as well.

The reagent is available commercially (Bio-Rad, Pierce — Appendix 3). Alternatively, dissolve 100 mg Coomassie Brilliant Blue G-250 in 50 ml 95% ethanol. Add 100 ml 85% (w/v) phosphoric acid, make up to 1 litre with water and filter through Whatman no. 1 paper (the reagent can be kept for a few weeks, re-filtering if a precipitate forms, but should be discarded after this time; the dye/ethanol stock keeps for years). Add 5 ml of the reagent to 100 μl of test solution (containing 10–100 μg protein), mix, leave for 5 min and read the absorbance at 595 nm. For a more sensitive assay make up the reagent to 200 ml instead of 1 litre and add 0.2–0.8 ml of test solution (containing 1–20 μg protein).

In common with most assays the colour yield varies somewhat between different proteins (see Section 1.1.2, note 1).

An alternative dye-binding assay has been developed recently (Winterbourne, 1986). This measures the amount of dye that binds to protein dried onto filter paper. It is more sensitive than the Bradford or Folin phenol, does not require protein to be in solution and is more specific for protein since small interfering molecules, e.g. peptides, are removed during the washing steps.

Materials and equipment

Protein solution or suspension to be measured
Standard protein (see Section 1.1.2, note 1)
0.4 g Coomassie Brilliant Blue R dissolved in 250 ml ethanol and 630 ml water
Glacial acetic acid

Destain solution: 10% (v/v) ethanol, 5% (v/v) acetic acid
Desorbing solution: 1M potassium acetate in 70% (v/v) ethanol
Whatman 3MM paper
Test tubes to hold 2 ml
Orbital shaker (Luckham — Appendix 3)
Visible light spectrophotometer

Procedure

1   Make a 1 mg/ml solution of the standard protein and calculate the exact concentration from its absorbance at 280 nm (Section 1.1.1).
2   Mark a grid of 1 cm squares in pencil on the paper.
3   In separate squares spot 1, 2, 5 and 8 μl of the standard and up to 8 μl of the test protein solutions. Allow to dry.
4   Mix 6 ml of acetic acid with 44 ml of Coomassie solution and filter. Immerse the paper in the mixture and agitate gently for 1 h.
5   Transfer the paper to destain solution, agitate gently for a few minutes, discard the liquid and repeat until a clear background is obtained (about three times).
6   Dry the paper at room temperature or in an oven.
7   Cut out the squares (including one with no protein) and place in separate test tubes. Add 1 ml of desorbing solution to each, mix, leave for 1 h and read the absorbance of the liquid at 590 nm.
8   Plot the absorbance against protein content for the standard and from this read off the amount of protein in the test solution.

1.2   PROTEIN FRACTIONATION

Two widely used fractionation techniques are described in this section — gel filtration and ion exchange chromatography. Other procedures are considered later (Chapters 7, 9 and 10).

1.2.1   Gel filtration

This is the procedure used most frequently in fractionating proteins. It consists of application of a protein mixture to a column of small beads with pores of carefully controlled size. Large proteins, above the 'exclusion limit' of the gel, cannot enter the pores and so are eluted from the column in the 'void volume' (i.e. the volume of the liquid between the beads; usually this is about 1/3 of the total column volume). Very small molecules enter the pores of the beads fully and so have to pass through the total volume of the column before being eluted. Intermediate size proteins partially enter the pores and so are eluted between the void and total volumes in positions logarithmically related to their molecular weight, with some modifications introduced by deviations from a 'normal' globular shape.

5

Choice of gel. The beads can be carbohydrate or polyacrylamide and are available in a wide variety of pore sizes and hence fractionation ranges (Fig. 1.1). Their method of use is similar, but consult the manufacturer's literature for special considerations.

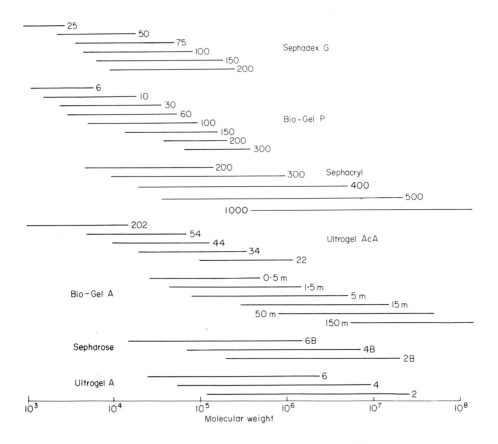

Fig. 1.1 Fractionation ranges of various gel filtration media taken from the manufacturer's literature. The bars indicate the range for which $\log_{10}$ molecular weight is linearly related to elution position (not for superfine grade of Sephadex); the gels are also useful outside these ranges for at least a factor of 2 from each end. Bio-Gel is manufactured by Bio-Rad; Sephadex, Sephacryl and Sepharose by Pharmacia; Ultrogel by LKB (Appendix 3). Sephadex is made from dextran (consisting mainly of glucose); Bio-Gel P from polyacrylamide; Sephacryl from cross-linked dextran; Ultrogel AcA from a mixture of polyacrylamide and agarose; Bio-Gel A, Sepharose and Ultrogel A from agarose (consisting mainly of galactose).

Choice of column. The column used should be of controlled diameter glass (e.g. precision bore tubing, Jencons — Appendix 3) with as low a dead space as possible at the bottom (outflow). Providing these points are considered, home-made columns are perfectly satisfactory except for upward flow applications (see below). Commercial columns are available from several manufacturers (Bio-Rad, LKB, Pharmacia,

Whatman — Appendix 3). The tubing connected to the column should be narrow (about 1 mm i.d.) to reduce dead space volume; this is not so important for the top (inflow) connection.

The most useful length of column for gel filtration is 90–100 cm (longer ones or two joined in tandem can be used for greater resolution). The choice of cross-sectional area is governed by the size of sample — both volume and amount of protein. The sample volume should not exceed 5% of the total column volume except for desalting (see below, note 7), and resolution is better with less, down to 1–2%. In general 10–30 mg of protein per cm^2 cross-sectional area is a good loading (equivalent to 10–30 mg of protein per 100 ml of gel for a 100 cm column). More protein will increase the yield but decrease the resolution and hence purity of the product, while lower loading will improve the resolution at the expense of yield.

Cross sectional area $= \pi \, (d/2)^2$
Column volume $= \pi \, (d/2)^2 h$

where d is the internal diameter and h is the length of column.

Packing the column. Ideally an extension reservoir should be attached directly to the top of the column so that the total volume of gel and buffer can be poured in one and allowed to settle. However, with care a column can be packed perfectly well by topping up the gel slurry repeatedly as it settles.

1 If the filtration medium is not supplied swollen, equilibrate the amount required to fill the column plus 10% with twice the column volume of the buffer (see manufacturer's literature for volume of swollen gel per unit of dry weight and minimum swelling times).
2 Degas the slurry in a Buchner side-arm flask under vacuum (a water pump with a non-return valve is sufficient) for 1–2 h with periodic swirling. Do not use a magnetic stirrer because this may break the beads.
3 Suspend the gel in about five times its volume of buffer and allow to stand. When the majority of the beads have settled, remove fines (i.e. small particles of beads or other debris) by aspirating the supernatant down to 1.5 × settled gel volume.
4 Clean the column with a weak solution of detergent and rinse with water. Clamp the column *vertically* (scaffolding attached to a wall is best) in an area free from draughts, direct sunlight, heaters and vibration.
5 Close the bottom outlet of the column and fill to 10–20 cm height with buffer. Swirl the gel slurry to resuspend it evenly and pour it down a glass rod onto the inside wall to fill the column (or column and reservoir). Allow to settle under gravity for 0.5–1 h to let air bubbles escape.
6 Adjust the height of the outlet end of the tube so that the vertical distance between it and the top of the reservoir or column is less than

7

the maximum operating pressure for the gel (see manufacturer's literature). Unclamp the bottom of the column and allow the gel to pack under this pressure.

7 (a) If an extension reservoir is used, leave the column to pack until the bed just runs dry. Then remove excess gel.

(b) If an extension reservoir is not used, top up the column periodically by syphoning off some excess supernatant, stirring the top of the gel if it has settled completely and then filling the column up to the top with resuspended slurry as in step 5.

8 When the column is packed (gel bed just runs dry) connect the top of the column to a buffer reservoir, remove air bubbles along this length of the tube and allow one column volume of buffer to run through the column. It can be eluted either by the pressure from the reservoir (the operating pressure is the vertical distance between the top of the buffer in the reservoir and the outlet end of the tube; this should never exceed the manufacturer's recommended maximum for the gel), or by a peristaltic pump between the reservoir and top of the column. As a general rule, the flow rate should be the volume contained in 2–4 cm height of column per hour (equivalent to one column volume in 1–3 days for a 90–100 cm long column). Some gels (e.g. Ultrogel and Sephacryl; Fig. 1.1) are designed for more rapid elution without damage to the bed (see manufacturer's literature) but the resolution invariably suffers.

Sample application. If a commercial column is used with flow adaptors touching the top of the gel bed, the sample is most conveniently applied by transferring the inlet tube from the buffer reservoir to the sample, allowing it to enter the tube and gel under operating pressure and then returning the tube to the buffer reservoir. Take care not to introduce air bubbles when the tube is transferred.

For home-made columns without flow adaptors, remove the top of the column (remember to adjust the height of the outlet end of the tube to compensate for the effective height being transferred from the top of the buffer in the reservoir to the top of the column). Either make the sample 5% in sucrose and layer it under the buffer directly to the top of the gel bed or allow the gel to just run dry and apply the sample directly to the top of the gel bed. The sample should be applied carefully by allowing it to run slowly down the inside wall of the column so that the gel bed is not disturbed. When the sample has entered the bed, carefully overlay the gel with buffer and reconnect the top of the column to the buffer reservoir. Check that this disturbance does not allow the gel to run dry during the next few hours of column elution.

Sample elution. For most gels, the maximum flow rate is governed by the operating pressure which the gel can withstand and by the resolution required (see manufacturer's literature and step 8 above). A wide range of fraction collectors are commercially available (Gilson, Isco,

LKB, Pharmacia — Appendix 3). Fractions should be collected by measured volume (or counted drops) rather than time to prevent fluctuations in flow rate from altering fraction size. As a general rule, a column volume of eluant from a 90–100 cm long column should be collected in about 100 fractions; the void volume is then eluted at fraction 30–35.

The eluant is usually monitored for its absorbance at 280 nm (proteins) or 215–230 nm (peptides; Section 1.1.1). This can be carried out by reading each collected fraction manually in a spectrophotometer or, more conveniently, by passing the eluant directly through the flow cell of a UV absorbance monitor (Isco, LKB, Pharmacia — Appendix 3). These monitors record transmission (inversely related logarithmically to absorbance) or absorbance at various wavelengths. The older monitors have a fixed wavelength of 254 nm and these detect proteins adequately. In addition radiolabelled proteins or peptides can be detected by taking an aliquot of each fraction for radioactivity measurement (Section 1.4).

Notes

1   The yield of protein should always be greater than 80% and is frequently 90–95%. New gel tends to adsorb protein non-specifically in a saturable fashion, and so the yield improves after the first use (for fractionation of very small amounts of protein the column should be saturated with albumin before use (e.g. Section 5.2.1).
2   Labile proteins can be fractioned at 4°C. Pack the column at room temperature and then transfer it to a cold room and allow it to equilibrate at the lower temperature before applying the sample. Transferring a column from cold to warmer temperatures usually causes bubbles to form and the column must then be repacked.
3   The columns (or swollen gel in a bottle) can be stored at room temperature or lower (do not freeze) in the presence of a bacteriostatic agent (0.02% sodium azide or 0.01% thimerosal). It is advisable to incorporate such an agent in the normal running buffer when columns are used for long periods. Azide interferes with UV absorbance measurements at 230 nm and lower (Section 1.1.1). It also forms potentially explosive lead and copper azide in some plumbing pipes; flush with running water when discarding.
4   For molecular weight determination the column can be calibrated by applying a mixture of standard proteins and noting their elution positions under standard conditions. The large carbohydrate polymer Blue Dextran (Pharmacia — Appendix 3), will mark the void volume of all gel filtration columns.
5   Gel filtration can be performed in a wide variety of buffers. While the majority of separations are carried out in neutral 'physiological' buffers, denaturing conditions are sometimes necessary to separate non-covalently associated polypeptide chains (e.g. Section 3.4.1) or to denature especially elongated proteins for determination of molecular

weight. The separation gels can withstand quite harsh conditions and some are especially strengthened for this purpose (see manufacturer's literature). However, viscous buffers (e.g. guanidine-HCl) reduce the flow rate and tend to cause the gel to compress when the operating pressure is increased. Very harsh denaturing solvents (e.g. 50% formic acid) should be washed out of the column when it is not in use.

6   Commercial columns with flow adaptors can be turned upside down so that the sample and buffer are eluted from bottom to top; all other arrangements (buffer reservoir, outlet, etc.) remain the same. This usually decreases zone broadening and allows a faster flow rate for a given operating pressure because gravity helps decrease the packing of the gel.

7   Gel filtration on small pore gels (e.g. Sephadex G-25, G-50 or other manufacturer's equivalent; Fig. 1.1) can be used to separate proteins from salt, solvent and other small molecules as a quick alternative to dialysis (Section 1.3). It is usually termed desalting. Because the separation is good, much larger sample volumes can be applied (up to 30% of column volume), the overall dilution of sample is small and shorter columns can be used (usually about 30 cm) — see Sections 3.4.1, 5.2.1 and 12.2.3 for examples.

8   To prevent a column without a pump from running dry whilst unattended, arrange the inlet tube so that part of it is below the outlet point of the column.

1.2.2   Ion exchange chromatography

Proteins are bound reversibly to ion exchangers by ionic interactions between oppositely charged groups. The proteins can then be eluted separately by gradually increasing the ionic strength of the buffer, which competitively disrupts the ionic interactions, or by changing the pH so that the interacting groups on the *protein* lose their charge (Fig. 1.2). The pH range is selected to maintain the charge on the *ion exchanger* throughout the procedure otherwise all the bound proteins will be eluted together.

Choice of ion exchanger. Various charged groups on insoluble supports are commercially available and widely used. They are listed together with their usable pH ranges in Table 1.2. Positively charged resins are termed 'anion exchangers' (because they bind and exchange anions); negatively charged resins are termed 'cation exchangers'.

Proteins are amphoteric and their net charge is variable: positive at low pH, negative at high pH and zero at their pI. The interacting charged groups on proteins are mainly carboxyl ($-COOH \rightleftharpoons -COO^- + H^+$) on the one hand and amino or tertiary amino ($-NR_2 + H^+ \rightleftharpoons -NR_2H^+$) on the other. Thus an anion exchanger binds proteins through their unprotonated carboxyl groups and is repelled by their protonated amino groups, and vice versa for a cation exchanger.

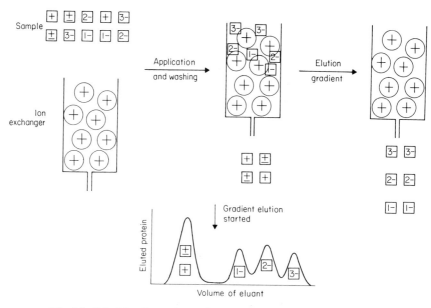

Fig. 1.2 Principle of ion exchange chromatography. The diagram shows the fractionation of variously charged molecules (squares) on an anion exchanger (circles). Positive, uncharged and weakly negative molecules are not bound to the exchanger and elute in the first unretarded peak. More highly charged negative molecules bind to the exchanger and can then be eluted separately (Section 1.2.2): the buffer counter ions have been omitted for clarity but they will bind to all otherwise free charges on both the ion exchanger and sample molecules. For cation exchangers all of the charges are reversed.

Table 1.2   Common ion exchangers

Ionic group	Nominal pH range	Available supports
Anion exchangers		
weak : diethylaminoethyl (DEAE)	2–9	dextran[2] agarose[1,2] beaded cellulose[2] fibrous cellulose[1,3] microgranular cellulose[3]
strong : quaternary amino-ethyl (QAE)	2–10	dextran[2] fibrous cellulose[1]
Cation exchangers		
weak : carboxymethyl (CM)	3–10[a]	dextran[2] agarose[1,2] fibrous cellulose[3]
strong : sulphoethyl (or propyl)	2–12[a]	dextran[2] microgranular cellulose[3]

Manufacturers (Appendix 3): ([1]) Bio-Rad; ([2]) Pharmacia; ([3]) Whatman.
([a]) Pharmacia recommend narrower pH ranges for the dextran and agarose exchangers: 6–10 for carboxymethyl and 2–10 for sulphopropyl.

11

As a general guide, proteins which differ in the total number of aspartic and glutamic residues should be separable by anion exchange while those that differ in their lysine, arginine and histidine content should be separable by cation exchange. This is however not a hard and fast rule because of many other factors which influence the binding. The strength of binding is related both to the protein's pI, and to the total number of charges. Hence, although two proteins with identical pI cannot be separated by equilibrium isoelectric focusing (Sections 7.5 and 9.2.2), they may be separable by ion exchange chromatography using a pH at which they contain significantly different numbers of charged residues per molecule.

Before attempting a novel separation of proteins it is worth electrophoresing them on polyacrylamide gels under both acid and alkaline conditions (Section 7.4). These separations serve roughly as analytical versions of cation and anion exchange chromatography respectively. For example, if a good analytical separation of a mixture is obtained by alkaline electrophoresis then it can probably be separated preparatively by an anion exchanger at a similar pH.

Choice of insoluble support. A variety of insoluble supports for the selected exchange group are available (Table 1.2). These are basically the classical cellulose support and the various beads used for gel filtration (Fig. 1.1).

Cellulose is still favoured overall for protein fractionation although the gel filtration beads are claimed to have a lower non-specific adsorption and are more frequently used for peptide fractionation, especially of small amounts. Some supports, notably Sephadex G-50 derivatives, change their volume alarmingly with changes in ionic strength. The newer physical forms of cellulose, microgranular and beaded (Whatman, Pharmacia — Appendix 3), are claimed to be more reproducible and to have a higher capacity and resolving potential than the older fibrous forms (Whatman, Bio-Rad — Appendix 3). Except when dealing with the most labile of proteins, manufacturer's claims of advantages of high column flow rates are not important because the vast majority of fractionations can be accomplished within 24 h.

A further consideration is the number of charged groups which are present in a unit volume of support (compare manufacturer's values) and which are available to the protein (e.g. Sephadex G-25 derivatives exclude proteins above 5000–10 000 molecular weight from a significant proportion of their charged groups whereas most of the charges on agarose and cellulose derivatives are accessible even to large proteins). This governs the capacity of the column and so will determine the expense, the dilution of sample and loss of protein through non-specific adsorption for a given fractionation. From the manufacturer's literature, the available capacity for protein is very similar (0.11–0.15 g albumin/ml of DEAE derivative) for microgranular cellulose, beaded cellulose and agarose (Whatman, Pharmacia — Appendix 3).

12

Non-specific adsorption to the support is saturable (Section 1.2.1, note 1) and less protein is lost on ion exchangers that have been used and recycled several times.

Preparation of ion exchanger. Some ion exchangers are sold pre-swollen and ready to use. The remainder should be regenerated before use and all exchangers need to be regenerated after each use. The procedure below is a general guide for cellulose exchangers — see manufacturer's literature for specific recommendations. Sephadex and Sepharose derivatives should only be exposed to 0.1 M acid or base.
1   Gently stir the ion exchanger into about 5 × its swollen volume of 0.5 M HCl (anion exchanger) or 0.5 M NaOH (cation exchanger). Leave for 30 min at room temperature with occasional swirling.
2   Filter out the resin by suction through a sintered funnel (porosity 3 or 4) or Whatman no. 54 paper. Wash the resin cake with distilled water until the pH of the filtrate is more than 4 (after acid) or less than 8 (after base).
3   Gently stir the ion exchanger into 5 × its swollen volume of 0.5 M NaOH (anion exchanger) or 0.5 M HCl (cation exchanger). Leave for 30 min at room temperature with occasional swirling.
4   Filter and wash with water as in step 2.
The exchangers have now been washed free of residual protein, and protons or hydroxyl ions left bound weakly to the charged groups of cation or anion exchangers, respectively. These can be displaced easily by the counter ions of the selected buffer when required.

Choice of buffer. The pH should be within the operational range of the ion exchanger (Table 1.2) and also not damaging to the protein. For a protein to bind to the exchanger the pH should be at least half and preferably one unit away from its pI (above it for anion exchangers, below it for cation exchangers). A pH too far from the protein's pI will induce excessively strong binding with consequent risks of denaturation and low recoveries.

A reasonable ionic strength for the application buffer is 0.01–0.05.

Ionic strength $(I) = \frac{1}{2}.\Sigma\ c_i.z_i^2$

where c_i is the molar concentration of each ion and z_i is the charge of each ion.
For simple monovalent fully ionized salts the ionic strength is equal to the molar concentration:

e.g. for 0.1 M NaCl, $I = \dfrac{0.1 \times 1^2 + 0.1 \times 1^2}{2} = 0.1$

(for buffer systems usually employed where the pH is between 4 and 10 the concentration of H^+ and OH^- ions is less than 0.1 mM and hence is negligible compared with the concentration of buffer and salts).

13

For the partially ionized groups of buffer molecules, acting as weak acids (HA $\rightleftharpoons$ H$^+$ + A$^-$), first calculate the proportion of ionized molecules from the Henderson-Hasselbach equation:

$$pH = pKa + \log_{10} [A^-]/[HA]$$

where [HA] is the concentration of undissociated buffer and [A$^-$] is the concentration of dissociated buffer.

E.g. 0.01 M sodium phosphate pH 7.0 exists as Na$^+$ + HPO$_4^{2-}$ + H$_2$PO$_4^-$ (we can ignore H$_3$PO$_4$ and PO$_4^{3-}$ at this pH).

For the reaction H$_2$PO$_4^- \rightleftharpoons$ H$^+$ + HPO$_4^{2-}$, the pKa = 7.21.

Hence $7.0 = 7.21 + \log_{10} [HPO_4^{2-}]/[H_2PO_4^-]$

$\therefore [HPO_4^{2-}]/[H_2PO_4^-] = 0.617$

Total phosphate concentration is 0.01M

$\therefore [HPO_4^{2-}] = 0.00381$ M and

$[H_2PO_4^-] = 0.00619$ M

The concentration of Na$^+$ balances out these charges

$\therefore [Na^+] = 2 \times 0.00381 + 0.00619 = 0.01381$ M

$$\therefore I = \frac{0.01381 \times 1^2 + 0.00381 \times 2^2 + 0.00619 \times 1^2}{2} = 0.01762$$

For reproducible fractionations the water used in buffers should be as pure as possible. The pH and conductivity of each batch of buffer must be carefully measured and adjusted. Charged bacterial inhibitors such as azide or thimerosal should not be added routinely to buffers (see note 1 below).

Choice of column. See Section 1.2.1 for the physical requirements of a chromatography column. There are even fewer rules for the sample loading of ion exchangers than for gel filtration. As a rough guide, most manufacturers quote a capacity for a standard protein under defined conditions. Allow a safety factor of at least 10 at first and then proceed empirically. In a novel separation check that the column is not overloaded by reapplying the unretarded fraction to a fresh column of regenerated exchanger.

A useful column length for ion exchange chromatography is 20–30 cm, although publication 607 from Whatman (Appendix 3) recommends the use of shorter columns. The volume of sample applied is not important — the binding of proteins is not influenced greatly by their concentration.

Equilibrium of exchanger. The regenerated exchanger should be equilibrated *fully* with the chosen starting buffer before use. The procedure below has been found satisfactory although many alternatives exist. The large variations in ionic strength will adversely affect some supports, notably those based on Sephadex G-50.

1 Add the regenerated exchanger (see above) to an equal volume of 10 × concentration of starting buffer. Mix and leave at room temperature for 30 min.

14

2   The exchanger will adsorb some of the buffer ions in exchange for protons or hydroxyl ions and consequently alter the pH. Gently stir the slurry and bring the pH back to the required value using the acid or basic forms of the buffer (e.g. for sodium phosphate buffer use sodium hydroxide for a cation exchanger and phosphoric acid for an anion exchanger).

3   Leave the slurry for a further 30 min, recheck its pH and adjust if necessary. The exchanger is now at the required pH with the required counter ion bound but the ionic strength is too high.

4   Wash the resin on a sintered funnel (porosity 3 or 4) or Whatman no. 54 paper with 5 × volume of starting buffer.

5   Remove the fines and degas the slurry and pack it into the column as described for gel filtration (Section 1.2.1).

6   Wash the column with starting buffer at the operating temperature until the pH and conductivity of the eluant is *exactly* the same as the starting buffer.

The column is now ready for use.

Sample application and elution. The sample should be dialysed exhaustively against the starting buffer; the final volume is not important. It is then applied to the column and the eluant monitored as described for gel filtration (Section 1.2.1).

After sample application, the exchanger should be washed first with at least two column volumes of the starting buffer to ensure complete elution of unbound protein. The bound proteins are then eluted by increasing the ionic strength of the buffer or changing its pH (downwards for anion exchangers, upwards for cation exchangers) or both. Variations in ionic strength are usually preferred because they can be controlled more carefully. A final ionic strength of 1.0 is usually sufficient to elute most proteins. Either the concentration of the buffer can be increased or this parameter kept constant and other ions increased (e.g. NaCl). The latter is usually better because the buffering capacity, and hence the pH, is constant throughout the separation procedure.

Except for well-characterized routine procedures, a gradient of gradually changing conditions is better than several stepped changes of eluting buffer which frequently cause artefactual peaks, although it is very difficult to produce a smooth pH gradient. Commercial gradient makers are available (LKB, MSE, Pharmacia — Appendix 3) but they are expensive and generally much more sophisticated than is required. Simple apparati for producing linear or concave or convex gradients can be made easily in any laboratory workshop (Fig. 1.3). Remember that the gradient will not quite reach the conditions in the final buffer.

As a rough guide, the total volume of the gradient should be 5–10 times the column volume. The size of fractions of eluant collected should be 1/5–1/10 of the column volume.

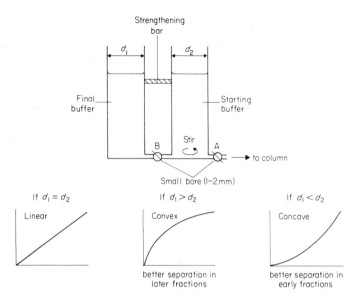

Fig. 1.3 A simple gradient maker. The relative diameters of the glass tubing used to construct the chambers govern the shape of the gradient produced. For convex or concave gradients the ratio should be 1.5–2.0. By adding a third tap so that both chambers have a direct outlet, one apparatus can be used to generate convex or concave gradients depending upon which chamber is chosen for mixing and draw off.

Clamp the apparatus vertically and close both taps. Fill the mixing chamber with starting buffer and flush air from both portions of small bore tubing by briefly opening both taps. Apply sample to the column and with tap A open wash the sample through with starting buffer. Remove excess starting buffer from the second chamber and fill with final buffer until the liquid in the two chambers is *exactly* level, ensuring that air is not introduced into the connecting tubing. Stir the liquid in the mixing chamber vigorously enough to mix to the full height of the liquid column but not enough to cause a vortex. Open tap B and the column will be eluted by the gradient.

Notes

1 Ion exchangers can be stored at 4°C in the presence of 0.03% toluene as a bacterial inhibitor. Alternatively the appropriately charged inhibitor may be used — 0.002% chlorhexidine for anion exchangers; 0.02% sodium azide for cation exchangers.

2 The pKa of most charged groups on a protein varies with temperature. Consequently a given separation of proteins will change if repeated at a different temperature. As a further complication, changes in temperature significantly alter the pKa of certain 'biological buffers', notably tris, and consequently change the pH of a buffer solution.

1.2.3 Hydroxylapatite

This form of calcium phosphate (also known as hydroxyapatite) has been widely used for fractionation of proteins and nucleic acids. It is a kind of ion exchanger (see Section 1.2.2) with the Ca^{2+} ions and to a

16

much lesser extent the phosphate groups interacting with charged groups on the macromolecules. Surface charge density, charge-to-mass ratio and other factors (?) play a role in the strength of adsorption of a protein and provide unique fractionation properties that can often resolve substances inseparable by other methods.

The usual buffer is sodium phosphate pH 6.8 (equimolar Na_2HPO_4 and NaH_2PO_4); most proteins bind in 10 mM and are eluted at 0.5 M. Apply the protein mixture to a column of hydroxylapatite (1 g dry weight for each 2 mg of protein allows a safety factor of about 5) in the low ionic strength buffer and elute with a gradient of increasing molarity (Section 1.2.2). CO_2 can absorb to hydroxylapatite forming a crust on top of the column and so degas all buffers.

1.2.4   HPLC

When these systems were first introduced the initials stood for High Pressure Liquid Chromatography because sophisticated pumps were used to force the material through very fine particles in columns of small cross-sectional area. The technology of the resins has now advanced to such a stage that reasonable flow rates can be obtained without such extreme pressure and 'Performance' is often substituted in the title; Pharmacia call their system FPLC.

Any fractionation of proteins by HPLC uses the same principles as chromatography in standard columns by gel filtration, ion exchange or affinity chromatography (Sections 1.2.1, 1.2.2, 1.2.3, 10.3, *et seq.*). The advantages over the conventional procedures are speed because of the small high-capacity columns, improved reproducibility because of the sophisticated pumps and accurate timers, and in some cases increased resolution because of the fine resins and control systems (e.g. Section 3.4.3, note 1). The disadvantage is the expense of the apparatus and the column materials. All buffers should be degassed and filtered. Systems suitable for protein fractionation are sold by Spectra-Physics, Bio-Rad and Pharmacia (Appendix 3).

1.3   DIALYSIS AND CONCENTRATION OF PROTEINS

If the solvent is volatile (e.g. dilute acetic or propionic acid or ammonium hydroxide or carbonate), a protein solution can be concentrated, to dryness if necessary, simply by evaporation of the frozen solution under vacuum (termed 'freeze-drying' or 'lyophilization'). Organic solvents or inorganic salts can be used to precipitate proteins but this is often selective and also causes some denaturation. Precipitation procedures are useful where the selectivity is advantageous (see for example Section 3.3.1) or the denaturation not important (Section 7.1.5) but they are not used routinely for concentration during general handling of proteins. Chromatography techniques where the protein binds to an insoluble support, such as ion-exchange, hydroxylapatite

17

and affinity chromatography (Sections 1.2.2, 1.2.3, 10.3), can be used for concentration by eluting in a small volume.

In the remaining cases, which comprise the vast majority of protein manipulation procedures, the protein in solution is separated from ions, water and other small molecules by filtration through a semi-permeable membrane. For dialysis the small molecules are simply exchanged for others by diffusion through the membrane with no change in sample volume (unless caused by an incidental osmotic pressure difference). The same principle applies to concentration but the small molecules are forced out of the protein solution by pressure of various kinds, so that the total sample volume is reduced. A rapid alternative to dialysis is desalting on a small pore gel filtration column (Section 1.2.1, note 7).

1.3.1 Dialysis

Although this widely used procedure is technically simple, a few notes are provided for guidance:

1   Select the size of visking tubing to hold the sample in a 10–30 cm length (Table 1.3).

2   Before use, boil the tubing in 10 mM EDTA for 1 min — this removes some impurities and decreases the pore size.

3   Close the tubing at both ends with two knots or small plastic clamps (Raven, Gallenkamp — Appendix 3). Knots may distort the membrane's pores. Clamps reduce the handling of sacs when dialysing radioactive samples.

4   The nominal molecular weight cut-off of standard visking tubing is 10 000, although it is not advisable to use it for proteins smaller than 15 000. Tubing with a nominal cut-off of 2000 is available (Sigma — Appendix 3), but it is very expensive.

5   Increasing the number of changes of buffer improves the exchange more than increasing the volume of each change (e.g. dialysis against four changes of 500 ml is considerably better than against two changes of 1 litre). The minimum time of dialysis against each change should be 4 h.

Table 1.3   Visking tubing

Size			Approximate capacity	
Inflated (inches)	Diameter (mm)	Flat width (mm)	ml/10 cm length	ml/25 cm length
8/32	6.3	10	3	8
18/32	14.3	22	16	40
24/32	19.0	30	28	71
36/32	28.6	45	64	160

1.3.2 Concentration

Protein solutions can be concentrated by applying pressure during dialysis which results in the outflow of small molecules and ions. There are several ways to apply this pressure.

Osmotic pressure. Place the sample in a small diameter dialysis sac (e.g. 8/32", Table 1.3) and lay it on a flat surface. Sprinkle it with dry polyethylene glycol 40 000 and leave it until the sample has concentrated to the required volume (usually a few hours).

Negative pressure or vacuum. Suspend a length of small diameter visking tubing (e.g. 8/32", Table 1.3) with one closed end inside a Buchner side-arm flask so that its top is open to the atmosphere through a funnel reservoir (Fig. 1.4). Place a little buffer in the Buchner flask and the protein solution in the dialysis sac and funnel and apply vacuum (a water pump is sufficient) until the sample has concentrated to the required volume.

Commercial concentrators. A number of different concentrators are available (Amicon, Millipore — Appendix 3). Instead of the conventional dialysis membrane they contain a physically strengthened semipermeable membrane filter. The filters are available in a range of nominal molecular weight cut-offs — from 500 to 300 000 — (remember that the nominal cut-off is not exact in practice) and with a range of chemical properties, the choice being governed by the buffer and sample used (see manufacturer's literature). Pressure is applied to the sample by compressed nitrogen, centrifugal force or an absorbent pad, depending upon the apparatus. The filters are expensive but can be reused many times with care; avoid scratching the surface of the membrane.

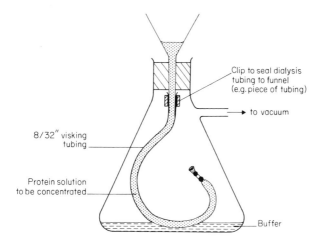

Fig. 1.4   Vacuum dialysis apparatus for protein concentration.

The commercial concentrators are convenient for general purpose use. However, they are expensive and some people claim that the membranes adsorb proteins non-specifically much more then visking tubing. Hence the above procedures using dialysis tubing are useful when handling small volumes or low concentrations of protein especially when cross-contamination of samples, from the reuse of membranes, must be avoided.

Care should be taken whatever method is used to ensure that the sample is not allowed to dry out, otherwise protein will be irreversibly adsorbed onto the membrane or dialysis tubing. All procedures can be carried out at the temperature of choice depending upon the lability of the protein.

1.4 MEASUREMENT OF RADIOACTIVITY

The isotopes commonly encountered in immunochemistry are presented in Table 1.4 together with their emissions. They can all be detected in two basic ways: measurement of the total activity in a sample (see below) or visualization of the distribution of activity throughout a chromatogram, electrophoretogram or tissue section or cell (Sections 1.5 and 12.4).

Although measurement is usually carried out on a small amount of radioactivity remember to follow the safety procedures outlined in Section 5.1.1. In addition, many of the solvents used are highly inflammable and of undetermined carcinogenicity, and so extra care is needed.

1 becquerel (Bq) = 1 disintegration per second
$1\mu Ci = 3.7 \times 10^4 Bq = 2.22 \times 10^6$ disintegrations per minute

The value for counts per minute (c.p.m.) obtained from a counter is related to, but always less then, the absolute disintegrations per minute (d.p.m.) occurring in the sample. The ratio between the two depends upon the efficiency of the machine at the set parameters and the absorption or quenching within the sample.

Isotopes that emit gamma rays (i.e. ^{125}I and ^{51}Cr in Table 1.4) are most easily quantitated by measuring this radiation directly in a gamma counter (solid scintillation counting). The efficiency for this is usually about 50%. However, for ^{51}Cr only 9% of the decay is of detectable energy and so the actual ratio of c.p.m. obtained to total activity is 50% of 9% = 4.5%.

The remaining isotopes in Table 1.4 emit the weaker β particles and these are measured by liquid scintillation counting. In this procedure the kinetic energy of the β particles is converted to photons of light by the scintillant and this radiation is detected by a photomultiplier tube. With care the efficiency can be about 50% for ^3H and greater than 85% for the other isotopes. However, changes in the sample geometry can alter these figures drastically (for example the efficiency of ^3H on glass fibre paper is only about 10% and the value is

20

Table 1.4 Physical properties of radioactive isotopes in common use

Isotopes	Half-life	Maximum β energy emitted (keV)	γ Emissions	Measurement[1]	Possible autoradiographic detection[2]		
					direct auto-radiography	fluorography	autoradiography with screen
[125]I	60.0 days	—	X-rays and γ rays	γ	+	+	+
[51]Cr	27.8 days	—	X-rays and γ rays	γ			
[32]P	14.3 days	1709	none	l.s.; C	+	+	+
[35]S	87.4 days	167	none	l.s.	+	+	–
[14]C	5730 years	156	none	l.s.	+	+	–
[3]H	12.35 years	18.6	none	l.s.	–	+	–

([1]) See Section 1.4: γ, solid scintillation counting in gamma counter; l.s., liquid scintillation counting; C, Cherenkov counting.
([2]) See Section 1.5: for detection of isotopes in cells or tissues see Section 12.4.

even lower on most other solid supports). ^{32}P emits β particles with sufficient energy to be detected without a scintillant — termed Cherenkov counting. This is usually measured in the tritium channel with about 20–40% efficiency.

The scintillant chosen depends upon the nature of the sample. One of the most efficient scintillator systems consists of a fluor dissolved in toluene or xylene, but unfortunately these solvents are incompatible with aqueous or polar specimens. They are useful, however, for steroids and lipids, aqueous samples dried *completely* onto glass fibre paper (see above and Section 5.1.2) and other samples in an appropriate solubilizer (see below). They are also cheap — either ready-made (Table 1.5), or mix the following:

2,5-diphenyloxazole (PPO)   7 g
1,4-bis-2-(5-phenyloxazolyl) benzene (POPOP)   0.5 g
Toluene   1 litre

A detergent can be added to make this system suitable for aqueous samples by forming an emulsion. Mixtures of aqueous samples in such scintillants form a colloidal suspension. They can take several interchangeable physical forms depending upon their composition — a clear or slightly opalescent homogeneous mixture, a two-phase system or a gel. The efficiency of counting varies dramatically between these forms; only the homogeneous mixtures (the clear solution and the gel) are suitable for counting. If a two-phase system is obtained more sample or more scintillant should be added to change it to one of the other forms. Samples containing strong alkalis cause a decrease in counting efficiency. A variety of commercial preparations of emulsion scintillants are available (Table 1.5). Alternatively, the following mixture can be used:

PPO   7 g
POPOP   0.5 g
Toluene   650 ml
Triton X–100   350 ml

Scintillants based on dioxan are an alternative to emulsion mixtures for aqueous samples. They are thermodynamically more stable and hence are not subject to abrupt changes in efficiency found with slight changes in composition of colloidal suspensions, but they are more expensive. They are commercially available (Table 1.5), but one well-tried scintillant is Kinard's mixture:

PPO   5 g
POPOP   0.05 g
naphthalene scintillation grade   80 g
1,4-dioxan   385 ml
xylene   385 ml
absolute ethanol   230 ml

A further option for counting aqueous or polar samples is the use of a quaternary ammonium base to solubilize them, the product being completely miscible with the efficient toluene or xylene based scintil-

Table 1.5 Common commercial liquid scintillation solutions (see Appendix 3 for manufacturers)

Scintillant type[1]	Amersham	Beckman	LKB	National Diagnostics	NEN	Nuclear Enterprises	Packard
For non-polar samples	OCS	ReadysolvNA	OptiScint Safe OptiScint T	Betafluor	Econofluor	NE233	Toluene Scintillator
Emulsion: clear 0–1.5 ml; gel 2.5–5 (or 10) ml	PCS PCS II	ReadysolvMP	OptiPhase MP OptiPhase Safe	Hydrofluor	Aquasol 1 & 2 Aquassure		Instagel
Economy version[2]	ACS ACS II	ReadysolvEP	OptiPhase X	Liquiscint			ES299
Solvent: 0–1 or 2 ml		ReadsolvHP		Ultrafluor Fluorodyne	Biofluor Riafluor	NE260	Picafluor 15
0–5 ml		ReadysolvCP	OptiPhase RIA	Monofluor	AtomLight	NE265	Picofluor 30
Solubilizer	NCS	BTS 450	OptiSolv	Solusol	Protosol		Soluene

(1) The volumes given refer to the approximate capacity for aqueous and polar samples of 10 ml of scintillant.
(2) With some loss of efficiency.

lants (see above). Commercial solubilizers are available (Table 1.5) and these can be used to solubilize anything from aqueous solutions to solid tissue. The solubilizer is added to the sample, incubated at 20–50°C until it is dissolved, cooled, neutralized with acetic or hydrochloric acid to prevent chemiluminescence and phosphorescence and the scintillant added (see manufacturer's literature for details). The cost per sample is more than for dioxan based scintillants and so they are only usually used when absolutely necessary (e.g. Section 7.1.4).

For most scintillants a higher fluorescence yield is obtained if the mixtures are bubbled with nitrogen to remove dissolved oxygen. To reduce background counts caused by chemiluminescence and phosphorescence, the samples in scintillant should be stored at room temperature in the dark overnight and then counted in the dark in a refrigerated counter. Plastic vial inserts are recommended for their cheapness although they swell or soften in some solvents.

For further information on liquid scintillation counting see Review 17 from Amersham (Appendix 3).

1.5 AUTORADIOGRAPHY (for autoradiography of cells and tissues see Section 12.4)

Radiation produced by radioisotopes will expose X-ray film and this can be used to visualize the distribution of radiolabelled antibodies and antigens. The basic method consists of placing a sheet of X-ray film in close contact with the medium containing the radiolabelled substance (e.g. polyacrylamide gel, chromatogram, etc.), enclosing it in a light-tight cassette and leaving it for a suitable period to expose (from a few hours to several months depending upon the isotope and activity). The film is then developed and fixed, and the presence of radiolabelled protein inferred from black bands or spots on the film.

High energy radiation can be detected by simple autoradiography, but low energy emissions may not penetrate the coating on X-ray film. The more sensitive fluorography technique is used to detect ^{3}H and small amounts of higher energy emitters. Isotopes commonly encountered in immunochemistry together with the type of radiation produced and techniques suitable for their detection are summarized in Table 1.4.

Many modifications to simple autoradiography have been devised usually in order to achieve greater sensitivity. These are discussed after a description of the basic technique.

1.5.1 Direct autoradiography

Polyacrylamide gels should be dried onto paper (Section 7.1.3). Chromatograms or gel transfers (Section 8.4) should also be dried *thoroughly*.

The cheapest autoradiography protocol involves clamping the gel or chromatogram onto a sheet of X-ray film between glass plates, securing the assembly with adhesive tape and placing it in several layers of black plastic. However, commercial cassettes exclude light more reliably. Plastic cassettes are less than half the price of metal cassettes, but they cannot be used for exposures at $-70°C$, a temperature which allows considerable enhancement in some cases (see note 2 below and Section 1.5.3).

Many films are suitable for autoradiography but they vary in their sensitivity, resolution and darkness of background. Most are double-sided (i.e. they have a layer of sensitive emulsion on both sides of a plastic support sheet) which makes for ease of handling when setting up the exposure in the dark. In addition, the use of an intensifying screen (see note 2 below) means that the film is exposed from both sides and so double-sided film is essential for this. For direct autoradiography of the weaker beta emitters (i.e. ^{14}C and ^{35}S) that do not penetrate the film support and hence cannot expose any emulsion on the far side, then single-sided film will give a clearer background by reducing general exposure. Amersham (Appendix 3) produce film with a very clear base to reduce background thus improving sensitivity and clarity.

Materials and equipment

Polyacrylamide gel or chromatogram or transfer membrane containing
    radiolabelled protein(s) (Chapter 7, Section 8.4)
X-ray film (Kodak X-Omat S or Industrex C)
Cassette (Cuthbert-Andrews, Hanimex — Appendix 3)
Developer and fixer for film
Dark room fitted with appropriate safelight

Procedure

Carry out steps 1 and 3 in total darkness or under safelight illumination only but avoiding direct illumination of the film.
1 In the dark room place a sheet of X-ray film into the cassette. Superimpose the polyacrylamide gel or chromatogram on the film and close the cassette.
2 Expose for 36–48 h preferably at $-70°C$.
3 Allow cassette to warm to room temperature. In the dark room develop the film according to the manufacturer's instructions.
4 If the film is overexposed (very black with diffuse bands or spots), expose for a shorter period. If the image is weak or invisible, expose for a longer period or use an intensifying screen if appropriate (note 2 below).

Notes

1 A metal cassette or clamping between glass plates holds the film in

close contact with the sample. Flexible cassettes should be placed under a heavy weight during exposure.

2   Intensifying screens (which consist of a plastic sheet impregnated with phosphor crystals) will increase the sensitivity of autoradiography to some radiations. The film is clamped between the sample and the screen which produces photons in response to radiation that has passed through the film. These photons are able to expose the film on the opposite side from the sample, thus enhancing the effect of the rays themselves. The screens are only effective for high energy emitters (e.g. ^{125}I, ^{32}P) because lower energy radiation does not pass through the film. Various types of screen are available (Laskey & Mills, 1977). The use of only one screen is recommended. Two screens increase sensitivity but may produce diffuse bands because of the longer distance travelled by both the radiation and photons. Exposure must be at $-70°C$ if intensifying screens are used (Section 1.5.3).

3   The X-ray film itself can be used to intensify a weak image by the addition of ^{35}S-thiourea. This binds to the silver grains in the original image and will expose a second X-ray film to give a more intense copy of the first film. The major advantage is that an autoradiograph can be intensified long after the original gel has been discarded or the isotope decayed. However, a large amount of ^{35}S-thiourea is required and so the procedure is expensive. Full details are available from Amersham (Appendix 3).

4   Weak images can also be intensified chemically on the original film by binding chromium to the developed silver grains. Kodak manufacture one such Chromium Intensifier — follow their instructions and then redevelop the film. The procedure can be repeated several times, the limiting factor being the darkness of the background which is also intensified.

1.5.2   Fluorography

Incorporation of a scintillant (normally 2,5-diphenyloxazole, PPO) into a polyacrylamide gel or chromatogram results in photon production by the radiation emitted from the isotope (Bonner & Laskey, 1974; Review 23 from Amersham — Appendix 3). These photons efficiently expose X-ray film whereas low energy radiation does this very badly (direct autoradiography with ^3H is difficult although Amersham have produced a more sensitive film with which this is now possible). The procedure can also be used to reduce exposure times with higher energy isotopes (Table 1.4). See Section 1.5.3 for increasing sensitivity still further.

Materials and equipment

Tritium labelled proteins separated on a polyacrylamide gel and fixed (Chapter 7)

Dimethyl sulphoxide (DMSO)

17% (w/v) PPO in DMSO (store in the dark)

X-ray film (Fuji RX or Kodak X-OMAT S film)

Cassette suitable for $-70°C$ (Cuthbert-Andrews, Hanimex — Appendix 3)

Developer and fixer for film

Dark room fitted with appropriate safelight

Procedure

Warning   DMSO is harmful if absorbed through the skin — wear protective gloves.

1   Soak the gel in 2 changes of 100 ml DMSO (30 min each).

2   Incubate the gel for at least 3 h in PPO/DMSO (in the dark).

3   Wash the gel for 30 min in tap water. PPO should form a white precipitate in the gel at this stage.

4   Dry the gel onto paper (see Section 7.1.3).

5   Expose to X-ray film *at $-70°C$* as for autoradiography (Section 1.5.1).

Note

1   The gel can be stained and destained (Section 7.1.1) and a photographic record of the pattern made before the PPO/DMSO treatment. The protein stain is at least partially removed by the DMSO washes.

2   Alternative fluorography materials are commercially available ('Amplify' from Amersham; 'Autofluor' from National Diagnostics; 'Enlightning' and 'En³Hance' from NEN — Appendix 3). These avoid the hazards of DMSO and are simpler and faster to use with less washes. En³Hance is also available as a spray for even greater simplicity and for materials that would be washed out by the solvents (e.g. in tlc) but it is expensive.

3   If the fluor-impregnated substrate is exposed to sunlight or certain fluorescent lights just before placing in the cassette, then a very high background can result. Therefore always allow at least 1 min in the dark before loading into the cassette.

1.5.3   Pre-exposure of film

X-ray film is relatively insensitive to light and this makes the detection of very small amounts of radioactivity difficult by fluorography or when using screens. The insensitivity of the film seems to be due to the instability of a single silver atom produced in a silver halide crystal. Each photon produces only one silver atom and this quickly decays back to Ag^+ unless further photons strike the crystal to produce more silver atoms. Exposure of X-ray film at very low temperatures increases the half life of single silver atoms, and this explains the enhancing effect of exposure at $-70°C$, but in some cases even this will not produce acceptable autoradiographs.

Exposure of the X-ray film to a short pulse of light prior to fluorography increases the sensitivity considerably. The pulse of light produces more than one silver atom per halide crystal, but not enough atoms to cause appreciable blackening upon development. Photons produced by the radiation from the isotope are then able to expose the film efficiently, as the silver atoms produced by them are now all stable. The pre-exposure light intensity must be determined empirically so that maximum enhancement is achieved without too much background blackening.

Materials and equipment

Electronic flash gun
Kodak Wratten No 22 orange filter
Whatman no. 1 filter paper
Spectrophotometer
Dark room
X-ray film (Fuji RX or Kodak X-OMAT S film)

Procedure (from Laskey & Mills, 1975)

1   Set up the flash gun in the darkroom, place the Wratten filter over the light aperture and cover the filter with a sheet of filter paper (this causes diffusion of the light pulse).
2   Hold or clamp a sheet of X-ray film 70 cm from the flash and operate the gun once.
3   Process the film according to the manufacturer's instructions, together with a sheet of unflashed film as a control.
4   Cut a small piece from the exposed and control sheets and measure the absorbance at 540 nm (set spectrophotometer to zero absorbance with the control).
5   If the absorbance of the exposed sheet is about 0.15 then the pre-exposure conditions are correct. If the absorbance is greater than this, repeat the procedure using a greater distance between film and flash gun and vice versa.
6   Use a pre-exposed film for fluorography (place exposed side against gel) as described in Section 1.5.2 but see note 2 below.

Notes

1   This procedure will not increase the sensitivity of direct autoradiography as most radioisotopes emit particles which are individually of sufficient energy to render a grain fully developable. However, it will enhance the image if intensifying screens are used (Section 1.5.1, note 2; place exposed side against screen).

28

2 Avoid direct exposure of pre-exposed film to safelights during processing.

1.5.4 Radioactive marker pen

It is useful to place radioactive marks on the sample before exposure so that the autoradiograph can be aligned precisely with the sample (e.g. for comparison of radioactive and stained patterns). Alternatively a phosphorescent pen is available commercially (NEN — Appendix 3).

Materials and equipment

4 ball-point pens
^{14}C in any non-volatile chemical form (including waste material; if you have to buy, [^{14}C]urea is cheapest) — 50–100 μCi
Ethanol
Acetone
Conical centrifuge tubes, about 10 ml

Procedure

Wear gloves and work over a tray — this is messy.
1 Extract the ink from the pens into a tube by centrifuging the inverted ink reservoirs at 2000 g for 10 min.
2 Remove the nibs and wash out the reservoirs with ethanol and then acetone. Refit the nibs.
3 Add a *little* ethanol (about 10%) to the ink to make it slightly more runny and then mix in the ^{14}C. Vortex and centrifuge to bring the ink to the bottom of the tube.
4 Replace the ink into *two* pens. Transfer it, a little at a time, to the reservoirs with a Pasteur pipette and centrifuge it down to the nib. If the ink is too thick, add a little more ethanol; if it is too thin, evaporate some off in a water bath (approximately 40°C) in a fume cupboard.
5 Label the pens conspicuously and store inside a sealed container to prevent leakage of radioactive material.
6 If the pens subsequently dry up, centrifuge the ink back down into the nibs.

2 Production of antibodies

2.1 INTRODUCTION

The extreme specificity shown by individual antibodies for the corresponding antigen makes them ideal tools for the study and purification of proteins. In general, antibodies can be raised easily, even when only a small quantity of immunogen is available, and they are used widely in many biological investigations.

Until recently production of antibodies was limited technically to immunizing animals and, after an appropriate time, collecting the immune serum. Antibodies derived from such immune sera are termed 'conventional antibodies' (Section 2.2). However, Köhler and Milstein (1975) have introduced technology for the production of murine monoclonal antibodies *in vitro* by the construction of hybridomas (Section 2.3). Such reagents have the enormous advantage over conventional antibodies of being homogeneous — i.e. every immunoglobulin molecule is identical in antigen binding properties, allotype, heavy chain subclass, etc. In addition the hybridoma lines secreting the antibodies are immortal and so there is an inexhaustible supply of antibody. More recently techniques have been described for the production of human monoclonal antibodies by viral transformation of B lymphocytes.

Although monoclonal antibodies can be selected to be exquisitely specific they are often of low affinity (Section 6.1.1) and so may be inappropriate for some applications. The possibility of a monoclonal antibody also reacting with other apparently unrelated antigens by virtue of sharing the single small antigenic determinant, or epitope, recognized by the antibody should always be borne in mind.

2.2 CONVENTIONAL ANTIBODY PRODUCTION

Conventional antibody production requires methods for the introduction of immunogen into animals, withdrawal of blood for testing the antibody levels, and finally exsanguination for collection of immune sera.

These apparently simple technical requirements are complicated by the necessity of choosing a suitable species and immunization protocol which will produce a highly immune animal in a short time.

Choice of animal is determined by animal house facilities available, amount of antiserum required (a mouse will afford only 1.0–1.5 ml blood; a goat can provide several litres) and amount of immunogen available (mice will usually respond very well to 50 μg or less of

30

antigen; goats may require several mg). Another consideration is the phylogenic relationship between the animal from which the immunogen is derived and that used for antibody production. In most cases it is advisable to immunize a species phylogenetically unrelated to the immunogen donor and, for highly conserved mammalian proteins, non-mammals (e.g. chickens) should be used for antibody production. However, if antibodies are to be produced which will detect only subtle differences between proteins (e.g. allotypes) then closely related or even the same species should be used for immunogen isolation and antibody production.

2.2.1 Immunization protocols

A better antibody response is usually obtained by using an adjuvant with the first (priming) immunization. Normally the immunogen is prepared as a water in oil emulsion containing a heat-killed mycobacterium (Freund's complete adjuvant — FCA). The emulsion ensures that the antigen is released slowly into the animal's circulation and the bacteria stimulate the animal's immune system. Further booster (secondary) immunizations are necessary for high antibody levels and these are given either in phosphate buffered saline or as an oil emulsion (bacteria are not normally included in boosting injections; a suitable simple oil adjuvant is Freund's incomplete adjuvant — FIA).

Five routes can be used for injection of immunogen. These are:
(a) intramuscular (i.m.)
(b) intravenous (i.v.)
(c) intradermal (i.d.)
(d) intraperitoneal (i.p.) and
(e) subcutaneous (s.c.)

Any of these can be used for the priming immunization, but i.p. injection is not normally used for large animals, and i.v. immunization cannot be used with particulate antigens or adjuvants. I.d. immunization is very effective in producing a primary response. Immunization by i.d., i.m. or s.c. injection is better in several sites, rather than a single large injection in one site.

Methods for preparing immunogens with Freund's adjuvant and suggested immunization protocols are given in this section.

Preparation of water in oil emulsion for immunization

Materials and equipment

Immunogen in 2 ml phosphate buffered saline (PBS — Appendix 2)
Freund's complete adjuvant (FCA) (primary injection)
or Freund's incomplete adjuvant (FIA) (booster injections) (Difco — Appendix 3)
Emulsifier (Silverson — Appendix 3)
Glass Universal container

31

Procedure

1   If FCA is used shake vigorously to resuspend the bacteria. Pipette 2 ml of adjuvant into the glass Universal.
2   Add 2 drops of immunogen solution to the adjuvant and mix *immediately* with the emulsifier for 5–6 seconds. Continue to add immunogen 2–4 drops at a time, emulsifying after each addition until all the immunogen has been mixed with adjuvant.

Notes

1   The above preparation is stable for several weeks at 4°C; do not freeze. If detergent is present in the immunogen, the emulsion is more difficult to prepare and is less stable.
2   The final emulsion should be thick and creamy. Before injection syringes should be filled with the emulsion without the needle attached and then expelled through a needle of the same bore as that to be used for immunization.
3   Smaller volumes of emulsion can be prepared but considerable losses occur onto the emulsifier blades and container walls. Alternatively the mixing can be carried out on a vortex, but this is tedious and produces a less satisfactory emulsion. Also 2 syringes joined through a 1 mm diameter connection can be used (Herbert & Kristensen, 1986).

Immunization procedures

The best immunization protocol for a particular immunogen and species can only be established by trial and error. The protocols outlined below have been used successfully for various antigens. It is advisable to immunize more than one animal.

Rabbits. Primary immunization of 50–200 μg protein in FCA injected i.d. into 6–8 sites on the animal's back (0.1–0.2 ml/site). Alternatively inject i.m. or s.c. Boost at 10 day intervals with 50–200 μg protein prepared in PBS (*no azide*) or FIA (i.m., s.c., i.v. or i.p.; 0.25–2 ml/site).

Guinea-pigs and rats. Primary immunization of 10–100 μg protein in FCA injected i.d. into 4–6 sites on the animal's back (0.1 ml/site). Alternatively inject i.m. or s.c. Boost at 7–8 day intervals with 10–50 μg prepared in PBS or FIA (i.m., i.p., i.v. or s.c.; 2 or 4 sites).

Mice. As for rats but use 5–50 μg protein for each immunization.

Sheep and goats. Primary immunization of 0.5–10 mg protein in FCA injected i.d., i.m. or s.c. into several sites. Boost after 14–28 days with 0.5–10 mg protein in PBS or FIA i.m., i.v., or s.c. (several sites for i.m. and s.c.). It may be possible to use less antigen in some cases, especially if long resting periods are used.

Chickens. Primary immunization of 50–200 μg protein in FCA injected i.m. into the breast muscle (2–4 sites; 0.25–0.5 ml/site). Boost after 10 days with 50–200 μg protein in PBS or FIA as for primary immunization.

Notes

1 The period between injections given above is the minimum that should be used.
2 Allowing animals resting periods of several months between later boosts may be advantageous.

2.2.2 Bleeding

The procedure used to obtain blood depends on whether the animal should recover from the bleeding. For test bleeds (removal of blood in order to monitor the antibody response) only a small quantity of blood is taken and the animal allowed to recover. When the animal's serum contains a high level of antibody, it may be advisable to sacrifice it and obtain a large volume of blood. Alternatively, weekly bleeding of rabbits and large animals will yield a lot of blood over 1 or 2 months.

The methods normally used to test bleed and exsanguinate animals are listed in Table 2.1. These procedures should be learnt from an experienced worker.

Table 2.1 Methods for test bleeding and exsanguinating animals

Animal	Test bleed	Exsanguination or collection of large samples
mice and rats	tail bleed or heart puncture	heart puncture
guinea-pigs	heart puncture	as mice and rats
rabbits	bleed from ear vein	as mice and rats or bleed from jugular vein
goats and sheep	as rabbits	bleed from jugular vein
chickens	bleed from wing vein	bleed from brachial vein

2.2.3 Isolation of serum from blood

Antibodies are present in the serum fraction of blood. Serum should be separated from cells as soon as possible after collection of blood; otherwise cells lyse and release contaminating proteins including proteolytic enzymes which will degrade the antibodies.

33

Materials and equipment

Blood preferably collected in a glass container (see note 1)
Bench centrifuge
Small plastic tubes suitable for frozen storage

Procedure

1   Allow blood to clot at room temperature (about 1 h). Then leave overnight at 4°C (this causes the clot to contract).
2   Detach clot from the walls of the container, and pour off all clot-free liquid into a centrifuge tube.
3   Centrifuge clot for 30 min at 2500 *g* at 4°C and remove any expressed liquid (contamination with a few cells does not matter). Add this to the clot free liquid from step 2.
4   Centrifuge the pooled liquid for 15–20 min at 1500 *g* at 4°C. Store the serum aliquoted at −20°C or −70°C or add a bacterial inhibitor (Section 3.2) and store at 4°C (chicken serum should not be frozen).

Notes

1   Blood clots more quickly in glass than in plastic containers.
2   See Section 4.2.2 for isolation of plasma from blood.
3   Mouse and rat immunoglobulins are more labile than those from most other species. Allow blood to clot as in step 1 and separate serum immediately.

2.2.4   Preparation of serum from plasma

If an anticoagulant has been added to blood and the plasma isolated (Section 4.2.2), the preparation can be defibrinated to yield an analogue of serum. This is preferable to plasma as a starting material for the isolation of most proteins (including immunoglobulins) because several contaminants (clotting factors, etc.) have been removed and also the sample cannot clot during subsequent procedures. However, some proteins are degraded by endogeneous proteases during the procedure.

Acid citrate-dextrose. Warm the plasma to 37°C and add 1/100 volume of thrombin solution (100 i.u./ml in 1 M calcium chloride). Stir vigorously to induce clot formation and incubate at 37°C for 10 min followed by 1 h at room temperature to ensure completion. Centrifuge at 40 000 *g* for 15 min and store the supernatant as serum (Section 2.2.3).

Heparin. Proceed as for citrated plasma but add 1/100 volume of 5 mg/ml protamine sulphate solution together with the thrombin. If a clot does not form quickly, add more protamine sulphate until it does.

2.3 MONOCLONAL ANTIBODIES

Fusion of spleen cells from an immune animal with neoplastic B cells (normally a B cell line derived from a tumour) can produce hybrid cells (hybridomas) which exhibit characteristics of both parent cells. Such hybridomas may secrete antibody of a specificity shown by the immune donor and also be immortal (a characteristic of the neoplastic B cell line).

Cells can be induced to fuse by mixing them together at high density in the presence of polyethylene glycol (some viruses also induce cell fusion). The efficiency of fusion is usually fairly low but hybridomas can be selected for if the parent neoplastic cell line is conditioned to die in selective medium. The tumour cells are killed by the selective medium, normal non-fused spleen cells die after a period in culture, but hybridomas inherit the ability to survive in the selective medium from the normal parent cell.

If individual hybridomas are isolated by cloning, it is possible to produce large quantities of the secreted monoclonal antibody (all the antibodies secreted by a single B cell or clone have identical antigen-binding specificities). The hybridomas can be grown in culture or injected intraperitoneally into animals of the same strain as the donor of spleen and tumour cells and the resultant ascitic fluid used as a source of monoclonal antibody.

Hybridoma technology requires facilities for, and knowledge of, tissue culture, facilities for freezing and storing viable cells, and a quick and reliable method for screening hybridomas for antibody secretion. It is advisable to learn the cell culture, fusion and cloning techniques from an experienced worker rather than trying to set them up in isolation.

Although production of murine hybridomas is now routine and fairly straightforward, human hybridomas are much more problematical. For this reason transformation of human B lymphocytes using Epstein-Barr virus (EBV), which leads to their immortality, has been a more successful approach for the production of human monoclonal antibodies. Although this procedure is still under development, a method which has been used successfully is described (Section 2.3.6).

2.3.1 Cell fusion and selection of antibody-secreting hybridomas

The neoplastic B cell line used for hybridoma production should have two properties:
1 The cells should be killed by a selective medium in which hybridomas survive. Usually medium containing hypoxanthine, aminopterin and thymidine (HAT) is used. This selectively kills cells deficient in the enzyme hypoxanthine-guanine phosphoribosyl transferase (HGPRTase). There are two pathways available to the cell for synthesis of nucleic acid: (a) *de novo* synthesis and (b) syntheses by 'salvaging' nucleotides produced by breakdown of nucleic acid. Aminopterin

35

(and thus HAT medium) inhibits *de novo* synthesis of nucleic acid, but for normal cells this is not lethal as the salvage pathway can still function (the hypoxanthine and thymidine present in HAT medium ensures that there is no deficiency of nucleotides). However, the enzyme HGPRTase is essential for the operation of the salvage pathway, and so, if the tumour cell line is deficient in this enzyme, it will be unable to synthesize nucleic acid, and therefore die when grown in HAT medium. HGPRTase deficient cell lines are produced by selection in medium containing 8-azaguanine. Cells possessing HGPRTase incorporate the 8-azaguanine into their DNA and die whereas HGPRTase deficient cells survive.

2   The tumour cells should not secrete a paraprotein or the antibody secreted by the hybridoma will be contaminated with this protein. Preferably these cells should not even synthesize immunoglobulin light chains or these may combine with the monoclonal antibody heavy chain and produce unwanted hybrid immunoglobulin molecules.

Several HAT-sensitive, non-secreting B cell lines have been produced from BALB/c strain mice and from Lou strain rats. These are all suitable for hybridoma production (Table 2.2). A HAT-sensitive human line has also been developed, but human hybridoma production is problematical (see Section 2.3.6 for an alternative).

Table 2.2   Some rodent B cell tumour lines used for hybridoma production

Cell line	Species/strain	Synthesis
NS1	mouse; BALB/c	light chain
NSO	as above	nothing
X63.Ag8.653	as above	nothing
Y3	rat Lou	light chain
Y2B	rat Lou	nothing

The exact methodology for hybridoma production varies considerably between laboratories; one such protocol is given below.

Materials and equipment

Facilities and equipment for cell culture, including a humidified 5–7% CO_2 37°C incubator
B-tumour cells (Table 2.2)
Immune animal (either BALB/c mouse or Lou rat — see Section 2.2.1 and note 1)
Equipment for dissection of animal
Sterile medium (Table 4.1) and fetal calf serum (FCS) — see note 2

36

PEG solution: sterile 50% w/v polyethylene glycol molecular weight 1500 (BDH — Appendix 3) prepared in medium (autoclave the solid PEG prior to adding double strength medium). Store in the dark

Stock aminopterin (1000×): 17.6 mg aminopterin (Sigma — Appendix 3) dissolved in a small volume of 0.1 M sodium hydroxide and made up to 100 ml with water. Store frozen in the dark

Stock hypoxanthine/thymidine (HT) solution (100×): 136.1 mg hypoxanthine and 38.75 mg thymidine (Sigma — Appendix 3) made up to 100 ml with water. Warm to 70°C to dissolve, sterilize by filtration and store frozen

Stock HAT (50×): 10 ml stock aminopterin plus 100 ml stock HT plus 90 ml water. Sterilize by filtration and store frozen in the dark

All glass homogenizer (Jencons — Appendix 3)

37°C water bath

Stop watch

Inverted microscope (Zeiss, Leitz — Appendix 3)

Equipment for counting viable cells (Section 4.1.1)

Centrifuge for sedimenting cells from suspension

Plastic conical-bottomed screw-capped centrifuge tubes, 325 mm × 115 mm (Falcon — Appendix 3)

24-well plates coated for tissue culture (Costar, Flow — Appendix 3)

Procedure

Cells must be grown and processed using aseptic conditions.

1   Grow tumour cells in medium containing 5–10% v/v FCS in spinners or bottles (see note 2). Keep cell density around 2×10^5 cells/ml. Usually about 2×10^7 cells or $3–4 \times 10^7$ cells are needed for mouse or rat fusions respectively.

2   Prepare medium containing 20% v/v FCS. Warm these and the PEG solution to 37°C. Also warm serum-free medium to this temperature.

3   Kill immune animal (see note 3) and remove its spleen aseptically. Trim away any residual connective or fatty tissue and place it in a homogenizer (see note 8).

4   Add 15 ml medium and disrupt using three passes of the pestle with a twisting motion.

5   Discard pieces of disrupted capsule, etc. and transfer the cell suspension to a sterile conical centrifuge tube. Centrifuge for 7.5 min at 300 *g*.

6   Wash cells twice by suspending in 40 ml medium in a conical centrifuge tube and centrifuging for 7.5 min at 300 *g*. Count viable cells (Section 4.1.1); most cells should be viable.

7   Count tumour cells and place required number in a conical centrifuge tube (see note 4). Wash once as in step 6.

8   Resuspend tumour and spleen cells in 10–20 ml medium. Mix together and centrifuge for 7.5 min at 300 g. Discard supernatant.

9   Warm cells to 37°C and disrupt the cell pellet by tapping the tube. Add 1 ml PEG solution over 1 min (mouse) or 30 sec (rat) *shaking all the time* (see note 5). Mix for a further 1 min, then add 1 ml medium over 1 min and then 8 ml of this medium over 5–6 minutes (increase the rate of medium addition as more medium is added). *Agitate all the time*, the cells must not be allowed to clump.

10   Add a further 10 ml warm medium dropwise and then centrifuge for 7.5 min at 300 g.

11   Resuspend cells thoroughly in 200 ml medium/20% FCS and plate out into eight 24-well Linbro plates (1 ml into each well).

12   Prepare HAT medium by adding 10 ml stock HAT solution to 500 ml medium/20% v/v FCS. Warm this to 37°C and add 1 ml to each well.

13   Feed with HAT medium every 6–8 days — remove half of the medium from each well and replace with an equal volume of fresh HAT medium. Check for hybridoma growth and tumour cell death using the inverted microscope.

14   After 10–14 days feed wells containing hybridomas with warm HT medium (10 ml stock HT added to 500 ml medium/20% FCS) every 2–3 days (see note 6).

15   Screen wells containing hybridomas for antibody secretion when the medium becomes yellow-orange (acid) and hybridomas are nearly confluent (see note 7).

16   Expand positive wells into further Linbro plates or bottles (after a further 5–8 days, cells will grow in medium containing 10% (v/v) FCS — see also Section 2.3.4) or clone (Section 2.3.2) or store frozen in liquid nitrogen. For this, resuspend about 10^7 hybridomas in 0.5–1 ml medium containing 20% (v/v) serum and 10% (v/v) DMSO. Store at -20°C for 12–18 h, then at -70°C for 24 h and then transfer to liquid nitrogen. For alternatives, see Section 4.1.

Notes

1   Animals should be test bled (Section 2.2.2) to ensure that they have responded to antigen before the spleen cells are fused. Give a booster injection (Section 2.2.1) preferably intravenously (no adjuvant) 3–4 days before the fusion is to be carried out.

2   Some laboratories use horse serum, newborn calf serum, serum substitute, or derivatives, or mixtures of these with FCS instead of FCS. These are cheaper than FCS, but often contain immunoglobulins which will contaminate the secreted monoclonal antibody. There is considerable variation between batches of sera in their ability to support cell growth. Each batch should be checked for its ability to support the growth of *hybridomas*. Most medium suitable for culturing lymphocytes can be used for hybridoma technology. The authors have

successfully used both RPMI 1640 and DMEM; however, do not change medium at sensitive stages. It is usual to add penicillin and streptomycin to medium.

3   Bleed the immune animal (preferably by heart puncture) just before killing it. This provides a positive control when assaying hybridomas for antibody secretion.

4   Usually a tumour cell to spleen cell ratio of 1:8 works well. However, ratios ranging from 1:4 to 1:12 have been used successfully.

5   Correct timing is important for cell fusion. Continual agitation is necessary to avoid cell clumping.

6   It is necessary to keep cells for a few days in medium containing HT after treatment with HAT to allow them to eliminate aminopterin.

7   Antibody secretion by hybridomas is detected most conveniently by solid phase radiobinding immunoassays (Section 11.1), immunofluorescence microscopy (Section 12.2) or flow microfluorimetry analysis (Section 12.2.2). Other procedures are not normally suitable for screening the large number of supernatants produced by the technique.

8   The use of a glass homogenizer to prepare the cell suspension is the quickest and most efficient procedure for mouse spleens. However, individual homogenizers should be evaluated for the production of a high yield of viable cells (see Section 4.1.1; a normal mouse spleen should yield about 10^8 lymphocytes). This method is not efficient for production of rat spleen suspensions, particularly if older animals are used. For these animals either disrupt the spleen using a wire gauze or tease the lymphocytes from the organ using two bent needles (Section 4.2.3).

2.3.2   Cloning hybridomas

Cloning is the process by which an individual cell is isolated and allowed to grow into a homogenous colony of cells. This colony can be selected and grown to provide the secreted monoclonal antibody. Cloning should be carried out 2–3 times to ensure that the antibody is monoclonal. Two different methods for this cloning are described below:

1   Cloning in soft agar

In this method high dilutions of cells are prepared in low concentration agar gel. The dilution of cells which produces discrete clones is selected and colonies of suitable size are picked from the plate and grown in culture.

Materials and equipment

Hybridomas (Section 2.3.1)

0.5% w/v agar (see note) prepared medium containing 15% v/v FCS
(see note 2, Section 2.3.1)
Sterile 9 cm Petri dishes for tissue culture (Flow — Appendix 3)
24-well plates coated for tissue culture (Costar, Flow — Appendix 3)
Inverted microscope
Heated water bath
Equipment for tissue culture including 5–7% CO_2 37°C incubator

Procedure

1   Add 12–14 ml of molten 0.5% w/v agar to each Petri dish (3
dishes are required per Linbro well or bottle of hybridomas). Allow
agar to gel and dry for 20 min at room temperature.
2   Suspend hybridomas in Linbro well or bottle and transfer 2–4 ×
10^3 cells in 0.2 ml of medium to one well of a fresh 24-well Linbro
plate. Add 0.8 ml medium to this and make three more serial 1:5
dilutions (i.e. 0.2 ml cells + 0.8 ml medium. Final dilutions are 1/5,
1/25, 1/125 of original). Discard 0.2 ml from the final well.
3   Allow agar solution to cool to about 45–47°C and add 1 ml to each
well, mix and transfer the contents of each well into separate agar-
containing Petri dishes. Incubate at 37°C in CO_2 incubator.
4   Check daily for cell growth using the microscope and discard
plates containing overgrown or no cells. When clones grow into colonies of about 20–100 cells pick them individually from the plate using
a Pasteur pipette. Incubate them in 1 ml medium/15% serum in
separate wells of a 24-well Linbro plate. Screen for antibody
secretion (see step 15 and note 7, Section 2.3.1).

Note

Some agar is toxic for hybridomas; check for this. Prepare agar solution by adding 2 g agar powder to 30–40 ml water, autoclaving, cooling
to 55°C and adding medium (at 55°C) containing 15% serum up to
400 ml. This is sufficient for cloning 10 hybridoma lines.

2   Cloning by limiting dilution

In this method cells are diluted so that they can be individually
pipetted into separate containers. The cells are plated out at theoretical concentrations of 1 cell/well, 1 cell/2 wells and 1 cell/5 wells.
Their growth is monitored and wells containing only one colony are
grown for monoclonal antibody production. The method given below
uses 96-well microtitre plates and a spleen cell feeder layer to enhance
hybridoma growth at the very low cell densities employed.

Materials and equipment

Hybridomas from fusion well (Section 2.3.1)

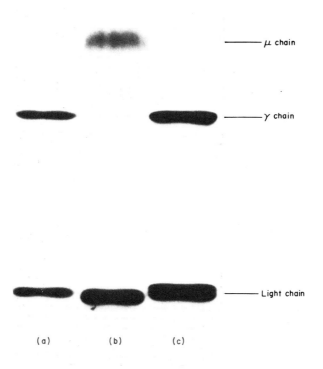

Fig. 2.1 Secretion products of three hybridoma cell lines. The products were biosynthetically radiolabelled with [³H]leucine (Section 5.4.1) and the culture supernatants reduced and analysed by SDS-polyacrylamide gel electrophoresis (Section 7.3.1) followed by fluorography (Section 1.5.2). (a) and (c) secrete IgG (detected as γ and light chain), whereas (b) secretes IgM (detected as μ and light chain).

Non-immune mouse of the same strain as hybridoma's parents
Medium (Table 4.1) containing 15% v/v FCS (see note 2, Section 2.3.1)
96-well microtitre plates coated for tissue culture (Costar, Flow — Appendix 3)

Procedure

1   Kill the mouse and remove its spleen aseptically. Prepare a suspension of spleen cells in medium/FCS (total volume 5 ml) as described in Section 2.3.1, steps 3–6.
2   Add one drop of spleen cell suspension (about 50 μl) to each well of the microtitre plate.
3   Prepare dilutions of hybridomas from one fusion well in medium/ FCS — 2 ml each of 20 cells/ml, 10 cells/ml and 4 cells/ml.
4   Add one drop (about 50 μl) of each hybridoma suspension to 32 wells of the microtitre plate. Add one drop of medium/FCS to each well and place in the CO_2 incubator for 1–3 weeks.
5   Check for cell growth, selecting wells containing only 1 colony (colonies should be visible macroscopically after 2–3 weeks). Assay for antibody secretion (Section 2.3.1, step 15 and note 7).

2.3.3   Production of ascitic fluid

Hybridomas will grow in the peritoneal cavity of animals of the same strain as the tumour cell line donor and spleen cell donor (Section 2.3.1), and secrete monoclonal antibody into the ascitic fluid formed within the cavity. By this procedure, large amounts of a monoclonal antibody can be produced (10 mg/ml of fluid) without the need for large-scale cell culture. The ascitic fluid will also contain immunoglobulins derived from the recipient animal. However, the monoclonal antibody can be purified from ascitic fluid by affinity chromatography (Section 10.3.1) or partially purified by several other procedures (Sections 3.3.1, 3.5, 10.3.2).

Materials and equipment

Hybridomas (about 10^7 cells/animal)
Pristane (Aldrich — Appendix 3)
Animals of the same strain as spleen cell donor and tumour cell line donor (see note 1)
Phosphate buffered saline *without* azide (PBS) (Appendix 2). Sterilize by autoclaving
Syringes (1 or 2 ml) with narrow gauge (23–27) hypodermic needles
Large gauge (19–21) hypodermic needles
Conical centrifuge tubes

42

Procedure

1 Inject each mouse intraperitoneally with 0.5 ml pristane (see note 3).
2 Grow hybridomas in culture.
3 Seven days after pristane injection (step 1), centrifuge the hybridomas (7.5 min, 300 g) discard the supernatant and resuspend the cell pellet in sterile PBS (2×10^7 cells/ml).
4 Inject 0.5 ml cell suspension i.p. into each animal using narrow gauge needles.
5 Inspect animals daily for swelling of the abdomen (indicating fluid production) and tap off ascitic fluid into conical centrifuge tubes using wide gauge hypodermic needles.
6 Remove any cells by centrifuging for 10 min at 500 g. Store the fluid frozen in aliquots.
7 Continue to tap fluid from animals at 1–2 day intervals.

Notes

1 If tumour cell line donor and spleen donor are not of the same strain use athymic (nu/nu) or F_1 hybrid animals for ascitic fluid production.
2 Injection of hybridomas does not always result in production of ascitic fluid. Occasionally the hybridomas do not survive or (more often) solid tumours are produced.
3 Lou rats do not require priming with pristane.
4 Re-injection of ascites derived cells (or ascites fluid) into new animals may increase the monoclonal antibody concentration in the ascites fluid, thus facilitating subsequent purification of the antibody and economizing on the use of animals.

2.3.4 Production of monoclonal antibodies *in vitro*

Monoclonal antibodies can be produced *in vitro*, rather than in ascites fluid, by culturing cells and harvesting the supernatant. However, the concentration of antibody is fairly low (5–40 μg/ml) and subsequent purification can be problematical. This approach can be scaled up by the use of spinner culture vessels (0.5–10 l) and purification problems reduced by using a low concentration (1–3%) of serum or serum-free medium. In some cases it is possible to select for high secretor clones.

2.3.5 Determination of class and subclass of monoclonal antibodies

The class of an antibody can be found by biosynthetically radio-labelling the hybridoma secretion products followed by analysis using SDS-PAGE and fluorography or radiography (Fig. 2.1), or by double immunodiffusion using class-specific antisera. In addition the IgG subclass can be determined using the latter technique and subclass-specific antisera.

43

1 Biosynthetic radiolabelling (see also Section 5.4)

Materials and equipment

Cloned hybridomas (2–5×10^6 cells in log phase growth, at least 95% viable)
Leucine-free DMEM (Gibco — Appendix 3)
[^{3}H]leucine, specific activity 120–190 mCi/mmol, sterile, 1 mCi/ml (Amersham — Appendix 3)
Flat-sided tissue culture tubes (Flow — Appendix 3)
Materials and equipment for cell culture (Section 2.3.1)

Procedure

1 Centrifuge hybridomas ($300 \, g$, 5 min), resuspend in 1 ml of leucine-free DMEM and transfer cell suspension to a tissue culture tube.
2 Add 200 μCi [^{3}H]leucine (i.e. 0.2 ml) and incubate at 37°C for 6 h.
3 Centrifuge at $300 \, g$ for 10 min, discard cells (**caution radioactive**) and analyse the supernatant by SDS-PAGE (Section 7.3.1) and fluorography (Section 1.5.2).

Note

The supernatant can be stored at -20°C prior to analysis.

2 Double immunodiffusion

Materials and equipment

Cloned hybridomas in log phase growth
Class- and/or subclass-specific antisera (Serotec — Appendix 3)
Saturated ammonium sulphate (Section 3.3.1) **or** membrane concentrator (Section 1.3.2), e.g. minicon system, 15 000 mol. wt cut-off (Millipore — Appendix 3)
PBS
Materials and equipment for cell culture (Section 2.3.1)
Materials and equipment for double immunodiffusion (Section 6.3.1)

Procedure

1 From a healthy culture of hybridomas, subculture in 10–50 ml medium containing 3% FCS until cells are confluent. Remove cells by centrifugation at $300 \, g$ for 10 min.
2 Concentrate supernatant about 20-fold by precipitation with 45% saturated ammonium sulphate (Section 3.3.1; Fig. 3.2) or using a membrane concentrator. After ammonium sulphate the precipitate should be redissolved in and dialysed against PBS before analysis.

44

3   Analyse supernatant by double immunodiffusion using the specific antisera (Section 6.3.1).

Note

Hybridoma supernatants can be stored at $-20°C$ prior to analysis if convenient.

2.3.6   Viral transformation of human B lymphocytes for the production of monoclonal antibodies

Human B lymphocytes can be transformed by Epstein-Barr virus (EBV) enabling them to grow continually in culture usually without impairing their ability to secrete antibody. Thus cloned EBV transformed B cells can be used to produce human monoclonal antibodies of selected specificity. Major problems with this approach seem to be the instability of such cell lines with respect to antibody secretion and the considerable difficulty of cloning positive cultures (the cells form large clumps which are polyclonal and almost impossible to disaggregate). A possible solution to these problems is to fuse the transformed lymphocytes with a mouse myeloma line such as NSO (Section 2.3.1) yielding hybridomas which are easier to work with because they do not clump appreciably in culture, and which grow as stable antibody secretors.

1   EBV transformation

Materials and equipment

Cell line *secreting infectious* EBV, e.g. the marmoset lymphoblastoid line
   B95-8 (ECACC — Appendix 3)
Human peripheral blood, 25–50 ml (see note 1)
RPMI 1640 medium (Section 4.1)
Fetal calf serum inactivated by heating at 56°C for 20 min (FCS)
Material and equipment for cell culture (Section 2.3.1)
96-well microtitre plates (Nunc, Flow, Costar — Appendix 3)

Procedure
Warning   EBV can cause infection and disease in humans — use appropriate facilities and care. Also all human blood should be treated as potential sources of hepatitis and HIV (AIDS virus).
Cells must be processed and grown under aseptic conditions.
1   Grow B95-8 cells in RPMI 1640 containing 15% (v/v) FCS (10–50 ml). The supernatant contains infectious EBV. Just prior to transformation, remove cells by centrifuging culture for 10 min at 300 *g* **(care   infectious virus).**

45

2   Prepare lymphocytes from blood as described in Section 4.2.1 —
the dextran step may be omitted (Section 4.2.1, note 2).
3   Wash the cells twice by re-suspending in RPMI and centrifuging
for 7–8 min at 300 g. Adjust the final cell suspension to 10^7 cells/ml.
4   Add an equal volume of B95-8 cell supernatant and incubate for
1.5–2 h at room temperature.
5   Wash the cells three times with RPMI as in step 3 and resuspend
at 10^6 cells/ml in RPMI containing 15% FCS (see note 2). Plate out in
microtitre plates (about 150 μl/well).
6   Check for colony growth using an inverted microscope. Screen
supernatants from colony-containing wells for antibody (see Section
2.3.1, note 7).
7   Clone cells from positive wells by limiting dilution (Section 2.3.2,
subsection 2) **but** use irradiated (3000 rads) human lymphocytes as
feeder cells (see note 3). Screen colony-containing wells for antibody
secretion (see Section 2.3.1, note 7).
8   Grow positive clones in culture, cryopreserve (Section 4.1) or fuse
with a myeloma line (subsection 2 below).

Notes

1   It is possible (and probably better) to use human lymphocytes from
spleen, lymph nodes or tonsil.
2   Some workers suggest that the addition of the mitogen phytohaemagglutinin (PHA) after EBV infection (step 5) is advantageous as
it will prevent cytotoxic T cell response to EBV infected cells as well as
stimulating growth factor production. For this add PHA (HA15, Wellcome — Appendix 3) to 1% (v/v). It is also possible to remove T cells
by E-rosetting (Section 4.3.2) or to enrich for antigen-specific B cells
using antigen-coated erythrocytes (Section 4.3.3) or other materials
(Section 4.3.4).
3   This cloning is particularly problematical because of aggregation; it
is unlikely to yield properly cloned lines, especially at the first attempt.
It is probably better to fuse positive cells with a myeloma line (subsection 2 below).

2   Fusion of EBV transformed lymphocytes with myeloma cells

Fusion is carried out as described in Section 2.3.1 except that the
HAT selection medium is supplemented with ouabain. The aminopterin in the HAT medium kills non-fused myelomas and the ouabain
selectively destroys human cells but not human/mouse hybridomas.
Such lines are easily cloned in soft agar (Section 2.3.2).

Materials and equipment

EBV transformed antibody secreting human B cells (subsection 1
   above)

Mouse myelomas, e.g. NSO (Section 2.3.1 and Table 2.2)
Materials and equipment for cell fusion (Section 2.3.1)

Procedure

1   Fuse cells as described in Section 2.3.1 except substitute EBV transformed human lymphocytes for murine splenocytes. Use a myeloma: lymphocyte ratio of 1:1.
2   Select fused cells using HAT medium (Section 2.3.1) supplemented with 1 μM ouabain.
3   Inspect for colony growth and screen and clone cells as described in Section 2.3.1.

Note

It is possible to use a human myeloma cell line instead of mouse. However, many human fusion partners give very low fusion efficiency.

3 Purification of immunoglobulins, constituent chains and fragments

3.1 INTRODUCTION

Antibodies are the major tools of the trade for immunochemists. They are able to recognize specifically every molecular structure (within certain dimensional limits) that man has isolated or synthesized, and they can distinguish between molecules as confusingly similar as two proteins differing by only one amino acid residue. Immunochemistry is the use of antibodies for the detection or purification of molecules. These antibodies are generally detected by an artificial label attached before use. This label can be radioactive (radioimmunoassay, Chapter 11; gel staining, Chapter 8; autoradiography, Section 12.4), fluorescent (immunofluorescence techniques, Section 12.2), enzymic (ELISA, Section 11.4; immunohistochemistry, Section 12.3) or alteration of a physical property like solubility (affinity chromatography and immunoprecipitation, Chapter 10). Antibodies belong to a group of proteins called 'immunoglobulins'. They are all made up of a common structural unit comprising two heavy and two light chains. The heavy chain constant region determines the class and subclass of the immunoglobulin, whilst the light chains (either kappa or lambda) are common to all classes (Table 3.2). The variable regions of both heavy and light chains determine the antigen binding specificity. Most of the techniques described in this book use immunoglobulins, or immunoglobulin fragments, as antibodies, target antigens or biological effector molecules and this chapter is concerned with preparation, purification and care of such tools.

Immunoglobulins have been isolated from only a limited number of species and modifications appropriate for each animal are indicated where known. For preparations from other species, try the method given, assay for the immunoglobulin at each stage (using, for example, immunoelectrophoresis, Section 6.4.3, and gel electrophoresis, Section 7.3) and modify the procedure accordingly. Fortunately, immunoglobulin structure is conserved throughout all mammals (and to a lesser extent birds, amphibians and marsupials) and so only minor changes should be necessary. The methods described are not necessarily the only ones available. They are, however, tried and trusted and recommended for initial preparations at least. The procedures are described for the amount of starting material usually encountered. They can be scaled up or down as required, but remember that it is the length of the column or slab in gel filtration and electrophoresis that governs the separation and so this parameter should be kept constant and the diameter or thickness of the matrix varied with the amount of the sample.

If pure antibody with a certain specificity (as distinct from pure immunoglobulin of a certain class) is required, then direct application of the immune sera (or ascites fluid or culture supernatant in hybridoma studies, Section 2.3) to an affinity column of insolubilized antigen (Section 10.3.1) is recommended. The bound antibody can then be eluted and purified further by the techniques described in this chapter.

The structural heterogeneity of immunoglobulins makes it almost impossible to isolate a class of immunoglobulin which is totally representative of the spectrum of molecules comprising that class *in vivo*. For example, the IgG pool obtained from serum by ion exchange chromatography (Section 3.3.1) will have lost some of the acidic molecules. Similarly, the IgA pool prepared from milk (Section 3.7.2) will contain neither the very basic molecules nor monomeric forms. Consequently these pools may be deficient in certain subclasses, subgroups or light chain types. These considerations are especially important when purifying certain monoclonal immunoglobulins (e.g. myeloma proteins or hybridoma antibodies) which may not fractionate with the bulk of molecules of that class.

3.2 MANIPULATION AND STORAGE OF IMMUNOGLOBULINS

Fortunately for the progress of immunology, immunoglobulins are robust proteins. They survive for long periods in the circulation and in the harsher environment of external secretions. In the laboratory, they can be kept at room temperature for several days (allowing convenient column chromatography), heated to 56°C (allowing the selective destruction of complement activity in antisera; Section 4.1), exposed to pH 2 or 11 for short periods (allowing their elution from antigen columns, Section 10.3.1) and precipitated and redissolved by changes in ionic strength. They even retain their antigen binding activity in low concentrations of urea or detergents. However, there is no point in destroying precious antibodies or fragments by carelessness and the following general procedures should be adopted.

1 Serum and other immunoglobulin solutions (except for IgM) are ideally stored frozen (at −20°C or better still −70°C) but repeated thawing and freezing should be avoided by aliquoting. Chicken proteins and serum should not be frozen. IgM can be stored at −20°C if glycerol is added to 50% v/v.

2 Alternatively, store at 2–4°C with the addition of 0.1% sodium azide or 0.01% thimerosal to retard bacterial growth (see Section 1.2.1 for azide warning). This is useful if freezer space is limited or if a solution is sampled repeatedly.

3 Pure immunoglobulins and fragments can be freeze-dried but this usually causes some aggregation when they are reconstituted.

49

4   Immunoglobulins are happiest in neutral isotonic buffers (e.g. phosphate buffered saline, Appendix 2). Carrier protein (e.g. albumin or haemoglobin) should be added to solutions of low protein concentration (less than 0.1 mg/ml) where possible (for example in immunoassays, Chapter 11).

5   After extremes of pH have been applied, the solution should be neutralized as quickly as possible and then dialysed into a neutral isotonic buffer.

6   Conversely, high concentrations of denaturing agent (e.g. guanidine-HCl) should be removed gradually by dialysis against very small volumes (1–3 × sample volume) of neutral isotonic buffer to allow the molecule to refold slowly to its native configuration.

7   Temperatures of 2–4°C are recommended where possible and convenient during isolation and use.

8   Immunoglobulins from certain species, notably chicken, mouse and rat, are more labile than others and greater care should be taken with these (see Section 3.4.5).

3.3   ISOLATION OF IgG

This immunoglobulin is the most abundant in the circulation (Table 3.1) and so serum is the usual starting material for its isolation. However, a method has been developed recently for purifying IgG from eggs (Section 3.3.2). As well as being convenient for the immunochemist, this novel idea may have clinical application by providing neatly wrapped antibodies for oral administration (e.g. in intestinal infections). The use of hybridoma technology for the production of monoclonal antibodies (Section 2.3) requires the isolation of IgG (and

Table 3.1   Human immunoglobulins in normal serum

Class	Subclasses	Normal serum concentration (mg/ml)		Approximate κ:λ ratio of L chain*
IgG		8.0	–15.0	2:1
	IgG1	5.0	–10.0	2:1
	IgG2	1.8	– 3.5	1:1
	IgG3	0.6	– 1.2	1:1
	IgG4	0.3	– 0.6	5:1
IgM		0.5	– 2.0	3:1
IgA		1.0	– 4.0	1:1
	IgA1	0.8	– 3.4	
	IgA2	0.2	– 0.6	
IgD		0.003	– 0.3	1:10
IgE		0.0001–	0.0007	

* The ratios for immunoglobulins present at low levels in the circulation are derived from the frequency with which myelomas containing each type of light chain occur. These values may not represent the normal state.

IgM, Section 3.5) from cell culture supernatants and rodent ascites fluid (see note 3, Section 3.3.1). All these procedures involve a combination of salt precipitation and ion exchange chromatography and occasionally gel filtration, although affinity chromatography is useful in some cases (e.g. Section 10.3.2).

3.3.1 Isolation of IgG from serum

Materials and equipment

Rabbit serum — 50 ml
Sodium sulphate, anhydrous
0.07 M sodium phosphate pH 6.3
DEAE-cellulose (e.g. Whatman DE32 or DE 52; Table 1.2) — 50 ml wet settled volume
Heated water bath
Column chromatography equipment (Section 1.2.1) including a column 1.6 cm × 30 cm

Procedure

1 Warm the serum to 25°C, add 9 g sodium sulphate to make an 18% (w/v) solution and stir to dissolve. Incubate for 30 min at 25°C and warm a centrifuge to 25°C.
2 Centrifuge at 3000 g for 30 min at 25°C.
3 Discard the supernatant, note the volume of the protein precipitate and redissolve it in water up to 25 ml.
4 Warm the solution to 25°C and add sodium sulphate to make a 14% (w/v) solution (about 2.2 g) — remember to allow for the salt carried over in the first precipitate. Stir to dissolve and incubate for 30 min at 25°C.
5 Repeat step 2 and discard the supernatant. Redissolve the precipitate in water up to 15 ml and dialyse against phosphate buffered saline (for storage) or 0.07 M phosphate buffer (for further purification).
6 Equilibrate the ion exchanger with the phosphate buffer, pack into the column (Section 1.2.2) and wash with the same buffer at room temperature. When both exchanger and sample are *fully* equilibrated, apply the sample to the column and elute with starting buffer all at room temperature. Monitor the absorbance at 280 nm and collect 10 ml fractions.
7 IgG is eluted by the starting buffer in a single asymmetric peak (Fig. 3.1) and impurities are bound and retarded by the exchanger (some may be visible as green or red bands on the column). The early fractions are purest and so discard pools B and C (Fig. 3.1) if purity is paramount (note, however, the effect of structural heterogeneity, Section 3.1).
8 Calculate the protein yield from the absorbance at 280 nm and

51

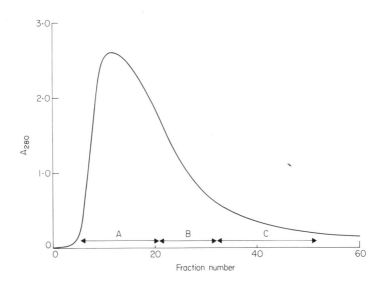

Fig. 3.1 Isolation of IgG from rabbit serum on DEAE cellulose in 0.07 M sodium phosphate pH 6.3, following sodium sulphate precipitation (Section 3.3.1). The earlier peaks are purer but are less representative of the heterogeneous IgG pool. See Figs. 6.4, 7.6 and 11.5 for analyses of human IgG.

volume of pool (Section 1.1.1). This should be 8–10 mg/ml of serum, of which about 10% will have the relevant antibody activity if immune serum was used.

Notes

1 Ammonium sulphate (40–45% saturated; add 24–27 g of solid to each 100 ml serum; Fig. 3.2) may be substituted for sodium sulphate and the whole procedure carried out at room temperature or lower. This is recommended for more labile IgG (e.g. from mouse) but it gives a slightly less pure product.
2 If high purity is not required the ion exchange step can be omitted and the procedure terminated after step 5. Alternatively serum can be applied directly to the DEAE-cellulose after dialysis against the starting buffer; to improve retention of impurities use 5 ml wet settled volume of exchanger per ml of serum and 10 mM sodium phosphate pH 8.0.
3 Other species:
Human — use 20 mM sodium phosphate pH 8.0 for the ion exchange step.
Goat — use 14% (w/v) sodium sulphate in step 1 and 20 mM sodium phosphate pH 7.5 for the ion exchange step.
Mouse and rat (including monoclonals) — by definition every monoclonal is different (see discussion in Section 3.1) but the following points are generally true. DEAE fractionation does not work well, except for some monoclonals which happen to have a suitable charge; an HPLC

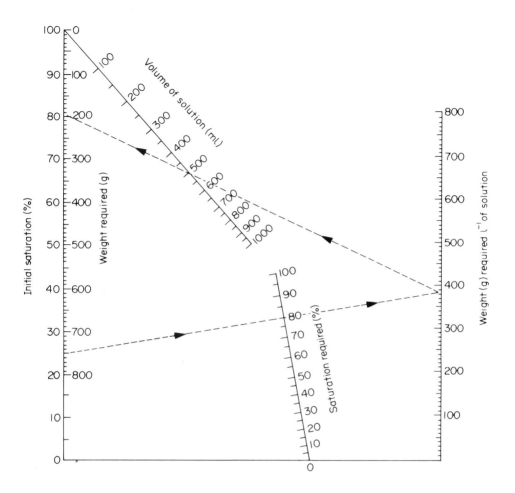

Fig. 3.2 Nomogram to calculate the amount of solid ammonium sulphate to add to a given volume of liquid to achieve desired saturation. Reproduced from Dixon (1953) with permission. The solubility of ammonium sulphate, unlike that of sodium sulphate, varies little with temperature (100% saturated is 3.9–4.1M from 0 to 25°C). However, added solid sodium sulphate does not greatly change the volume of the solution and so a nomogram is not necessary. To prepare a stock 100% saturated ammonium sulphate solution stir 1000 g of solid in 1 litre of water at 50°C. Let stand overnight at room temperature and use the supernatant.

system (Section 1.2.4) improves the resolution in some cases (Clezardin *et al.*, 1985; see, for example, Fig. 7.7). For mouse, affinity chromatography on insolubilized protein A (Section 10.3.2) is recommended for isolation from serum, culture supernatant and ascites fluid. We have not found fractionation on hydroxylapatite to be satisfactory in most cases. Removal of lipids from ascites fluid is recommended before fractionation to increase yield and purity and one simple method involves addition of silicon dioxide powder followed by centrifugation (Neoh *et al.*, 1986). A 25–50% pure preparation, which is adequate for many purposes, can be obtained simply by precipitation with ammonium sulphate (see note 1) or polyethylene glycol 6000 (PEG). For the latter add an equal volume of 20% (w/v) PEG in PBS, incubate for 15 min on ice and centrifuge at 2000 g for 30 min. A novel purification by adsorption chromatography has been reported (Belew *et al.*, 1987).

4 Human IgG is analysed by various techniques in Figs. 6.4, 7.6 and 11.5.

3.3.2 Isolation of IgG from chicken eggs (from Jensenius *et al.*, 1981)

It is easier to obtain eggs than blood from chickens. The yolk contains 10–20 mg of IgG per ml including antibody specificities present in the circulation. Hence 0.5–1.0 g of IgG can be collected per chicken per week. No other class of immunoglobulin is detectable in the yolk. The major problem in the isolation is removal of lipids which are present at high concentration.

Materials and equipment

Chicken egg
Tris buffered saline containing 0.1% sodium azide (TBS — Appendix 2)
10% (w/v) dextran sulphate in TBS
1 M calcium chloride in TBS
Sodium sulphate, anhydrous
36% (w/v) sodium sulphate (this is a supersaturated solution; it should be heated to dissolve the salt).

Procedure

1 Break eggshell and separate the yolk from white. Cut the yolk membrane and pour out the yolk (about 10 ml).

2 Add TBS to a final volume of 50 ml, mix and centrifuge at 2000 g for 20 min at 20°C.

3 Discard the pellet and add 3 ml of dextran sulphate and 7.5 ml of calcium chloride solutions to the supernatant. Mix and incubate for 30 min at room temperature.

4 Centrifuge at 2000 g for 20 min at 20°C and store the supernatant. Resuspend the precipitate in 50 ml of TBS, recentrifuge and pool the two supernatants, discarding the final pellet. (If the first supernatant is cloudy, add more dextran sulphate and calcium chloride and repeat the incubation and centrifugation.)

5 Add TBS to the pooled supernatants to a final volume of 100 ml. Add 20 g of sodium sulphate, stir to dissolve and incubate at room temperature for 1 h.

6 Centrifuge at 2000 g for 20 min at 25°C. Discard the supernatant and note the volume of precipitate.

7 Redissolve the protein precipitate in TBS to a final volume of 10 ml. Add sodium sulphate solution to make a final concentration of

9% (w/v), allowing for salt carried over in precipitate. Mix and incubate for 1 h at room temperature.

8 Centrifuge at 2000 *g* for 20 min at 25°C. Discard the pellet and note the volume of the supernatant.

9 Add sodium sulphate solution to make a final concentration of 14% (w/v), allowing for 9% salt already present. Mix and incubate for 1 h at room temperature.

10 Repeat step 6 and dissolve the precipitate in 5–10 ml of TBS and dialyse against TBS. The yield should be 10–15 mg/ml of yolk.

Notes

1 The sodium sulphate is nearly saturated in some steps and the incubations can be carried out at 25–30°C if necessary.

2 The procedure does not give completely pure IgG but the preparation is free from other classes of immunoglobulin because of their absence from yolk. Further purification (e.g. gel filtration on Sephadex G-200) can be carried out if necessary.

3 Chicken IgG should not be frozen but it is stable for many months at 4°C in TBS containing a suitable preservative (Section 3.2, note 2).

3.4 PREPARATION OF FRAGMENTS OF IgG

The nomenclature for the constituent chains and fragments of IgG is given diagrammatically in Fig. 3.3 and listed in Table 3.2.

3.4.1 Separation of heavy and light chains

The disulphide bonds between heavy (γ) and light (L) chains are easily split by reducing agents (under conditions which leave intrachain bonds intact) and they can then be alkylated to prevent their re-oxidation. However, the two chains are still held together by non-covalent forces and a dissociating agent is required during chromatography for their separation (Fleischman *et al.*, 1963).

Materials and equipment

0.5 M tris-HCl pH 8.0 containing 2 mM EDTA

IgG (Section 3.3.1) — 50 mg in 2.5 ml of the tris buffer

0.1 M dithiothreitol in the tris buffer (freshly made)

0.21 M iodoacetic acid in the tris buffer (freshly made)

Oxygen-free nitrogen

1 M propionic acid — degas under vacuum before use

Sephadex G-25 (medium) in 1 M propionic acid packed into a 1.0 cm × 30 cm column (Section 1.2.1)

Sephadex G-100 (fine) in 1 M propionic acid packed into a 1.6 cm × 100 cm column (Section 1.2.1)

Column chromatography equipment (Section 1.2.1)

55

Table 3.2 Polypeptide chain composition of human immunoglobulins

Isotype	Molecular weight (×10⁻³)	% carbohydrate	H chain designation	H chain domains	Chain composition	Molecular weight of chains (×10⁻³) total	polypeptide	% carbohydrate of chains
IgG1	146	2–3	$\gamma 1$	4	$2\gamma 1$ 2L	51 23	49 23	3–4 < 0.5
IgG2	146	2–3	$\gamma 2$	4	$2\gamma 2$ 2L	51 23	49 23	3–4 < 0.5
IgG3	170	2–3	$\gamma 1$	4	$2\gamma 3$ 2L	60 23	57 23	3–4 < 0.5
IgG4	146	2–3	$\gamma 4$	4	$2\gamma 4$ 2L	51 23	49 23	3–4 < 0.5
IgM	900	10–12	μ	5	10μ 10L 1J	67 23 15	57 23 14	12–16 < 0.5 7.5
IgA1[a]	160	7–10	$\alpha 1$	4	$2\alpha 1$ 2L	56 23	50 23	10–15 < 0.5
IgA2[a]	160	7–10	$\alpha 2$	4	$2\alpha 2$ 2L	53 23	48 23	10–15 < 0.5
Secretory IgA[b]	390	7–10	$\alpha 1$ or $\alpha 2$	4	4α 4L 1J 1SC[c]	53–56 23 15 75	48–50 23 14 63	10–15 < 0.5 7.5 15–16
IgD	165	10–12	δ	4	2δ 2L	60 23	51 23	14–17 < 0.5
IgE	185	10–12	ϵ	5	2ϵ 2L	70 23	59 23	13–16 < 0.5

([a]) Data are given for the monomeric form which predominates in human sera. Polymeric forms also exist (up to pentamer); these contain 1 molecule of J chain per polymer in addition to α and L chains.

([b]) Data are given for the dimer (Fig. 3.9); a tetrameric form is also common in man.

([c]) SC, secretory component, derived from a membrane-bound poly-Ig receptor used to transport the IgA through epithelial cells during its secretion (Mostov *et al.* 1984).

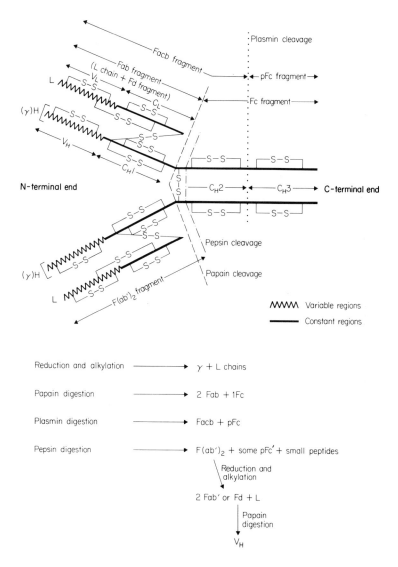

Fig. 3.3 Diagrammatic representation of rabbit IgG showing its constituent chains, domain structure, variable and constant regions, sites of proteolytic cleavage, nomenclature of chains and fragments and pathways for their isolation. See Section 3.4.5 for mouse and rat monoclonals.

Procedure

1 Add 0.275 ml of dithiothreitol solution to the IgG, flush with nitrogen and incubate in a sealed tube at room temperature for 1 h with stirring (final dithiothreitol concentration is 10 mM).

2 Cool the mixture on ice and cover with foil. Add 0.275 ml of iodoacetic acid solution and incubate in an ice bath for 30 min with stirring.

3   Add 20 µl of dithiothreitol solution and incubate at room temperature for 15 min.

4   Apply the mixture to the G-25 column and elute with 1 M propionic acid. Collect 1 ml fractions (by hand is convenient) and monitor the absorbance at 280 nm.

5   Apply the protein peak from step 4 (eluted in the void volume) directly to the G-100 column and elute with 1 M propionic acid. Collect 2.5 ml fractions and monitor the absorbance at 280 nm.

6   The first peak (Fig. 3.4) consists of aggregated protein and any intact IgG. The second peak is heavy chain and the third peak light chain.

7   Calculate the protein yields from the absorbance at 280 nm and volume of the pools (Table 1.1). The yield of L chain should be 25–28% of the total yield of γ and L chain; a lower value indicates the presence of light chain (presumable dimeric) in the heavy chain pool.

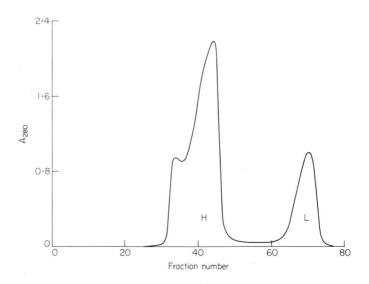

Fig. 3.4   Fractionation of partially reduced and alkylated IgG on a Sephadex G–100 column in 1 M propionic acid (Section 3.4.1). The first peak contains aggregated protein, the second (H) heavy chain and the third (L) light chain.

Notes

1   Alkylation of methionine residues occurs at low pH and so a strong buffer is employed and a second addition of reducing agent is used to remove excess alkylating agent before acidification.

2   Iodoacetamide or ethyleneimine can be substituted for iodoacetic acid according to the charge required on the cysteine residues.

3   Light chains (except mouse κ chain) are soluble in neutral buffers,

58

and so can be dialysed and stored frozen. Heavy chains are only sparingly soluble at neutral pH and, unless very dilute solutions are appropriate (e.g. in immunoassays), they are best stored in 0.01 M acetic acid or freeze dried.

4 Dialysis against 1 M propionic acid can be substituted for the desalting procedure (step 4) but this causes more aggregation (i.e. increased first peak in Fig. 3.4).

5 The procedure is applicable to the IgG from most species tested so far.

6 In certain disease states, free homogeneous light chain (termed 'Bence-Jones protein') is present in the urine. It can be easily isolated in non-denatured form by precipitation at 4°C using 65% saturated ammonium sulphate (add 43.5 g to each 100ml of urine, Fig. 3.2) followed by gel filtration on Sephadex G-75 in 10 mM tris-HCl pH 7.3 containing 0.5 M sodium chloride.

3.4.2 Preparation of Fab and Fc fragments

Native IgG is hydrolysed in the hinge region (Fig. 3.3) by papain to yield two antigen-binding fragments (Fab) and one dimer of the C-terminal half of the heavy chain (Fc; Porter, 1959). These are all of similar size (50 000 molecular weight) but they can be separated by ion exchange chromatography. In general, proteolytic fragments of immunoglobulins can be separated under non-denaturing conditions because they are not held by non-covalent bonds (compare the interactions between γ and L chains — Section 3.4.1).

Materials and equipment

0.1 M sodium phosphate pH 7.0, containing 0.01 M cysteine 2 mM EDTA
Rabbit IgG (Section 3.3.1) — 50 mg in 3 ml of the phosphate buffer
Papain (Worthington — Appendix 3)
0.01 M sodium acetate pH 5.5
1 M sodium acetate pH 5.5
CM-cellulose (e.g. Whatman CM32 or CM52; Table 1.2) — 25 ml wet settled volume
Column chromatography equipment (Section 1.2.1) including a column 1.0 cm × 30 cm and linear gradient maker 2 × 100 ml (Section 1.2.2)

Procedure

1 Dissolve 1 mg of papain in 100 μl of 0.1 M sodium phosphate buffer and quickly add 50 μl of this to the IgG. Mix gently and incubate at 37°C overnight (16 h).

2 Dialyse against water and then 3 × 500 ml of 0.01 M sodium acetate pH 5.5.

3   Equilibrate the ion exchanger with the 0.01 M acetate buffer and pack into the column (Section 1.2.2). Wash with the same buffer at room temperature.

4   When both sample and exchanger are *fully* equilibrated, apply the sample to the column and elute with at least 60 ml of starting buffer until the absorbance at 280 nm has returned to baseline. Then apply a linear gradient, total volume 200 ml, from 0.01 M to 1 M acetate all at room temperature. Collect 5 ml fractions and monitor the absorbance at 280 nm.

5   Protein eluted with the starting buffer and the first peak in the gradient consists mostly of Fab. The third peak is Fc. The protein yield in the three peaks should be about 90% of the original IgG.

Notes

1   These preparations are not completely pure (test by immuno-electrophoresis, Section 6.4.3, and polyacrylamide electrophoresis, Section 7.3). They can be further purified by affinity chromatography using insolubilized anti-Fc or Protein A to remove Fc and undigested IgG from Fab, and insolubilized anti-L chain to remove Fab and undigested IgG from Fc (Sections 10.3.2 and 10.3.3).

2   A fragment very similar to Fab (termed Fab') can be obtained by reduction of the divalent pepsin fragment $F(ab')_2$ (Section 3.4.3).

3   The cysteine used to activate papain (step 1) also partially reduces interchain disulphide bonds but the chains remain together, held by non-covalent forces (Section 3.4.1). The disulphide bonds reform as the reducing agent is removed (step 2). This complication may be avoided by activating 10 mg of papain in 1 ml of 0.1 M sodium phosphate pH 7.0, 2 mM EDTA 0.01 M cysteine at 37°C for 30 min and rapidly removing the reducing agent by desalting (Sections 1.2.1 and 3.4.1) on a column (1.2 cm × 30 cm) of Sephadex G-25 (medium) in 0.1 M sodium phosphate pH 7.0 2 mM EDTA. This activated papain can then be added to the IgG solution in the absence of reducing agent.

4   Papain will produce Fab and Fc fragments from the IgG of other species, including human, mouse, rat and guinea-pig, but they are not necessarily resolved by CM-cellulose chromatography. For example, separation of mouse and human fragments is by DEAE-cellulose chromatography using a gradient from 0 to 0.2 M NaCl in 5 mM tris HCl pH 7.5 for mouse and from 0 to 0.3 M NaCl in 0.1 M sodium phosphate pH 8.0 for human (Fab elutes first followed by any IgG then Fc; papain is in the fall through). In decreasing order of suscepti-bility to digestion the subclasses are IgG3> IgG1> IgG4> IgG2 for human; IgG2b> IgG3> IgG2a> IgG1 for mouse; IgG2a> IgG2c> IgG2b> IgG1 for rat. See Section 3.4.5 for a fuller discussion of monoclonals.

3.4.3   Preparation of F(ab')₂, Fab' and pFc' fragments

Native IgG is also hydrolysed by pepsin (Nisonoff *et al.*, 1975). However, this enzyme cleaves on the C-terminal side of at least one γ-γ chain disulphide bond to give a divalent antigen binding fragment, F(ab')₂. It also degrades part of the Fc portion to small peptides to leave a dimer of the C-terminal quarter of the γ chain, pFc' (Fig. 3.3). The F(ab')₂ fragment can be reduced to the monovalent Fab' fragment.

Materials and equipment

0.1 M sodium acetate pH 4.5
IgG (Section 3.3.1) — 50 mg in 2.5 ml of the acetate buffer
Pepsin (Worthington — Appendix 3)
2 M tris
Tris buffered saline (TBS — Appendix 2)
Sephadex G-200 (fine) in TBS packed into a column 1.6 cm × 100 cm (Section 1.2.1)
Column chromatography equipment (Section 1.2.1)
For Fab':
1 M tris-HCl pH 7.5
0.2 M EDTA, disodium salt
0.1 M dithiothreitol in the 1 M tris buffer, freshly made
0.21 M iodoacetamide in the 1 M tris buffer, freshly made

Procedure

1   Dissolve 2 mg of pepsin in 200 μl of the acetate buffer and add 100 μl of this to the IgG solution. Mix gently and incubate at 37°C overnight (16 h).
2   Neutralize with 2 M tris (approximately 300 μl — this irreversibly inactivates the enzyme) and centrifuge at 2000 *g* for 10 min to remove any precipitate.
3   Apply the supernatant to the G-200 column and elute with TBS. Collect 2.5 ml fractions and monitor the absorbance at 280 nm.
4   The first major peak is F(ab')₂ (Fig. 3.5). In front of this is undigested material and just behind it any Fab' or intact Fc formed. These minor products are sometimes not completely resolved from F(ab')₂ and form shoulders on the main peak. pFc' is in the next peak and small peptides are eluted in the total column volume (Fig. 3.5).
Fab'. F(ab')₂ can be directly reduced to Fab' if required.
1   Pool the fractions containing F(ab')₂ and concentrate to 5 ml (this should give a protein concentration of about 6 mg/ml). Add 0.5 ml of the 1 M tris buffer and 50 μl of EDTA solution.
2   Add 50 μl of the dithiothreitol solution and incubate in a sealed tube at room temperature for 1 h with stirring.

61

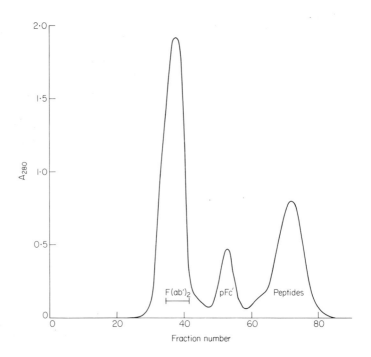

Fig. 3.5 Fractionation of pepsin digested human IgG on a Sephadex G–200 column in TBS (Section 3.4.3). The shoulder on the leading edge of the F(ab')₂ peak contains undigested IgG and should be discarded.

3   Cool on ice, cover with foil and add 50 μl of the iodoacetamide solution. Incubate in an ice bath for 30 min with stirring.

4   Add 5 μl of dithiothreitol solution, incubate at room temperature for 15 min and apply the mixture to the G-200 column. Elute as for the peptic digest above. There will be a small peak of undissociated F(ab')₂ in its original position followed by a major peak of Fab'.

Notes

1   The separation between undigested IgG and F(ab')₂ varies between species, and subclasses of one species, being best for rabbit. If the IgG is a shoulder on the main peak, pure F(ab')₂ can still be obtained in a reasonable yield by discarding the early fractions (Fig. 3.5). The use of Sephadex G-150 may improve the separation in some cases. HPLC (Section 1.2.4) is useful for this.

2   The subclasses of human IgG vary in their susceptibility to digestion in the order IgG3 = IgG4> IgG2> IgG1. This is most apparent in the yield of pFc' which is maximal for IgG3 after 2 h digestion but for IgG1 only after 24 h digestion. (IgG1 comprises about 70% of normal pool IgG.)

3   F(ab')₂ can be obtained from many species, including rabbit, human, guinea-pig, horse, goat and sheep (see, however, note 1). For

mouse and rat monoclonals see Section 3.4.5. The susceptibility of IgG differs between species. Sheep, horse and goat are relatively resistant and are digested better in 0.1 M sodium formate pH 3.6. The pFc' fragment can only be obtained from human and to a lesser degree rabbit. Digestion of rabbit IgG with plasmin produces pFc and Facb fragments (Fig. 3.3; Connell & Porter, 1971).

4   For comments on reduction and alkylation see Section 3.4.1. The interchain disulphide bonds of Fab' are mostly cleaved but the Fd and L chains remain held together by non-covalent bonds. The Fab' is usually purer than the corresponding Fab fragment obtained by ion exchange chromatography (Section 3.4.2).

3.4.4   Preparation of Fd and V_H fragments

After cleavage of the interchain disulphide bonds of rabbit $F(ab')_2$, L chain can be partially removed from the γ chain fragment (termed Fd; Fig. 3.3) under dissociating conditions (Fleischman et al., 1963). Although these chains are of similar size they can be resolved by gel filtration because of the tendency of Fd to form dimers at low pH. The Fd fragment can be hydrolysed by papain under carefully controlled conditions to produce the intact V_H domain (Fig. 3.3) in about 50% yield (Mole et al., 1975). The C_H1 domain is completely degraded.

3.4.5   Fragmentation of mouse and rat monoclonal IgG

The subclasses of mouse and rat IgG appear to vary even more in their susceptibility to proteolytic digestion than in human IgG (Section 3.4.2, note 4; Section 3.4.3, note 2). On top of this every monoclonal antibody is different. The points below are given for a general guide — do an analytical scale digestion first and analyse the products by SDS-PAGE (Section 7.3.1) at varying digestion times. The method used to prepare the IgG can affect the digest (e.g. the acid from an affinity column and precipitation will increase aggregation — see Section 3.2); often a partially pure preparation (Section 3.3.1, note 3) can be digested successfully with subsequent fractionation removing the contaminants as well as the unwanted fragments. For a fuller discussion, see Lamoyi & Nisonoff (1983) and Parham (1986).

Susceptibility to digestion:
mouse, papain and pepsin — IgG2b> IgG3> IgG2a> IgG1
rat, papain — IgG2a> IgG2c> IgG2b> IgG1
rat, pepsin — IgG2c> IgG2b> IgG2a> IgG1

Mouse IgG1

This subclass gives similar fragments to rabbit IgG (Fig. 3.3) — i.e. $F(ab')_2$ and degraded Fc with pepsin; Fab and Fc with papain. In addition, by pre-activating the papain so that the digest can be carried out in the absence of reducing agent, $F(ab')_2$ and Fc can be obtained

63

because of a different arrangement of inter-heavy-chain disulphide bonds from rabbit.

Pepsin. To the IgG at 2–5 mg/ml in 0.1 M sodium citrate pH 3.5 add pepsin (enzyme:IgG ratio 1:50 by weight). Incubate at 37°C for times between 5 min and 24 h and analyse the products — usually 8–12 h works. For the preparative run, stop the reaction and fractionate the products as in Section 3.4.3, step 2 onwards.

Papain. To the IgG at about 5 mg/ml in the buffer of Section 3.4.2 add papain (enzyme:IgG ratio 1:100 by weight) and incubate at 37°C for times between 1–8 h. The fragments are reasonably stable and so the digest can usually be allowed to go to completion. If the monoclonal happens to precipitate out in the buffer, the ionic strength and pH can be varied (from 5.5 to 8) without stopping the papain from working. For the preparative run, fractionate by DEAE chromatography in 5 mM tris HCl using a gradient of NaCl from 0 to 0.2 M — Fab elutes first, sometimes in the fall-through, followed by any undigested IgG and finally Fc (papain is in the fall-through).

Pre-activated papain. To the IgG in the above papain buffer but without the cysteine add pre-activated papain (Section 3.4.2, note 3; enzyme:IgG ratio 1:25 by weight). Incubate and analyse as above. Fractionate the preparative run on DEAE as above (F(ab′)$_2$ is usually in the fall-through) and purify further by gel filtration (Section 3.4.3) or affinity chromatography on Protein A (Section 10.3.2).

Mouse IgG2a

This subclass is a little more sensitive than IgG1 to digestion. Pepsin will give the usual F(ab′)$_2$, but with some Fab′, and degrade the Fc; papain will give the usual Fab and Fc.

Pepsin. Digest as for IgG1 but increase the pH to 4.2; times are usually 3–6 h. Because of the increased sensitivity, conditions that leave some intact IgG may have to be selected to minimize the further digestion to Fab′. This increased contamination by IgG can be removed after gel filtration by affinity chromatography on Protein A (Section 10.3.2).

Papain. Digest as for IgG1. Again increased contamination by IgG and F(ab′)$_2$ can be removed by gel filtration on Sephadex G-100 and affinity chromatography on Protein A (Section 10.3.2).

Mouse IgG2b

This is the most sensitive subclass and there is no good method for producing F(ab′)$_2$. Pepsin cleaves the other side of the inter-heavy-chain disulphide bond from usual to give an Fab fragment and a fragment consisting of Fab joined to Fc (called Fab/c) which is then digested further. Papain will give Fab and Fc with short digestion times. Fractionate as for IgG2a.

Mouse IgG3

Pepsin will give $F(ab')_2$ and degrade the Fc; papain will give Fab and Fc.

Pepsin. Digest as for IgG1 but increase the pH to 4.5; times are usually 10–20 min. Fractionate as for IgG2a.

Papain. As for IgG2a.

Rat IgG

IgG1 should be handled as for mouse IgG1. Other rat subclasses are also digested by pepsin to give $F(ab')_2$ but this is then cleaved further, so pick the optimal time from an analytical digest.

3.5 ISOLATION OF IgM

The concentration of IgM in the circulation (Table 3.1) is high enough for it to be isolated from normal serum. However, the preparation is facilitated by the use of serum from patients with Waldenström's macroglobulinaemia, a disease characterized by greatly elevated IgM levels in the circulation. Similarly, certain murine plasmacytomas are available which actively secrete IgM. Such monoclonal proteins are not representative of the heterogeneous IgM pool. IgM normally exists as a pentamer of the basic immunoglobulin unit, covalently bonded together through their Fc regions by virtue of a small polypeptide chain called 'J chain' (Fig. 3.6). Because of its large size (molecular weight 900 000), gel filtration is an important fractionation step in the preparation. Most IgM molecules are insoluble at low ionic strength and so a euglobulin precipitation step (i.e. precipitation at low ionic strength) is a useful preliminary procedure. However, some IgM molecules are not precipitated by this means and other methods must be employed in certain cases (see note 2 below).

Materials and equipment

Serum from normal human donors — 100 ml
or
Serum from macroglobulinaemic patients — 10 ml
2 mM sodium phosphate pH 6.0
Tris buffered saline (TBS — Appendix 2)
Sepharose 4B or 6B in TBS packed into a column 2.6 cm × 100 cm
(Section 1.2.1)
Column chromatography equipment (Section 1.2.1)

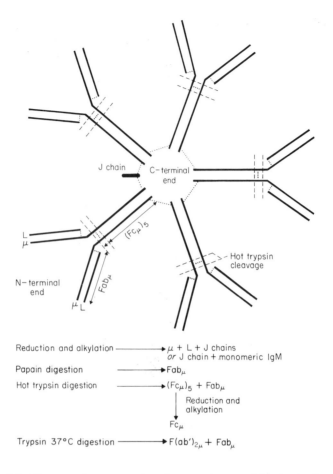

Reduction and alkylation   → μ + L + J chains
                                    or J chain + monomeric IgM

Papain digestion   → Fab_μ

Hot trypsin digestion   → $(Fc_\mu)_5$ + Fab_μ
                                      ↓ Reduction and
                                         alkylation
                                Fc_μ

Trypsin 37°C digestion   → $F(ab')_{2\mu}$ + Fab_μ

Fig. 3.6 Diagrammatic representation of pentameric serum IgM, showing its constituent chains, site of hot tryptic cleavage, nomenclature of chains and fragments and pathways for their isolation. The number and position of interchain disulphide bonds is not definitive. For mouse monoclonal IgM see Section 3.6.4.

Procedure

Warning   all human sera should be treated as potential sources of hepatitis and HIV (AIDS virus).

1   Dialyse the serum against at least three changes of 10 volumes of 2 mM phosphate pH 6.0 at 4°C.

2   Centrifuge at 2000 *g* for 10 min at 4°C, discard the supernatant and resuspend the precipitate in cold phosphate buffer and recentrifuge. Repeat this washing procedure at once.

3   Dissolve the final euglobulin precipitate in a total volume of 10–15 ml TBS at room temperature and centrifuge at 2000 *g* for 10 min.

4   Apply the supernatant to the column of Sepharose and elute with TBS at room temperature. Collect 6 ml fractions and monitor the absorbance at 280 nm.

5 A small peak of large molecules or aggregated material is followed by the first large peak containing pentameric IgM (Fig. 3.7). Smaller contaminants, including IgG, are eluted later, after the position of marker protein ferritin.

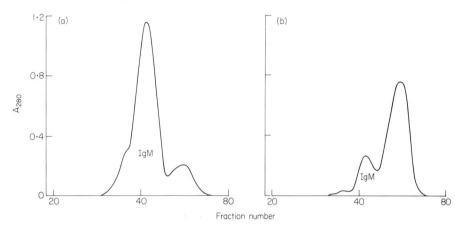

Fig. 3.7 Isolation of IgM from human serum on a Sepharose CL–4B column in TBS, following euglobulin precipitation (Section 3.5). (a) Serum from a patient with Waldenström's macroglobulinaemia; (b) serum from a normal donor. These preparations are analysed in Figs. 6.4, 7.6 and 11.5.

Notes

1 The yield of IgM from normal donors should be about 0.5 mg/ml serum and from macroglobulinaemic patients 5–15 mg/ml, depending upon the concentration in their circulation. The supernatant from step 2 may be saved for the isolation of IgG or IgA (Sections 3.3.1 and 3.7.1).

2 If the majority of the IgM in the macroglobulinaemic serum is not present in the euglobulin precipitate (steps 1 and 2), then bring the pH of the serum to 8.0 with 2 M tris and make the solution 6% (w/v) in polyethylene glycol 6000 (PEG). After 30 min at 4°C, centrifuge and wash the precipitate as in step 2 using 6% PEG in 10 mM tris-HCl pH 8.0 and continue from step 3.

3 The IgM obtained from macroglobulinaemic sera should be greater than 95% pure. The purity of normal pool IgM will be lower (about 80% — see Figs. 6.4, 7.6 and 11.5) because of the lower concentration in the starting material. The purity can be improved by affinity chromatography (Chapter 10) on insolubilized protamine sulphate, to which IgM binds, or Pevikon block electrophoresis (Section 9.2.3).

4 IgM tends to precipitate upon long term storage. It is best stored at 4°C or in 50% v/v glycerol at −20°C and not frozen (Section 3.2).

5 The procedure is applicable to other species, the limiting factor being the amount of serum available from small animals. However, the euglobulin precipitation step does not work well for all species (the mouse is especially bad) and precipitation with PEG (note 2 above) or

ammonium sulphate should be used in these cases (start with 6% PEG or 45% saturated ammonium sulphate and check for complete precipitation). Mouse IgM is obtained most easily from the plasmacytoma MOPC 104E grown *in vivo* by applying the procedure, with the above modifications, to the serum and ascites fluid. This method can also be used for the isolation of IgM monoclonal antibodies produced by hybridoma techniques (Section 2.3); Sepharose gel filtration alone (steps 4 and 5) will give a reasonably pure preparation from culture supernatants containing no, or immunoglobulin-free, serum. Affinity chromatography on protamine sulphate is an alternative for small amounts (Section 10.3.2, note 3). Simple precipitation with 6% PEG (note 2) of delipidated ascites fluid will give reasonable pure IgM in high yield (Neoh *et al.*, 1986). A novel purification by adsorption chromatography has been reported (Belew *et al.*, 1987).

6 Two human IgM preparations (from normal and macroglobulinaemic sera) are compared by several analytical techniques in Figs. 6.4, 7.6 and 11.5.

3.6 PREPARATION OF FRAGMENTS OF IgM

The constituent chains and fragments of IgM are represented diagrammatically in Fig. 3.6 and listed in Table 3.2.

3.6.1 Separation of heavy, light and J chains

Reducing agents split the disulphide bonds between μ, L and J chains which can then be separated under dissociating conditions in a manner analogous to IgG (Section 3.4.1). Any non-covalent bonds between J and μ chains are very weak and monomeric IgM can be obtained separate from J chain by mild reduction and gel filtration under non-dissociating conditions (Section 3.6.2).

Procedure

As for IgG (Section 3.4.1). The yield of L chain should be 20–25% of the total yield of μ and L chain.

Note

The L chain peak will also contain J chain, which chromatographs anomalously for its smaller size. If pure L chain is required, carry out an initial gel filtration in TBS to remove J chain (Section 3.6.2) and then rechromatograph in propionic acid. Alternatively, the L and J chain mixture can be separated by affinity chromatography (Chapter 10) using the appropriate insolubilized antibodies.

68

3.6.2 Isolation of J chain from IgM: preparation of monomer IgM

Materials and equipment

0.5 M tris-HCl pH 8.0 containing 2 mM EDTA

Human IgM (Section 3.5) — 150 mg in 7.5 ml tris buffer

0.5 M dithiothreitol in the tris buffer, freshly made

1.05 M iodoacetic acid in the tris buffer, freshly made

Tris buffered saline (TBS — Appendix 2)

Sephadex G-200 (fine) in TBS packed into a column 2.6 cm × 100 cm (Section 1.2.1)

0.01 M tris-HCl pH 8.0

0.01 M tris-HCl pH 8.0 containing 0.7 M sodium chloride

DEAE-cellulose (e.g. Whatman DE32 or DE52; Table 1.2) — 15 ml wet settled volume

Column chromatography equipment including a column 1.0 cm × 20 cm and a linear gradient maker 2 × 50 ml (Sections 1.2.1 and 1.2.2)

Procedure

1 Add 75 μl of dithiothreitol solution to the IgM and incubate in a sealed tube at room temperature for 1 h with stirring (final concentration of dithiothreitol 5 mM).

2 Cool on ice and cover with foil. Add 75 μl of iodoacetate solution and incubate in an ice bath for 30 min with stirring.

3 Apply the mixture to the G-200 column and elute with TBS. Collect 6 ml fractions and monitor the absorbance at 280 nm and 230 nm.

4 J chain is eluted as a small peak in the position of 50 000 molecular weight proteins after the IgM.

5 Dialyse this pool against the 0.01 M tris-HCl buffer. Equilibrate the ion exchanger with the same buffer and pack into the column (Section 1.2.2). Wash with the starting buffer at room temperature.

6 When both sample and ion exchanger are *fully* equilibrated, apply the sample to the column and elute with at least 30 ml of starting buffer until the absorbance has returned to baseline. Then apply a linear gradient, total volume 100 ml, from 0 to 0.7 M NaCl in 0.01 M tris-HCl pH 8.0. Collect 2 ml fractions and monitor the absorbance at 230 nm and 280 nm.

7 J chain is eluted with approximately 0.4 M buffer after L chain and other contaminants. The yield should be 1.5–2.0 mg (60–80% of theoretical).

Notes

For further information on J chain see Koshland (1975).

1 J chain exhibits an anomalously high molecular weight both on

69

polyacrylamide gel electrophoresis in SDS (approximately 20 000) and on gel filtration (20 000 to 50 000 depending on the chromatography buffer).

2   J chain is not easily detected because of its low absorbance at 280 nm (Table 1.1) and the small amount present in IgM (1 mole per 10 moles of μ or L chain) and so the additional monitoring at 230 nm is advised (azide absorbs at low wavelengths and should not be included in the buffers). Alternatively, 100 μCi of iodo[2–^{14}C]acetic acid (Amersham — Appendix 3) can be added in step 2 and the mixture incubated on ice for 5 min before the addition of unlabelled iodoacetate (Section 3.8.1). This introduces the ^{14}C label into the reduced cysteine residues and an aliquot of each eluted fraction can be taken for liquid scintillation counting (Section 1.4).

3   J chain is identified most easily by polyacrylamide gel electrophoresis in alkaline urea (Section 7.3.3) when it migrates as a very fast (anodic) band (Fig. 7.4).

4   In some species (notably rabbit and chicken) J chain is not completely resolved from L chain by DEAE chromatography. Use affinity chromatography on anti-(L chain) columns instead (Section 10.3.3).

5   To improve resolution of monomer IgM from any unreduced pentameter use Sephacryl S300 or Sepharose 6B instead of G-200.

3.6.3   Preparation of Fc_μ, $F(ab')_{2\mu}$ and Fab_μ fragments

Pepsin does not give fragments in high yield. Papain, under the conditions described for IgG (Section 3.4.2), cleaves native human IgM to yield the Fab_μ fragment. Trypsin at 37°C produces $F(ab')_{2\mu}$ and Fab_μ. However, the Fc portion of IgM is highly susceptible to proteolytic degradation and few methods produce intact Fc_μ in good yield. High temperature (above 50°C) causes a conformational change in the IgM molecule which allows trypsin to cleave the hinge region rapidly whilst leaving the globular portions intact (Plaut & Tomasi, 1970). This procedure allows the isolation of Fab_μ and a pentamer of Fc_μ, which can be reduced to monomeric Fc_μ.

Materials and equipment

Human IgM (Section 3.5) — 50 mg in 5 ml 0.05 M tris-HCl pH 8.0 containing 10 mM calcium chloride

Tris buffered saline (TBS — Appendix 2)

TPCK-treated trypsin (Worthington — Appendix 3) — 10 mg/ml in 0.001 M HCl

Soybean trypsin inhibitor — 10 mg/ml in TBS

Heated water bath

Sepharose 4B or 6B in TBS packed into a column 1.6 cm × 100 cm (Section 1.2.1)

Column chromatography equipment (Section 1.2.1)

70

1   Warm the IgM solution to 65°C and add 200 μl of trypsin solution. Mix gently and incubate at 65°C for 10 min.
2   Add 200 μl of inhibitor solution and cool rapidly on ice to about room temperature.
3   Centrifuge at 2000 *g* for 10 min and apply the supernatant to the Sepharose column. Elute with TBS and collect 2 ml fractions. Monitor the absorbance at 280 nm.
4   A small peak of undigested IgM is followed by three peaks containing pentameric Fc_μ and Fab_μ and finally peptides produced by degradation of portions of the polypeptide chains (Fig. 3.8).

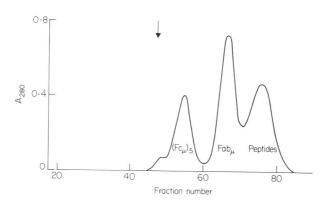

Fig. 3.8   Fractionation of a 65°C tryptic digest of human IgM on a column of Sepharose CL–4B in TBS (Section 3.6.3). The arrow indicates the elution position of pentameric IgM.

Notes

1   A dimer of Fab_μ is observed occasionally eluting just ahead of the Fab_μ peak.
2   The yields of Fc_μ and Fab_μ are approximately 20% and 40% respectively of the protein digested (60–70% of theoretical for both fragments). Both fragments are reasonably pure, but they can be purified by affinity chromatography using the appropriate insolubilized antibodies (Section 10.3.3).
3   Pentameric Fc_μ can be reduced to the monomeric form by 1 mM dithiothreitol followed by gel filtration on Sephadex G-200 in TBS, as described for $F(ab')_2$ (Section 3.4.3). The interchain disulphide bonds are also cleaved by this procedure but the chains remain held together by non-covalent forces.
4   Tryptic digestion of IgM at elevated temperatures is well characterized only for the human protein. For other species see Beale and Van Dort (1982). For mouse monoclonal antibodies see Section 3.6.4.

5   Digestion under the above conditions but at 37°C for 6–16 h will give $F(ab')_{2\mu}$ as well as Fab_{μ} but degrades the Fc completely.

3.6.4   Fragmentation of mouse monoclonal IgM

This is less well characterized than for IgG. Every monoclonal antibody is different — do an analytical scale digestion first and analyse the products by SDS-PAGE (Section 7.3.1) at varying digestion times. See the caution on the effect of the method of purification of the immunoglobulin in Section 3.4.5. IgM precipitates much more easily than IgG (see Sections 3.2 and 3.5) and this could adversely affect the digestion.

Trypsin at elevated temperatures and pepsin at 37°C give $F(ab')_{2\mu}$ which is then further digested to Fab_{μ} (Beale and Van Dort, 1982). Trypsin at 37°C with a reducing agent gives Fab_{μ} in 20% of theoretical yield (Bidlack & Mabie, 1986). No method gives intact Fc fragment.

Hot trypsin. Digest at 55°C in 0.1 M tris-HCl pH 8.3 containing 0.2 M NaCl and 10 mM $CaCl_2$ as for human IgM (Section 3.6.3, steps 1 and 2); usual time is 1–4 h. Fractionate the preparative digest on a Sephadex G-200 column in PBS; undigested IgM elutes first followed by $F(ab')_{2\mu}$ then Fab_{μ} and finally small peptides.

Pepsin. Digest as for IgG (Section 3.4.3, steps 1 and 2) but include 0.2 M NaCl in the buffer; usually 4 h gives a good yield of $F(ab')_{2\mu}$ and by 8 h Fab_{μ} is also formed. Fractionate as for hot trypsin above.

Trypsin. To the IgM in 0.05 M tris-HCl pH 8.1 add 1/10 volume of 0.1 M cysteine and then trypsin (enzyme:IgM ratio 1:50 by weight), gas with nitrogen and incubate in a gas-tight container at 37°C; usual time is 4 h. Stop the reaction with soybean trypsin inhibitor (Section 3.6.3) and alkylate with iodoacetamide (Section 3.4.1), final concentration 15 mM, to prevent aggregation by disulphide exchange. Fractionate as for hot trypsin above.

3.7   ISOLATION OF IgA

The concentration of IgA in the circulation of humans is sufficiently high to allow its isolation from normal serum (Table 3.1). In addition, certain patients have a serum IgA myeloma. However, most other species have a lower serum IgA level and the starting material of choice is an external secretion, usually milk or colostrum, in which IgA is the major class of immunoglobulin. Alternatively, an appropriate transplantable plasmacytoma (e.g. MOPC 315) can be used to induce high serum IgA levels in mice.

Serum IgA is present in several polymeric forms, ranging from the monomer to pentamer. In man the monomeric form usually predominates, but the relative amount of each polymeric form varies between species. Like IgM, the basic immunoglobulin units are covalently linked by J chain to form the polymer. IgA in secretions exists mainly as dimer, although a tetrameric form is also common in man. In addition to α chain, L chain and J chain, secretory IgA contains a fourth polypeptide chain termed secretory component (Fig. 3.9 and Table 3.2). This latter chain is a proteolytic fragment of a membrane-bound poly-Ig receptor that is involved in transporting the IgA through epithelial cells during its secretion (Mostov *et al.*, 1984). For further information on IgA see Heremans (1974).

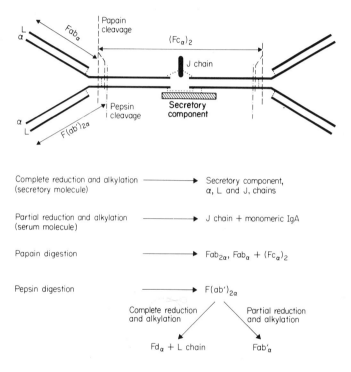

Fig. 3.9 Diagrammatic representation of dimeric rabbit secretory IgA showing its constituent chains, sites of proteolytic cleavage, nomenclature of chains and fragments and pathways for their isolation. Not all molecules of secretory component and light chain are covalently bound. The proteolytic digestion products vary between species and between the serum and secretory molecules (see Sections 3.8 and 3.8.5).

3.7.1 Isolation of IgA from serum

Materials and equipment

Serum from normal human donors — 100 ml
2 mM sodium phosphate pH 6.0
0.1 M zinc sulphate
1 M sodium carbonate

Vacuum filtration equipment
Saturated ammonium sulphate
0.2 M EDTA, disodium salt
20 mM sodium phosphate pH 8.0
0.3 M sodium phosphate pH 8.0
DEAE-cellulose (e.g. Whatman DE32 or DE52; Table 1.2) — 100 ml
   wet settled volume
Column chromatography equipment including a column 2.6 cm ×
   20 cm and a linear gradient maker 2 × 300 ml (Section 1.2.2)
Heated water bath

Procedure

**Warning all human sera should be treated as potential sources
of hepatitis and HIV (AIDS virus).**

1   Dialyse the serum against at least three changes of 2 litres of the
2 mM phosphate buffer to induce euglobulin precipitation. Centrifuge
at 2000 *g* for 10 min at 4°C.
2   Discard the pellet (or isolate IgM from it — Section 3.5) and add
100 ml zinc sulphate solution to the supernatant with vigorous stirring
at 20–25°C. Add sodium carbonate solution in drops to raise the pH to
6.8–6.9 also with vigorous stirring.
3   Allow to stand for 1 h at 20–25°C and then filter by suction
through Whatman no. 1 paper. Incubate the filtrate at 28°C for 30 min
and centrifuge at 2500 *g* for 15 min at 28°C to remove the newly
formed precipitate.
4   Add 0.7 × volume (about 150 ml) of saturated ammonium sulphate to the supernatant. Mix and leave at room temperature for 30
min. Centrifuge at 2500 *g* for 30 min, discard the supernatant and
redissolve the precipitate in 20 ml of water.
5   Add 1 ml of EDTA solution and dialyse against at least 3 × 1 litre
of 20 mM phosphate buffer. Equilibrate the ion exchanger in the same
buffer and pack into the column (Section 1.2.2) and wash with the
same buffer at room temperature.
6   When both the sample and ion exchanger are *fully* equilibrated,
apply the sample to the column and elute with at least 200 ml of
starting buffer until the absorbance at 280 nm has returned to baseline. Then apply a linear gradient, total volume 600 ml, from 20 mM to
0.3 M phosphate pH 8.0. Collect 10 ml fractions and monitor the
absorbance at 280 nm.
7   IgA elutes as a broad peak (because of its heterogeneity) with
approximately 0.1 M buffer.

Notes

1   The yield from normal serum should be 0.2–0.5 mg/ml. A substantial amount of IgA is precipitated by Zn^{2+}, but this step is worth
while because it removes the majority of IgG.

74

2   Sera from myeloma patients or mice with a plasmacytoma usually has sufficiently high IgA levels to allow omission of the preliminary euglobulin and zinc precipitation steps and produce reasonably pure IgA by ammonium sulphate precipitation and DEAE chromatography alone.

3   The procedure will not give completely pure IgA from normal serum. Other immunoglobulins can be removed by affinity chromatography using appropriate insolubilized antibodies (Section 10.3.3). Repetition of the ammonium sulphate precipitation step will decrease the amount of albumin trapped in the precipitate. Gel filtration can be used for further purification (for example, to remove pentameric IgM — Section 3.5), but the higher polymers of IgA will also be lost by this procedure.

3.7.2   Isolation of secretory IgA from milk and colostrum

Materials and equipment

Rabbit milk or colostrum — 20 ml
Isotonic saline — 0.9% (w/v) sodium chloride
Ultracentrifuge and cellulose nitrate tubes (or equivalent)
Concentrated hydrochloric acid
2 M tris base
Microfiltration equipment with 0.45 μm filter (Millipore, Sartorius — Appendix 3)
Sephadex G-200 (fine) in 0.1 M sodium phosphate pH 6.8 packed into a column 3.2 cm × 100 cm (Section 1.2.1)
0.01 M sodium phosphate pH 7.5 containing 0.1 M sodium chloride
0.01 M sodium phosphate pH 7.5 containing 0.25 M sodium chloride
DEAE-cellulose (e.g. Whatman DE32 or DE52; Table 1.2) — 30 ml wet settled volume
Column chromatography equipment including a column 1.6 cm × 20 cm (Section 1.2.1)

Procedure

1   Mix the milk with 10 ml of isotonic saline and centrifuge at 100 000 g for 1 h at 4°C in a cellulose nitrate tube.

2   Puncture the tube with a hypodermic needle and remove the clear aqueous layer between the floating fatty layer and the pellet. This solution (termed 'clarified colostrum') can be stored at −20°C for extended periods if desired.

3   Stir the solution and bring the pH to 4 with hydrochloric acid. Centrifuge at 30 000 g for 30 min at 4°C.

4   Discard the pellet (mostly casein) and neutralize the supernatant with 2 M tris. Centrifuge as in step 3 and pass the supernatant through the 0.45 μm filter.

5 Apply to the G-200 column and elute with 0.1 M sodium phosphate pH 6.8 at 4°C. Collect 10 ml fractions and monitor the absorbance at 280 nm. Dimeric IgA is eluted in the first major peak after a small amount of excluded material (aggregated protein and IgM) and before IgG (Fig. 3.10).

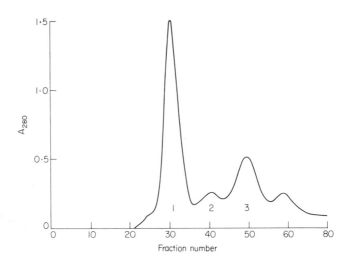

Fig. 3.10 Isolation of secretory IgA from rabbit milk on a Sephadex G–200 column in 0.1 M sodium phosphate pH 6.8 following removal of lipid and casein (Section 3.7.2). The dimeric IgA molecule is contained in peak 1 from which it can be purified by DEAE chromatography. IgG is present in peak 2 and free secretory component in peaks 2 and 3 from which it can be purified (section 3.8.4). Human secretory IgA is analysed in Figs. 6.4, 7.6 and 11.5.

6 Dialyse the IgA peak against 0.01 M sodium phosphate pH 7.5 containing 0.1 M sodium chloride. Equilibrate the ion exchanger in the same buffer and pack into the column (Section 1.2.2). Wash with this starting buffer at 4°C.

7 When both sample and exchanger are *fully* equilibrated apply the sample to the column and elute with at least 60 ml of starting buffer, at 4°C, until the absorbance has returned to baseline. Then elute with 150 ml of the buffer containing 0.25 M sodium chloride at 4°C. Collect 5 ml fractions and monitor the absorbance at 280 nm.

8 IgG and free secretory component are eluted by the starting buffer. IgA is eluted by the higher salt buffer.

Notes

1 The yield of IgA is 4–5 mg/ml of milk. There is no difference in the yield from early colostrum or later milk in the rabbit.

2 The IgA preparation is not completely pure but it is free from detectable levels of IgG and IgM. The purity can be improved by gel

76

filtration on Sephadex G-200 in 3 M guanidine-HCl but this causes partial aggregation of the protein and removes some non-covalently bound secretory component and L chain (Section 3.8.3).

3 The procedure is applicable to other species, including human (see HIV caution, Section 3.7.1) and guinea-pig.

4 A preparation of human secretory IgA is analysed by various techniques in Figs. 6.4, 7.6 and 11.5.

3.8 PREPARATION OF FRAGMENTS OF IgA

The constituent chains and fragments of dimeric secretory IgA are represented diagrammatically in Fig. 3.9 and listed in Table 3.2.

J chain binds the immunoglobulin units together covalently as for IgM (Section 3.5); it is not found in monomeric IgA, or IgG, IgD or IgE. Secretory component is present only in the IgA (and possibly IgM) which is secreted into the milk, saliva, gastric juices, parotid fluid, etc. The vast majority is covalently bound to the α chain in humans but half is bound only by non-covalent forces in rabbit and the proportion varies for other species. In the rabbit this is related to the subclass in that all of the *f* molecules and some of the *g* molecules bind secretory component covalently, whereas the remainder of the *g* molecules only bind it non-covalently (Johnstone & Mole, 1977). In addition, some IgA molecules (human allotype $A_2m(1)$ of the IgA2 subclass, myelomas from BALB/c mice and a small proportion of pooled rabbit IgA) contain only non-covalently bound L chains.

3.8.1 Separation of heavy, light and J chains

Serum IgA from human and mouse can be dissociated into its constituent chains after mild reduction and alkylation as for IgG and IgM. The procedure is described in Sections 3.4.1 and 3.6.1.

Disulphide-linked L chain dimers can be dissociated from human IgA2 molecules of the $A_2m(1)$ allotype and from BALB/c mouse IgA by application to the Sephadex column in propionic acid without prior reduction (see above).

However, the secretory molecule is more resistant both to reduction of its covalent interchain bonds and to disruption of non-covalent interactions, especially in the rabbit. Different methods for the reduction of the secretory molecule are therefore employed.

Materials and equipment

0.5 M tris-HCl pH 8.2

Rabbit secretory IgA (Section 3.7.2) — 50 mg in 5 ml of the tris buffer containing 7 M guanidine-HCl

0.5 M dithiothreitol in the tris buffer, freshly made

1.05 M iodoacetic acid in the tris buffer, freshly made

10–100 μCi iodo[2–^{14}C]acetic acid, optional (Amersham — Appendix 3)

Sephadex G-100 (fine) in 5 M guanidine-HCl (Appendix 2) packed into a column 1.6 cm × 100 cm (Section 1.2.1)

Column chromatography equipment (Section 1.2.1)

Procedure

1 Add 50 μl of dithiothreitol solution to the IgA and incubate in a sealed flask at room temperature for 2 h with stirring (dithiothreitol is in 4-fold molar excess over cystine residues).

2 Cover with foil and add the iodo[2–^{14}C]acetic acid; incubate at room temperature for 5 min. Add 50 μl of unlabelled iodoacetate solution and incubate at room temperature for a further 20 min.

3 Apply the mixture directly to the G-100 column and elute with 5 M guanidine-HCl. Collect 2.5 ml fractions and monitor the absorbance at 280 nm. Also take 20 μl from each fraction for liquid scintillation counting (Section 1.4).

4 The first peak contains α chain and secretory component and the second L chain (Fig. 3.11). J chain is eluted immediately after L chain and is detected by its radioactive content. These fraction are analysed in Fig. 7.4.

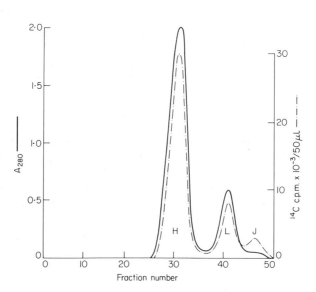

Fig. 3.11 Fractionation of completely reduced and alkylated (iodo[2–^{14}C] acetate) rabbit secretory IgA on a column of Sephadex G–100 in 5 M guanidine–HCl (Section 3.8.1). The first peak (H) contains α chain and secretory component and peaks L and J contain light and J chain respectively. These pools are analysed in Fig. 7.4. Reproduced from Johnstone & Mole (1977).

78

Notes

1 Reduction in a strong denaturing agent cleaves every disulphide bond, including intrachain bonds (compare Section 3.4.1). This causes extensive unfolding of the chains into almost random structures.

2 It has not yet been possible to separate α chain and secretory component because of aggregation of the chains (presumably induced by the total reduction and denaturing solvents). Rabbit α chain has never been purified.

3 L and J chains from other species may not be resolved by the gel filtration.

4 J chain has a low absorbance at 280 nm (Table 1.1). However, it incorporates a large amount of ^{14}C because of its high cysteine content (6–7 mol/mol).

5 The yield of L chain should be about 20% of the total yield of α and L chain for the secretory molecule and 25% for serum IgA.

3.8.2 Isolation of J chain from IgA

J chain can be isolated from rabbit secretory IgA, but only after total reduction (Section 3.8.1). It is more easily obtained from polymeric serum IgA (Section 3.7.1), especially in humans, by the gentle procedure described for IgM (Section 3.6.2), which yields J chain and monomeric IgA in an undenatured condition. Alternatively it can be isolated from the L chain pool after separation of H and L chains (Sections 3.4.1 and 3.6.1 — J chain elutes just ahead of L chain but is not completely separated). DEAE chromatography (Section 3.6.2) or affinity chromatography using insolubilized anti-(L chain) (Section 10.3.3) will separate L and J chains.

3.8.3 Isolation of bound secretory component from secretory IgA

For species in which a considerable proportion of secretory component is bound to IgA only by non-covalent forces (e.g. rabbit), it can be isolated by chromatography of secretory IgA under dissociating conditions as described below. For the human molecule this will give a low yield (10–20% released) and an alternative approach is to isolate it directly from milk or colostrum (Section 3.8.4) where it is present as a free polypeptide chain as well as in association with IgA.

Materials and equipment

Rabbit secretory IgA (Section 3.7.2) — 50 mg
3 M guanidine-HCl containing 1 mM iodoacetamide
Sephadex G-200 (fine) in 3 M guanidine-HCl packed into a column
   1.6 cm × 100 cm (Section 1.2.1)
Column chromatography equipment (Section 1.2.1)

79

Procedure

1 Concentrate the IgA to 10–20 mg/ml and dialyse overnight against 500 ml of 3 M guanidine-HCl containing iodoacetamide.
2 Apply to the G-200 column and elute with 3 M guanidine-HCl. Collect 2.5 ml fractions and monitor the absorbance at 280 nm.
3 The first peak, eluted in the void volume, consists of IgA and the second contains dissociated secretory component. The third is very variable and contains L chain, which is bound only by non-covalent forces in some IgA molecules (Section 3.8). Careful pooling of fractions gives secretory component free from IgA and L chain.

3.8.4 Isolation of free secretory component from milk or colostrum

Materials and equipment

As for Section 3.7.2 but omit ion exchanger
Ammonium sulphate

Procedure

1 Carry out steps 1–5 Section 3.7.2. Free secretory component is eluted together with IgG in the second and third major peaks of the G-200 column (Fig. 3.10). Analyse for it by polyacrylamide gel electrophoresis in SDS (Section 7.3.1) and pool the appropriate fractions.
2 Add 27 g of ammonium sulphate to each 100 ml of secretory component pool, stir to dissolve and leave at room temperature for 30 min. Remove the precipitated immunoglobulin by centrifuging at 3000 *g* for 30 min.
3 Dialyse the supernatant (e.g. against phosphate buffered saline — Appendix 2) to remove ammonium sulphate and store.

Note

Any residual IgA can be removed by applying the sample to DEAE-cellulose in 0.01 M sodium phosphate pH 7.5 containing 0.1 M sodium chloride at 4°C. Secretory component is eluted with starting buffer. However, immunoglobulin is removed more efficiently by affinity chromatography using insolubilized anti-(L chain) antibodies (Section 10.3.3).

3.8.5 Preparation of F(ab')$_{2\alpha}$ Fab'$_\alpha$ and Fc$_\alpha$ fragments

IgA is the most resistant of all immunoglobulins to proteolytic digestion and secretory IgA is even more resistant than its serum counterpart. The resistance is especially evident in the rabbit and probably reflects the harsh conditions of pH, ionic strength, detergents and proteases in which secretory IgA must function.

Mouse IgA is cleaved by papain under identical conditions to those used for IgG (Section 3.4.2) to give Fc_α and Fab_α in good yield. The fragments can be separated on DEAE-cellulose using a linear gradient from 0.05 M to 0.3 M sodium chloride in 0.01 M sodium phosphate pH 7.9 to elute Fab_α and a step to 0.1 M sodium phosphate pH 7.9 containing 0.3 M sodium chloride to elute Fc_α.

Human and rabbit IgA are partially digested by papain, pepsin and trypsin to yield Fab_α or $F(ab')_{2\alpha}$ fragments; the Fc portion can be obtained in some cases but in variable yield. Susceptibility to papain correlates with subclass in the rabbit, the *f* molecules being resistant to this protease. An extracellular protease of *Streptococcus sanguis*, which is common in the human gut, specifically cleaves only human IgA1 molecules into Fc_α and Fab_α (Plaut *et al.*, 1974). Peptic digestion gives the most complete cleavage of rabbit secretory IgA and a good yield of $F(ab')_{2\alpha}$ although the Fc portion is degraded. The digestion is only complete if carried out at very low pH, conditions which totally degrade IgG to small peptides.

Materials and equipment

0.1 M glycine-HCl pH 2.4
Rabbit secretory IgA (Section 3.7.2) — 50 mg in 5 ml of the glycine
  buffer
Pepsin (Worthington — Appendix 3)
2 M tris base
Sephadex G-200 (fine) in 0.1 M sodium phosphate pH 6.8 packed into
  a column 1.6 cm × 100 cm (Section 1.2.1)
Column chromatography equipment (Section 1.2.1)

Procedure

1   Dissolve 2 mg pepsin in 200 μl of the glycine buffer and add 100 μl of this solution to the IgA. Mix gently and incubate at 37°C overnight (16 h).
2   Neutralize with tris (this irreversibly inactivates the enzyme) and centrifuge at 2000 *g* for 10 min to remove any precipitate.
3   Apply the supernatant to the G-200 column and elute with 0.1 M sodium phosphate pH 6.8. Collect 2.5 ml fractions and monitor the absorbance at 280 nm.
4   The first peak, eluted in the void volume, consists of intact and partially digested IgA. The second peak contains the $F(ab')_{2\alpha}$ fragment and the third peak consists of small peptides produced by complete degradation of portions of the molecule (Fig. 3.12).
5   $F(ab')_{2\alpha}$ can be reduced to Fab'_α using 10 mM dithiothreitol and rechromatography on the same G-200 column as described in Section 3.4.3 for the IgG fragment.

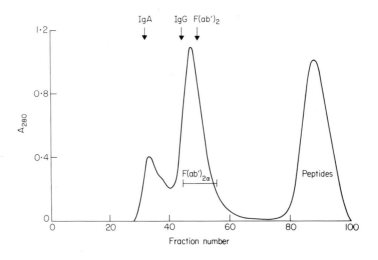

Fig. 3.12 Fractionation of pepsin digested rabbit secretory IgA on a Sephadex G–200 column in 0.1 M sodium phosphate pH 6.8 (Section 3.8.5). The arrows indicate the elution positions of standard proteins. Reproduced from Johnstone & Mole (1977).

Notes

1   The yield of F(ab′)$_{2\alpha}$ is 30–35% of IgA digested (50% of theoretical). J chain, Fc$_\alpha$ and secretory component are degraded to small peptides.

2   A small amount of Fc$_{2\alpha}$ is present between the first two peaks of Fig. 3.12.

3   Human IgA is digested at pH 4.5 like IgG (Section 3.4.3). For serum IgA a good yield of F(ab′)$_{2\alpha}$ is obtained after 8 h digestion. Secretory IgA is slightly more resistant and gives a poorer yield.

4   Monomeric mouse serum IgA gives a good yield of Fab′$_\alpha$ directly by digestion at pH 4.5 for 6 h. This is probably caused by exposure to a reducing agent during the preparation of monomeric IgA. Further digestion with pepsin at pH 3.6 for 4 h produces a fragment containing the variable region of both α and L chains, termed 'Fv' (Inbar *et al.*, 1972). This may only work for one particular immunoglobulin, MOPC 315, although a somewhat more complicated approach may be more generally applicable (Sharon & Givol, 1976).

3.8.6   Preparation of Fd$_\alpha$

This fragment is prepared from rabbit F(ab′)$_{2\alpha}$ by a procedure analogous to that used for the isolation of Fd from IgG (Section 3.4.4). The chains can only be separated after total cleavage of all disulphide bonds (compare the separation of chains in intact rabbit secretory IgA — Section 3.8.1). The Fd$_\alpha$ aggregates at low pH and is obtained pure in good yield by gel filtration under dissociating conditions (Johnstone & Mole, 1977).

82

3.9 ISOLATION OF IgE

Interest in this class of immunoglobulin is centred on its function as the mediator of reaginic hypersensitivity reactions. IgE antibodies are produced against many allergens.

The concentration of IgE in normal serum is extremely low (Table 3.1) and this precludes its isolation from this source. However, patients sensitized to various allergens or suffering from parasitic infections, and mice experimentally immunized with parasite extracts, have a higher circulating IgE level and it is possible to prepare an IgE-enriched fraction from such sources. Unfortunately not all of the antibodies in these cases are of the IgE class and so affinity chromatography using insolubilized antigen (Section 10.3.1) will not give a pure preparation of IgE.

Purification is facilitated greatly by use of serum containing an IgE myeloma as starting material. Such myelomas occur occasionally in humans and frequently in inbred rats of the strain Lou/WST that produce immunocytomas spontaneously, one-third of which are IgE. For further information on IgE see Möller (1978).

Materials and equipment

Human serum containing IgE myeloma protein — 20 ml
Sodium sulphate
0.01 M sodium phosphate pH 8.0
0.2 M sodium phosphate pH 8.0
DEAE-cellulose (e.g. Whatman DE32 or DE52; Table 1.2) — 50 ml
  wet settled volume
Tris buffered saline (TBS — Appendix 2)
Sephadex G-200 (fine) in TBS packed into a column 3.2 cm ×
  100 cm (Section 1.2.1)
Column chromatography equipment (Section 1.2.1) including a linear
  gradient maker 2 × 200 ml (Section 1.2.2) and a column 1.6 cm ×
  30 cm.

Procedure

Warning   all human sera should be treated as potential sources of hepatitis and HIV (AIDS virus).

1   Carry out two precipitations with 18% (w/v) sodium sulphate as described for IgG, allowing for the smaller volume (Sections 3.3.1, steps 1–5).

2   Dialyse the final pellet against the 0.01 M phosphate buffer. Equilibrate the ion exchanger with the same buffer and pack into the column (Section 1.2.2). Wash with the same starting buffer at room temperature.

3   When both sample and exchanger are *fully* equilibrated, apply the sample to the column and elute with at least 100 ml of starting buffer

83

until the absorbance has returned to baseline. Then elute with a linear gradient, total volume 400 ml, from 0.01 M to 0.2 M sodium phosphate pH 8.0 all at room temperature. Collect 10 ml fractions and monitor the absorbance at 280 nm.

4 The majority of the IgG is eluted with the starting buffer (see Section 3.3.1) and IgE is eluted in the gradient with about 0.03 M buffer ahead of the majority of the IgA. Pool the appropriate fractions (identified by double immunodiffusion, Section 6.3.1, or immuno-electrophoresis, Section 6.4.3) and concentrate to about 10 ml.

5 Apply to the G-200 column and elute with TBS. Collect 10 ml fractions and monitor the absorbance at 280 nm. IgE is eluted with IgA after IgM and before IgG.

Notes

1 The yield will depend upon the concentration of myeloma protein in the patient's circulation. The preparation will be reasonably pure if the myeloma is severe.

2 For preparation from allergen-sensitized patients, use 200–500 ml of serum and apply the final salt precipitate to 250 ml of DEAE-cellulose. Unlike the myeloma serum, no definite protein peak will be seen in the IgE position and identification by specific antisera is necessary (e.g. Sections 6.3.1, 6.4.3 and Fig. 11.8). Up to 200 mg of the appropriate pool can be applied to the G-200 column in step 5 above. The yield of IgE will be 1–10 μg/ml serum and contamination with IgG, IgA and IgD will be considerable. Further purification should be by affinity chromatography using the appropriate insolubil-ized antibodies (Section 10.3.3).

3.10 PREPARATION OF FRAGMENTS OF IgE

The constituent chains of IgE are described in Table 3.2. The heavy (ϵ) and light chains can be separated by gel filtration in 1 M propionic acid after cleavage of the interchain disulphide bonds in an analogous manner to IgG (Section 3.4.1). The yield of L chain should be about 20% of the total yield of ϵ and L chain. Patients with a serum myeloma protein usually have a corresponding light chain in the urine (Bence-Jones proteins).

Papain digestion of IgE under conditions which cleave IgG into Fab and Fc fragments (Section 3.4.2) produces an Fc_ϵ fragment but the Fab_ϵ portion is partially degraded and not recovered in good yield. Fc_ϵ is the first major peak eluted when the digest is applied to a Sephadex G-150 column in TBS. Peptic digestion using conditions described in section 3.4.3 cleaves IgE within 20 min to produce a pFc_ϵ fragment and most of the remainder of the molecule as a large $F(ab')_{2\epsilon}$. The latter is reminiscent of the Facb fragment of rabbit IgG (Section 3.4.3, note 3) and shares antigenic determinants with the N-terminal portion of papain fragment Fc$_\epsilon$. The products of peptic digestion can be separated by gel filtration on Sephadex G-200 in TBS (Section 3.4.3).

3.11 ISOLATION OF IgD

The function of IgD is obscure but it is one of the two classes of immunoglobulin most frequently observed on the surface of small B lymphocytes.

Its concentration in the circulation of normal individuals is low (Table 3.1) but approximately 100 times that of IgE. Myelomas of this class do occur occasionally, frequently associated with λ type light chain.

The procedure for the isolation of IgD from myeloma serum is the same as described for IgE (Section 3.9) but carry out all procedures at 4°C and precipitate with 45% saturated ammonium sulphate (Fig. 3.2) instead of the sodium salt or omit the precipitation step completely. IgD is more acidic than IgE and so will be eluted from the DEAE-cellulose column in slightly later fractions. This property increases the IgA contamination. The ion exchange step can be speeded up to decrease proteolysis by using a stepped instead of a gradient elution. Apply the sample in 15 mM sodium phosphate pH 8.0, elute unbound IgG with the same buffer and then elute IgD with 35 mM sodium phosphate pH 8.0. The procedure can also be applied to normal serum but the contamination with IgA and IgG is considerable. Further purification can be by affinity chromatography using appropriate in-solubilized antibodies (Section 10.3.3).

IgD in serum in quickly hydrolysed to fragments probably by the protease plasmin. The degradation is retarded by adding 5 mM ε-aminocaproic acid to freshly collected serum and to all chromatography buffers. This inhibits the formation of plasmin from plasminogen. For further information see Spiegelberg (1977).

3.12 PREPARATION OF FRAGMENTS OF IgD

The constituent chains of IgD are described in Table 3.2. The δ and L chains can be separated after reduction and alkylation of interchain disulphide bonds by gel filtration in 1 M propionic acid, as described for IgG (Section 3.4.1). The L chain yield is about 20% of the total yield of δ and L chain. Like other classes of immunoglobulin, IgD myelomas are often accompanied by a urinary Bence-Jones protein corresponding to the L chain.

IgD is extremely susceptible to proteolysis. It is cleaved by papain within minutes to produce Fab$_\delta$ and Fc$_\delta$. Digest as described for IgG (Section 3.4.2) but omit cysteine and EDTA and terminate the digestion after 1 h. Isolate the fragments by gel filtration on Sephadex G-100 in PBS. Alternatively digest with 1% TPCK-treated trypsin at pH 7.5 for 15 min at 37°C.

85

4 Isolation and fractionation of lymphocytes

Lymphocytes have been studied extensively. They produce antibody and mediate the cellular immune response, both of which involve specific interactions with a variety of other cells and soluble factors. They can be isolated as a suspension of highly viable cells and are an attractive object of study both in their own right and as models for other nucleated cells.

Peripheral blood is a convenient starting material in large animals. Cannulation of the thoracic duct provides another source of lymphocytes in suspension. Various solid tissues, notably tonsil, spleen, thymus and mesenteric lymph nodes, are also used frequently. Lymphocytes obtained from blood and lymph are nearly 100% viable. Disruption of solid tissue breaks about half of the lymphocytes but the dead cells can be removed to yield a 90–95% viable preparation.

A detailed discussion of the isolation and culture of lymphocytes is not appropriate in this book (for such a review see Ling & Kay, 1975). However, this chapter describes facile methods for the isolation, fractionation, storage and solubilization of lymphocytes; more specialized culture details are described in Section 2.3. These preparations are used throughout this book for immunochemical analysis both of lymphocytes and of various antibodies.

4.1 MANIPULATION AND STORAGE OF LYMPHOCYTES

In the appropriate environment, lymphocytes will remain viable for several days, although they will not grow and divide unless stimulated (e.g. by mitogen) or transformed (e.g. by virus). The medium should be sterile, isotonic, pH 7.0–7.5 and contain nutrients and some essential ions. For longer term culture, it is supplemented with 10% (v/v) serum (that has been depleted of complement activity by incubation at 56°C for 30 min) and with antibiotics. Fetal calf serum should be used where the absence of immunoglobulin is of paramount importance (e.g. for subsequent purification of monoclonal antibodies from culture supernatants — Sections 2.3.4; 3.3.1, note 3; 3.5, note 5; 10.3.2). This is very expensive and even difficult to obtain and so other sera should be used whenever possible. Three media are recommended:
1   Basal medium, Eagles with Earle's salts, buffered with 10 mM sodium hepes pH 7.3 (BMEE).
2   Roswell Park Memorial Institute (RPMI) 1640 supplemented with 10% heat inactivated serum, fresh 2 mM glutamine and antibiotics.

3 Dulbecco's Modified Eagles Medium (DMEM) supplemented with heat inactivated serum, and antibodies.

The constituents of these media are shown in Table 4.1. The

Table 4.1 Composition of culture media (mg/litre)

	BMEE	RPMI 1640	DMEM
$CaCl_2\ 2H_2O$	264.9		264.9
$Ca(NO_3)_2$		69.49	
$Fe(NO_3)_3\ 9H_2O$			0.10
KCl	400.0	400.0	400.0
$MgSO_4\ 7H_2O$	200.0	100.0	200.0
NaCl	6800	6000	6400
$NaHCO_3$		2000	3700
$NaH_2PO_4 2H_2O$	158.3		141.3
Na_2HPO_4		800.7	
glucose	1000	2000	4500
sodium phenol red	17.00	5.00	15.00
sodium pyruvate			110.0
L-arginine HCl	21.06	200.0	84.00
L-asparagine H_2O		56.82	
L-aspartic acid		20.00	
L-cystine disodium salt	14.21	59.15	56.78
L-glutamic acid		20.00	
L-glutamine	292.3	300.0	584.0
glutathione		1.00	
glycine		10.00	30.00
L-histidine HCl H_2O	10.50	15.00	42.00
L-hydroxyproline		20.00	
L-isoleucine	26.32	50.00	104.8
L-leucine	26.23	50.00	104.8
L-lysine HCl	36.53	40.00	146.2
L-methionine	7.46	15.00	30.00
L-phenylalanine	16.51	15.00	66.00
L-proline		20.00	
L-serine		30.00	42.00
L-threonine	23.82	20.00	95.20
L-tryptophan	4.08	5.00	16.00
L-tyrosine	18.11	20.00	72.00
L-valine	23.43	20.00	93.60
biotin	1.00	0.20	
D-Ca pantothenate	1.00	0.25	4.00
choline chloride	1.00	3.00	4.00
folic acid	1.00	1.00	4.00
i-Inositol	2.00	35.00	7.00
nicotinamide	1.00	1.00	4.00
p-aminobenzoic acid		1.00	
pyridoxal HCl	1.00	1.00	4.00
riboflavin	0.10	0.20	0.40
thiamin HCl	1.00	1.00	4.00
vitamin B12		0.005	
hepes	2383		
NaOH	to pH 7.3		

buffer in RPMI 1640 and DMEM is sodium bicarbonate and this requires an atmosphere of about 5% carbon dioxide to maintain the pH. Phenol red is reddish-orange at pH 7.3; pink is too alkaline and yellow-orange is too acid. BMEE with its hepes buffer, is used for general manipulation or storage of lymphocytes outside a CO_2 incubator and DMEM or RPMI 1640 containing 10% serum for culture periods longer than a few hours.

Lymphocytes can be stored in medium containing 5% serum at cell concentrations less than 2×10^7/ml at room temperature for 24 h with no appreciable drop in viability. At 37°C the cell concentration should be $1-2 \times 10^6$/ml. Chicken and rodent lymphocytes are especially fragile and are best used on the day of preparation.

For longer term storage the cells can be fixed with glutaraldehyde (Section 4.1.2). This procedure preserves most of the surface structure but destroys all functional activity. Alternatively, lymphocytes may be stored in liquid nitrogen after suspension at 10^7 cells/ml in BMEE medium containing 10% (v/v) dimethyl sulphoxide (DMSO) and 20% (v/v) inactivated fetal calf serum in a sealed ampoule and slow cooling (1°C/min down to -30°C and 3–5°C/min down to -125°C). If controlled cooling equipment is not available, the ampoules should be placed inside an insulating polystyrene container and left for 8 h at -20°C, then for 16 h at -70°C before transferring to liquid nitrogen. After thawing quickly in a 37°C water bath and diluting the DMSO the cells are of low viability (30–50%) but retain some functional capabilities (e.g. mixed lymphocyte reaction).

All procedures should be carried out under sterile conditions to minimize contamination. Lymphocytes are reasonably sturdy and will withstand centrifugal forces up to 500 g and vortexing with no appreciable drop in viability. After sedimenting and decanting, the cell pellet should be resuspended by gentle agitation in the residual supernatant followed by addition of fresh medium and vortexing. A nomogram and equation for relating centrifugal force (g) to rotation speed (r.p.m.) for individual centrifuges is given in Fig. 4.1. All centrifugal forces used in this book are g max — i.e. the force at the bottom of the centrifuge tube.

4.1.1 Counting cells and determining their viability

Materials and equipment

Cell suspension, 2×10^6/ml to 5×10^7/ml
Eosin, sodium salt 0.5% (w/v) in 0.9% (w/v) sodium chloride
Counting chamber, improved Neubauer ruling with thick coverslip
Light microscope, phase contrast facility is recommended
Laboratory cleaning detergent
Ethanol (70%)
2 or 3 channel tally counter

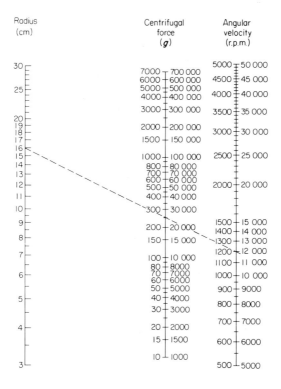

Radius (cm)	Centrifugal force (g)	Angular velocity (r.p.m.)

Fig. 4.1 A nomogram for calculating centrifugal force. For example, the force exerted on a point 16 cm radius from the centre of the spindle when rotating at 1200 or 12000 r.p.m. is 250 or 25 000 g respectively (dashed line). If the radius is measured to the bottom of the centrifuge tube (in extended position for swing-out rotors) the calculated centrifugal force will be the maximum exerted on the sample (g max).

Alternatively calculate: centrifugal force $= 118 \times 10^{-7} \times r \times v^2$
where r = radius (cm) and v = rotation speed (r.p.m.).

Procedure

1   Clean the counting chamber and coverslip sequentially with detergent, water and ethanol and dry thoroughly. Wet the edges of the coverslip, lay it across the ruled counting area and press down firmly on to the supports on either side.

2   Add 10 μl of cell suspension to 10 μl of eosin solution in a small tube (e.g. 10 mm $\times$ 50 mm). Mix gently.

3   Introduce the sample on to the ruled counting area under the coverslip. The space will fill by capillary action; 10 μl is sufficient.

4   Allow the cells to settle for 1 min and observe under the microscope (about 20 $\times$ objective). Erythrocytes are small clear cells; lymphocytes are of similar size but opaque under phase contrast; polymorphonuclear leucocytes are larger and opaque; platelets are small black dots; dead cells are red because eosin stains the nucleus.

89

5   The improved Neubauer ruling consists of 25 large squares enclosed by triple lines, each of which is divided into 16 smaller squares (Fig. 4.2). The volume encompassed by one large square to the height of the coverslip above the ruled area is 0.004 mm^3.

6   Count the number of lymphocytes and dead cells in five large squares (80 small squares) using the tally counter to record numbers. If the total is less than 100, count the number in the total counting area (25 large squares, 400 small squares). Cells are considered to be inside a square if they fall on the top or left perimeter line and outside if they are on the bottom or right.

7   Cell concentration in original suspension taken = number in five large squares $\times 10^5$/ml

Lymphocyte viability

$$= \text{(for any area)} \frac{\text{number of viable lymphocytes}}{\text{sum of viable and dead lymphocytes}} \times 100\%$$

(see Fig. 4.2 for examples of calculation.)

Notes

1   0.1% erythrosin can be used instead of the eosin solution; its colour is more easily seen by most people. Trypan blue is less visible than either of these reds and it is affected by any serum proteins present.

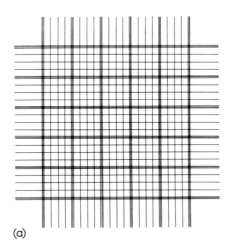

(a)

Fig. 4.2 Counting chamber for quantitation of cells. (a — *above*) Improved Neubauer ruling on chamber. (b — *facing page*) Examples of lymphocytes on 5 large squares. The dark cells are dead, stained red by eosin. The small cells are platelets. The count of viable lymphocytes in the squares (see Section 4.1.1 for protocol) is: A, 6; B, 12; C, 13; D, 11; E, 13. The total, 55, gives a concentration of 55×10^5 lymphocytes/ml in the original sample if diluted as in Section 4.1.1, although 100–200 cells should be counted for acceptable accuracy.

2   A mixture of 0.1 mg/litre crystal violet in 10% (v/v) acetic acid may be substituted for the eosin solution. This lyses the cells to leave the nuclei and so it cannot be used for viability. The shape of the nucleus is visible more clearly with this stain and so a better discrimination can be made between lymphocytes, polymorphonuclear leucocytes and monocytes. However, erythrocytes are not detected in this solution.

3   For adherent cells, a convenient assay of cell number is to apply the protein dye-binding technique (Section 1.1.3) to monolayers grown in multi-well plates after glutaraldehyde fixation (Winterbourne, 1986).

4.1.2   Glutaraldehyde fixation of lymphocytes

Glutaraldehyde cross-links proteins and turns the cell surface into a rigid cell wall, thereby allowing long term storage of lymphocytes. Low concentrations of glutaraldehyde do not drastically affect protein con-

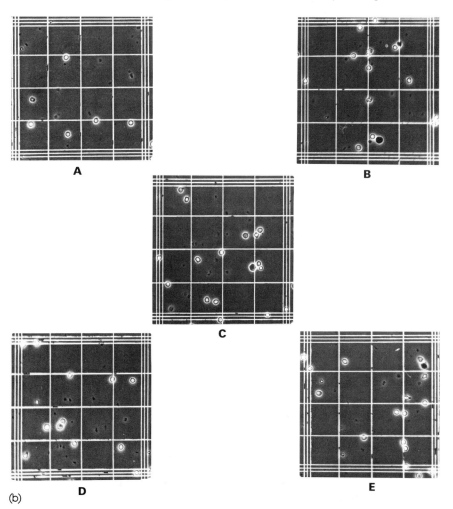

(b)

formation and the antigenicity of most proteins is retained. Hence the fixed cells can be used for immunochemical analyses (e.g. radioimmunoassay, Section 11.1.2, or immunocytochemistry, Chapter 12) although non-specific binding is increased and 0.5–1.0% albumin should be used throughout the procedures to alleviate this problem. Fixed cells do not retain functional activity and cannot be solubilized by detergents.

Materials and equipment

Lymphocytes — 2.5×10^7
Phosphate buffered saline (PBS — Appendix 2)
Glutaraldehyde — 0.25% in PBS, freshly made (glutaraldehyde is supplied as a 25% solution)
Sodium borohydride, 0.5% in PBS, freshly made
Bovine serum albumin, 1.0% (w/v) in PBS
Sodium azide — 10% (w/v) (see warning on use of azide in Section 1.2.1)
Polystyrene screw-capped round-bottomed tubes 16 mm × 100 mm (Sterilin — Appendix 3)

Procedure

Warning   borohydride in solution slowly liberates hydrogen.

1   Centrifuge the cells at 250 *g* for 5 min in a 16 mm × 100 mm tube, discard the supernatant and resuspend the pellet in 10 ml PBS. Repeat this washing procedure twice.
2   Resuspend the final cell pellet in 0.5 ml of PBS and remove any clumps of cell debris with a Pasteur pipette.
3   Add 0.5 ml of 0.25% glutaraldehyde solution, mix gently and incubate for 5 min at room temperature.
4   Add 0.25 ml of sodium borohydride solution, mix gently and incubate for 5 min at room temperature.
5   Add 0.25 ml of albumin solution and make up to a total volume of 10 ml with PBS. Wash the cells twice in PBS by centrifugation as described in step 1.
6   Resuspend the final cell pellet in 1 ml of albumin solution and remove any clumps of cells. Add 10 μl of azide solution, mix and store at 4°C or −20°C.

4.1.3   Removal of surface protein and its regeneration

In several immunochemical analyses of lymphocytes it is important to remove the protein from the outer surface without damaging the cell's integrity and then allow the cell to resynthesize the stripped proteins. This manoeuvre is useful in proving the vectorial nature of the action of 'surface labels' (Chapter 5), and demonstrating that a particular protein is synthesized by the cell and not taken up artefactually from the environment. It will also remove any extrinsically acquired protein which may mask surface antigens — e.g. autoantibodies (useful in fluorescence microscopy, Section 12.2.4, and radioimmunoassay, Chapter 12).

Materials and equipment

Human peripheral blood lymphocytes (Section 4.2.1) — 2×10^7
BMEE medium (Table 4.1)
RPMI 1640 medium containing 10% heat inactivated fetal calf serum
　(Table 4.1)
TPCK-treated trypsin (Worthington — Appendix 3)
Soybean trypsin inhibitor
Polystyrene screw-capped round-bottomed tubes 16 mm × 100 mm
　(Sterilin — Appendix 3)
Polystyrene culture flasks, 25 cm^2 (50 ml)
Heated water bath
Incubator, 37°C with 5% carbon dioxide atmosphere

Procedure

1　Suspend the lymphocytes in 2 ml BMEE medium in a 16 mm × 100 mm tube and warm to 37°C.
2　Dissolve 1 mg trypsin in 100 μl BMEE and add 20 μl of this to the lymphocyte suspension. Mix gently and incubate at 37°C for 15 min (final trypsin concentration 0.01%, w/v).
3　Dissolve 1 mg trypsin inhibitor in 100 μl BMEE and add 20 μl of this to the cell suspension. Mix and add 8 ml of BMEE. Mix and remove any sticky cell debris or DNA with a Pasteur pipette.
4　Centrifuge at 250 *g* for 5 min. Discard the supernatant, resuspend the pellet in 10 ml BMEE and recentrifuge.
5　Discard the supernatant and resuspend the cell pellet in 20 ml RPMI 1640 containing serum in the culture flask. Culture in the incubator for 24 h at 37°C.
6　The yield of cells should be 50–80% and viability 95–100%.

Notes

1　The tryptic digestion removes the vast majority of surface protein as determined by loss of surface radiolabel (Section 5.2.3).
2　The post-digestion culture allows the resynthesis of major surface proteins (e.g. histocompatibility antigens detected by immunoprecipitation, Section 10.4, and fluorescence microscopy, Section 12.2.4). The culture period can be extended to ensure complete regeneration but cells begin to die after 2–3 days.
3　The method works for other species but mouse lymphocytes are especially fragile and the yield and viability will be lower.

93

4   If an incubator equipped with carbon dioxide atmosphere is not available the RPMI medium can be buffered with 10 mM sodium hepes pH 7.3 for this short incubation.

4.2   ISOLATION OF LYMPHOCYTES

Lymphocytes can be isolated easily from peripheral blood by density gradient sedimentation after depletion of the erythrocyte content (Section 4.2.1). Alternatively, a more complicated procedure can be employed to obtain plasma, platelets, erythrocytes and lymphocytes from one blood sample (Section 4.2.2). The isolation from solid tissue is described in Section 4.2.3.

4.2.1   Isolation of lymphocytes from blood

Materials and equipment (all sterile if the cells are to be cultured)

Human blood freshly collected in heparin (10 i.u./ml) — 30 ml
Dextran molecular weight 250 000 (BDH, Sigma — Appendix 3) —
   3.5% (w/v) in 0.15 M sodium chloride
Hepes buffered BMEE medium (Table 4.1)
Heparin — 1000 i.u./ml, preservative-free
Isopaque-Ficoll mixture — Ficoll-Paque or Lymphoprep or Histopaque (Pharmacia, Nycomed, Sigma — Appendix 3)
Polystyrene conical-bottomed Universal containers 24 mm × 90 mm (Sterilin — Appendix 3)
Plastic conical-bottomed screw-capped tubes 30 mm × 115 mm (Falcon —Appendix 3)

Procedure

Warning   All human blood should be treated as potential sources of hepatitis and HIV (AIDS virus) and handled accordingly. It is inadvisable to work with one's own lymphocytes, especially if they are to be stimulated or transformed, because of the lack of HLA barrier to reintroduction.

1   Add 24 ml of dextran solution to the blood in a 30 mm × 115 mm tube, mix gently and allow to settle at 37°C for 30 min.
2   Transfer the turbid yellow supernatant (approximately 30 ml) to a fresh 30 mm × 115 mm tube leaving undisturbed the bottom red layer of agglutinated erythrocytes. Add 200 µl of heparin solution and 20 ml BMEE medium to the supernatant, mix and centrifuge at 200 *g* for 10 min at room temperature.
3   Discard the supernatant and resuspend the cell pellet in 20 ml of BMEE with 200 µl of heparin. Place 5 ml of Isopaque-Ficoll into each of two Universal containers and layer 10 ml of the cell suspension on top of each, taking care not to disturb the bottom dense layer.

94

4 Centrifuge at 450 g for 30 min at 20°C (temperature control is important).

5 Viable lymphocytes accumulate as a white turbid layer on top of the Isopaque-Ficoll layer; erythrocytes and dead cells sediment to the bottom of the tube. Transfer the lymphocytes to a fresh 30 mm × 115 mm tube using a Pasteur pipette, add BMEE to 40 ml and mix.

6 Centrifuge at 250 g for 5 min at room temperature and discard the supernatant. Resuspend the pellet in 40 ml BMEE and repeat the centrifugation.

7 Discard the supernatant, resuspend the pellet in 20 ml BMEE and determine lymphocyte yield and viability (Section 4.1.1). The yield should be about 10^6 lymphocytes/ml of blood and viability 98–100%.

Notes

1 If the dextran is unavailable, a 6% (w/v) solution of Ficoll 400 (Pharmacia — Appendix 3) may be used instead.

2 Blood can be diluted with an equal volume of BMEE and layered directly on to 2 volumes of Isopaque-Ficoll (step 3) as recommended by the manufacturers. However, this gives a less pure lymphocyte preparation and uses more Isopaque-Ficoll (60 ml compare with 10 ml).

3 As a general rule load 3–6 × 10^8 total cells (discounting platelets) in 5–10 ml on to 5 ml of Isopaque-Ficoll in a Universal container (24 mm × 90 mm) or 1.0–1.5 × 10^8 total cells in 2–3 ml on to 2 ml of Isopaque-Ficoll in a 16 mm × 100 mm tube.

4 A mixture of Isopaque-Ficoll consisting of 9.6% (w/v) metrizoate (Nycomed — Appendix 3) and a 9.9% (w/v) Ficoll 400 (Pharmacia — Appendix 3) should be used for most other mammalian species (compared with the commercially available mixtures of approximately 9.0% metrizoate and 5.7% Ficoll for human). A metrizoate-dextran mixture (Lympho-paque) for other species is also available commercially (Nycomed — Appendix 3).

5 Chicken lymphocytes cannot be isolated satisfactorily by Isopaque-Ficoll density sedimentation. For these mix freshly drawn heparinized blood with 3 volumes BMEE and centrifuge at 150 g for 6 min at 4°C. The large erythrocytes, platelets and granulocytes sediment to the bottom and the smaller lymphocytes remain in the supernatant. Centrifuge the supernatant at 500 g for 5 min, discard the supernatant and resuspend the pellet in RPMI 1640 containing 5% (v/v) serum. Repeat the centrifugation and resuspension.

6 A few individuals have lymphocytes with altered density that do not separate normally on the density gradients. These can be isolated in reasonable purity from the buffy coat (Section 4.2.2) by lysis of erythrocytes (Section 4.2.4).

7 The procedure can be applied to older blood samples (up to 24 h) but contamination with polymorphonuclear leucocytes is increased.

8 The procedure is also applicable to buffy coats that can sometimes

be obtained from Blood Transfusion Units to yield large numbers of lymphocytes ($1-4 \times 10^8$ from the buffy coat from each unit of blood).

4.2.2 Separation of lymphocytes, erythrocytes, platelets and plasma

Materials and equipment

Human blood freshly collected in heparin (10 i.u./ml) — 30 ml
Phosphate buffered saline (PBS — Appendix 2)
Hepes buffered BMEE medium (Table 4.1)
Heparin 1000 i.u./ml, preservative-free
Isopaque-Ficoll mixture — Ficoll-Paque or Lymphoprep or Histopaque (Pharmacia, Nycomed, Sigma — Appendix 3)
Polystyrene round-bottomed screw-capped tubes 16 mm × 100 mm (Sterilin — Appendix 3)
Polystyrene conical-bottomed Universal containers 24 mm × 90 mm (Sterilin — Appendix 3)
Plastic conical-bottomed screw-capped tubes 30 mm × 115 mm (Falcon — Appendix 3)
High speed centrifuge
Microfiltration apparatus with 0.45 μm filter (Sartorius, Millipore — Appendix 3)

Procedure

See **warnings** in Section 4.2.1

1 Divide the blood in to three 16 mm × 100 mm tubes (10 ml each) and centrifuge at 200 *g* for 10 min at room temperature. Erythrocytes form the bottom red layer; lymphocytes are contained in the white 'buffy coat' layer on top of this; the turbid yellow supernatant consists of platelets and plasma.
2 Centrifuge the three supernatants at 3000 *g* for 10 min at 20°C. Remove the supernatant, which is *plasma*, recentrifuge at 20 000 *g* for 15 min, pass through the 0.45 μm filter and store as for serum (Sections 2.2.3 and 3.2).
3 Resuspend the first pellet from step 2 in 10 ml of BMEE, add 100 μl of heparin and centrifuge at 3000 *g* for 10 min at 20°C.
4 Discard the supernatant and repeat the resuspension and centrifugation in step 3 to give *platelets*.
5 Transfer the buffy coats from step 1 to a 30 mm × 115 mm tube.
6 Add 5 ml of PBS to each erythrocyte layer from step 1, resuspend and centrifuge at 200 *g* for 10 min at room temperature.
7 A small buffy coat will again form on top of each erythrocyte layer. Add these buffy coats to the others from step 5.
8 Wash the erythrocyte layers by repeating step 6 twice, discarding the supernatant and top 5 mm of pellet each time. Resuspend the final pellet of *erythrocytes* in an equal volume of PBS; this preparation can be stored for several days at 4°C.

96

9   Add BMEE to the pooled buffy coats from steps 5 and 7 to bring the total volume to 50 ml. Add 200 μl of heparin, mix and centrifuge at 250 g for 5 min at room temperature.
10   Follow steps 3–6 in Section 4.2.1 to obtain *lymphocytes*.

Notes

See Section 4.2.1, notes 3–6.

4.2.3   Isolation of lymphocytes from solid tissue

Solid tissue is alternative to blood as a source of lymphocytes. The cells obtained from different tissues vary in their composition of T and B cells (Table 4.2) and subsets of these populations. The disruption of solid tissue breaks about half of the lymphocytes but the dead cells can be removed to yield a 90–95% viable preparation.

Table 4.2   B and T cell composition of lymphocytes from various sources

Source	% T cells	% B cells
human tonsil	55	45
human peripheral blood	60–80	10–20
human CLL peripheral blood[1]	<20	>80
mouse thymus	>90	< 5
mouse spleen	35	40
nude mouse spleen	0	>90
mouse thoracic duct lymph	80	20
lymph node	75–90	5–20

([1]) From patients with chronic lymphocytic leukaemia.

Mouse spleen

Materials and equipment

Two spleens from freshly killed mice
Hepes buffered BMEE medium (Table 4.1)
Two long large-gauge needles
2 × 1 ml disposable syringes
Isopaque-Ficoll mixture [9.6% (w/v) metrizoate (Nycomed — Appendix 3) and 9,9% (w/v) Ficoll 400 (Pharmacia — Appendix 3)] or ready-made metrizoate-dextran Lympho-paque (Nycomed — Appendix 3)
Polystyrene screw-capped round-bottomed tubes 16 mm × 100 mm (Sterilin — Appendix 3)
9 cm Petri dish

Procedure

1   Place the spleens in a Petri dish containing 10 ml BMEE. Bend each needle to form a right-angle half-way along the shaft and attach these to the syringes.

2   Pierce the end of the spleen with one of the needles (make an incision roughly 2–3 mm long) and hold closed end of the spleen with the shaft of the other needle. Expel the contents of the spleen through the hole into the medium by dragging the other needle shaft over the spleen from the closed to the open end. When all the cells are removed the spleen will be semi-transparent. Discard spleen membrane and transfer the cell suspension to a polystyrene tube. Centrifuge for 5 min at 250 g at room temperature.

3   Discard the supernatant, resuspend the pellet in 10 ml BMEE and repeat the centrifugation in step 2.

4   Discard the supernatant, resuspend the pellet in 4 ml BMEE and carefully layer 2 ml of the suspension on top of 2 ml Isopaque-Ficoll mixture in each of two 16 mm × 100 mm tubes.

5   Centrifuge at 1600 g for 20 min at 20°C (temperature control is important) and isolate and wash the lymphocytes as described in Section 4.2.1, steps 5–7. The yield of viable lymphocytes should be 1–5 × 10^7/spleen.

Notes

1   Tougher tissue (e.g. mesenteric lymph nodes) should be disrupted, after removal of fat, by cutting into small pieces with scissors and homogenizing in a polypropylene tube containing BMEE using a Teflon pestle with a 1 mm clearance. See also Section 2.3.1 and below.

2   For technical details of centrifugation on Isopaque-Ficoll see Section 4.2.1, notes 3 and 4.

Human tonsil

(Courtesy of David Darling and Susan King)

Materials and equipment (all sterile)

Tonsil
Hepes buffered BMEE medium (Table 4.1)
Stainless steel mesh with approximately 0.1 mm square holes
2 ml disposable syringe
Scissors and forceps
Isopaque-Ficoll mixture — Ficoll-Paque or Lymphoprep or Histo-paque (Pharmacia, Nycomed, Sigma — Appendix 3)
Plastic conical-bottomed screw-capped tubes 30 mm × 115 mm (Falcon — Appendix 3)

Polystyrene conical-bottomed Universal containers 24 mm × 90 mm
   (Sterilin — Appendix 3)
9 cm Petri dish

Procedure

See **warnings** in Section 4.2.1.

1   Add some medium to the tonsil in its container and shake to wash
off as much blood as possible.
2   Place tonsil in a Petri dish and cut out the lymphoid tissue (white,
spongy) avoiding areas with lots of blood vessels.
3   Hold lymphoid tissue with forceps and cut into small pieces with
scissors. Transfer these to a tube containing 20 ml of medium.
4   Shake the tube to release some cells into the medium and allow the
lumps to settle.
5   Hold the steel mesh over a Petri dish and pour the supernatant
through it in stages, transferring the filtrate to a fresh tube.
6   Place 5 ml medium in the Petri dish and some of the lumps on the
mesh. Use the plunger from the syringe to squash the tissue through
the mesh into the medium. Pool this filtrate with the other.
7   Discard the squashed lumps on the mesh, add fresh tissue pieces
and repeat step 6 until all of the tissue is disrupted.
8   Make up the cell-containing filtrate to 50 ml with medium, remove
an aliquot for counting (Section 4.1.1) and centrifuge the rest at 400 g
for 10 min.
9   Resuspend the cell pellet in medium to $1.5–2.5 \times 10^7$ live lymphocytes per ml and layer on top of Isopaque-Ficoll (6 ml cell suspension
on 5 ml Isopaque-Ficoll) in Universal containers as described in Section 4.2.1, step 3.
10   Follow Section 4.2.1, steps 4–7.

Notes

1   This method of tissue dispersal also works for thymus; if the
thymus is removed cleanly then the Isopaque-Ficoll step can often be
omitted. See above and Section 2.3.1 for alternatives.
2   For technical details of centrifugation on Isopaque-Ficoll see Section 4.2.1, notes 3 and 4.

4.2.4   Lysis of erythrocytes

As a rough, quick but effective alternative to density gradient centrifugation, lymphocytes can be obtained by specific lysis of the erythrocytes which are the major contaminants in most preparations. This
technique can be combined with other procedures (e.g. prior isolation
of the buffy coat, Section 4.2.2) to give a reasonably pure preparation,
although the lymphocytes may be damaged to some extent either by

the lysis buffer or the massive concentration of haemoglobin that is released.

Materials and equipment

Human lymphocytes and erythrocytes — 0.1 ml packed volume
Lysis buffer: 10 mM potassium bicarbonate containing 0.155 M
  ammonium chloride and 0.1 mM EDTA
BMEE medium (Table 4.1)
BMEE medium containing 5% w/v albumin

Procedure

1   Centrifuge the cells (300 *g*, for 5 min), discard the supernatant and resuspend the pellet in 0.9 ml lysis buffer. Incubate at room temperature for 5 min.
2   Add 4 ml BMEE, mix and overlay onto 2 ml albumin solution. Centrifuge at 300 *g* for 10 min.
3   Discard the supernatant and wash the cell pellet twice by resuspension in BMEE and centrifugation (300 *g*, 5 min).
4   Repeat the procedure if red cell contamination is still too high.

Note

For mouse cells the lysis buffer is 17 mM tris-HCl pH 7.2 containing 0.144 M ammonium chloride.

4.3   FRACTIONATION OF LYMPHOCYTES

Lymphocytes may be fractionated into T and B cells because of interactions between the surface of certain types of lymphocytes and inert supports or other cells. More sophisticated methods are available (Sections 4.3.3, 4.3.4, 10.3.6 and 12.2.2) but the procedures described in Sections 4.3.1 and 4.3.2 are simple and reliable. In each case a negative selection by removal of unwanted cells is recommended to avoid possible changes in surface structure induced by binding and subsequent elution. However, this approach will tend to yield a less pure preparation. Because of the heterogeneity of both B and T cells it is virtually impossible to obtain a preparation which contains all of the subpopulations of either type of lymphocyte (compare the purification of immunoglobulins, Section 3.1). A preparation of lymphocytes rich in the type of cell of interest may be obtained by selection of the appropriate tissue source (Table 4.2).

4.3.1   Enrichment of T cells

B cells (and other adherent cells) bind to nylon fibre whilst the majority of T cells do not (Greaves & Brown, 1974).

100

Materials and equipment

Lymphocytes from human peripheral blood (Section 4.2.1) — 3×10^7
Scrubbed nylon fibre, 3 denier, 1.5 inch, type 200 (Travenol —
  Appendix 3)
0.2 M hydrochloric acid
2 ml disposable syringe
Hepes buffered BMEE (Table 4.1) containing 5% (v/v) heat inacti-
  vated fetal calf serum or autologous plasma (Section 4.2.2)
Incubator, 37°C

Procedure

1   Soak the nylon fibre in the acid solution for 10 min and repeat
twice in fresh solution. Soak in water until the acid has been removed
(about 5 changes) and dry.
2   Pack 0.12 g of washed nylon fibre into the syringe barrel up to
1.2 ml volume (the assembly can be sterilized by autoclaving, for some
makes of syringe, or washing with alcohol).
3   Wash the column through with BMEE containing serum and then
seal top and bottom and incubate at 37°C for 10 min. Wash the
column through again.
4   Suspend the lymphocytes in 0.5 ml BMEE containing serum and
apply to the column. Allow the sample to enter the nylon fibre and then
seal the syringe bottom. Add further 0.5 ml of medium, seal the
syringe top and incubate at 37°C for 30 min.
5   Elute the nylon fibre with 3–4 ml of medium at about 1 ml/min to
obtain T cells.
6   The yield should be about 50% of total cells applied (i.e. 70%
yield of T cells).

Notes

1   Elution of B cells from the nylon fibre is not recommended.
2   Some subsets of T cells may also bind to nylon fibre although the
proportion of T cell subpopulations defined by monoclonal antibodies
against CD4 and CD8 is not affected by this separation.
3   This procedure works for lymphocytes from various tissues in most
mammalian species and T cell purity (less than 1% B cells after 1
passage of peripheral blood) is comparable with that obtained by most
other methods, e.g. affinity chromatography (Section 10.3.6). The
purity can be increased by applying the eluant to a fresh column of
nylon fibre.
4   For optimal reproducible yield and purity, it is important to carefully adjust both the density of packing of the fibre (0.1 g/ml) and the
loading of the column — for peripheral blood lymphocytes (10–20% B
cells) use 2.5×10^8 cells/g of fibre; for spleen and tonsil (50% B cells)
use 1.5×10^8 cells/g of fibre.

4.3.2 Enrichment of B cells

Human T cells bind specifically to sheep erythrocytes and form 'E rosettes' (i.e. one lymphocyte surrounded by many erythrocytes) if the erythrocytes are present in excess.

(Courtesy of David Darling and Susan King)

Materials and equipment (all sterile)

Lymphocytes from human peripheral blood or tonsil (Section 4.2.1 or 4.2.3) — 3×10^7
Sheep erythrocytes (TCS — Appendix 3)
0.15 M NaCl (isotonic saline)
2-aminoethylisothiouronium bromide (AET) (Sigma — Appendix 3)
5 M NaOH
water
0.22 μm filter (Millipore, Sartorius — Appendix 3)
RPMI 1640 (Table 4.1) containing 40% heat-inactivated fetal calf serum or human serum
Hepes-buffered BMEE (Table 4.1)
Isopaque-Ficoll mixture — Ficoll-Paque or Lymphoprep or Histopaque (Pharmacia, Nycomed, Sigma — Appendix 3)
Polystyrene screw-capped round-bottomed tubes 16 mm × 100 mm (Sterilin — Appendix 3)
Polystyrene conical-bottomed Universal containers 24 mm × 90 mm (Sterilin — Appendix 3)
Heated water bath

Procedure

1 Dissolve 0.983 g AET in 15 ml water, bring pH to 9 with NaOH and make up to 25 ml with water. Pass through 0.22 μm filter to sterilize.
2 Resuspend erythrocytes by inverting their container and transfer 6 ml to a Universal container. Add 4 ml of saline.
3 Centrifuge at 800 g for 5 min, discard the supernatant and resuspend the pellet in 10 ml of saline.
4 Repeat step 3.
5 Centrifuge at 800 g for 10 min, discard the supernatant and resuspend the pellet in 20 ml of AET solution (step 1).
6 Incubate at 37°C for 15 min, shaking occasionally.
7 Centrifuge at 800 g for 5 min, discard the supernatant and resuspend the pellet in 20 ml of saline.
8 Repeat step 7 two or three times until the supernatant is no longer reddish. Resuspend the final pellet in 20 ml serum-containing RPMI 1640. Use immediately or store at 4°C for up to one week (for use after storage, centrifuge at 800 g for 5 min and resuspend in fresh serum-containing medium).

102

9   Suspend the lymphocytes in 3 ml BMEE, add 3 ml of AET-treated erythrocytes (step 8) and mix.

10   Layer the suspension onto 5 ml of Isopaque-Ficoll in a Universal container and leave for 10 min at room temperature.

11   Centrifuge at 50 g for 10 min at 20°C (this settles the rosettes onto the interface) and then at 450 g for 30 min at 20°C.

12   T cell rosettes and excess erythrocytes sediment to the bottom of the tube. Unbound B cells accumulate on top of the Isopaque-Ficoll and can be recovered as described in Section 4.2.1, steps 5–7.

Notes

1   The preparation is still not pure because of the low proportion of B cells in peripheral blood lymphocytes. Steps 5–8 can be repeated to obtain a purer preparation. Lymphocytes containing a higher proportion of B cells may be isolated from an alternative source (e.g. tonsils or peripheral blood from patients with chronic lymphocytic leukaemia — Table 4.2).

2   T cells can be recovered from the pellet of rosettes after hypotonic lysis of the erythrocytes (Section 4.2.4) but see caution in Section 4.3.

3   Sheep erythrocytes also rosette pig T cells; guinea-pig T cells form rosettes with rabbit erythrocytes.

4.3.3   Specific rosetting techniques

The rosette method (Section 4.3.2) can be extended by coupling specific proteins to the surface of erythrocytes. The red cell acts simply as an inert support and should be of a species that does not bind the lymphocytes in their own right; the added protein provides the specificity for lymphocyte selection. For example, ox erythrocytes coated with immunoglobulin by addition of rabbit antiserum against ox erythrocytes will specifically form rosettes with lymphocytes that carry receptors for Fc (termed 'EA rosettes'). Use of individual classes of immunoglobulin isolated from the antiserum allows cells carrying Fc receptors specific for each class to be isolated. Furthermore, if IgM antibody is isolated from the serum and added to the ox erythrocytes together with fresh human serum as a complement source, then rosettes will be formed with lymphocytes which possess complement receptors (termed 'EAC rosettes').

The erythrocytes can be made even more specific by coupling them to an F(ab')$_2$ fragment (Section 3.4.2) with defined antigen binding activity. For example, erythrocytes coated with the F(ab')$_2$ fragment of an anti-immunoglobulin antibody will specifically form rosettes with B cells. The simplest and most common method uses chromic chloride to couple the protein to the cell by a poorly understood mechanism.

103

Materials and equipment

Chromic chloride, hydrated
0.15 M sodium chloride (isotonic saline)
Phosphate buffered saline (PBS — Appendix 2)
1 M sodium hydroxide
Erythrocytes — 0.5 ml packed volume
F(ab')$_2$ fragment of antibody — 0.5 mg in 0.5 ml of isotonic saline
Polystyrene conical-bottomed Universal containers 24 mm × 90 mm
   (Sterilin — Appendix 3)

Procedure

1   Make a 1% (w/v) solution of chromic chloride in isotonic saline
and adjust the pH to 5 with sodium hydroxide. Leave at room temperature for 3 weeks adjusting the pH to 5 thrice weekly. The 'aged'
solution can be stored at room temperature.
2   Wash the erythrocytes in 3 × 20 ml of isotonic saline by repeated
centrifugation (300 *g*, 5 min) and resuspension in a Universal container, discarding the supernatant each time.
3   Resuspend the final cell pellet in isotonic saline to a total volume of
4.5 ml. Add the F(ab')$_2$ fragment in 0.5 ml and mix.
4   Dilute 100 μl of the aged chromic chloride (step 1) in 10 ml of
isotonic saline and adjust the pH to 5.
5   Whilst vortexing the cell suspension add 5 ml of 0.01% chromic
chloride (step 4) dropwise. Incubate for 15 min at room temperature
vortexing every minute for the first 5 min and thereafter every 5 min.
6   Add 10 ml PBS, mix and centrifuge at 300 *g* for 5 min. Discard the
supernatant and repeat the resuspension and centrifugation twice.
7   Carry out the rosetting as described in Section 4.3.2, steps 9–12.

Note

A more expensive but better defined alternative is to use small inert
hydrophilic beads in place of erythrocytes. These can be purchased
with an N-hydroxysuccinimide carboxylate ester group for attachment
to proteins (Matrex Pel 102, Amicon — Appendix 3) and even with
antibodies of various specificities already coupled (Immunobeads, Bio-
Rad — Appendix 3).

4.3.4   Other fractionation techniques

Lymphocytes can also be fractionated using antibodies or lectins
coupled to agarose beads instead of erythrocytes (Section 10.3.6). The
separation is then by affinity chromatography instead of rosette sedimentation. Alternatively the ligands can be coupled to iron beads
which are subsequently removed with a magnet. Both of these separation methods are made more precise by the use of monoclonal antibodies with defined specificity.

The most reproducible and reliable method for cell fractionation employs fluorescently conjugated monoclonal antibodies to label the lymphocytes of interest which can then be isolated by a flow micro-fluorimetry (Section 12.2.2). The definition of lymphocyte populations is being improved constantly by this means. Such purified populations should prove of great use in elucidating the relationship between surface markers and lymphocyte function. Unfortunately the expense of the sorting equipment places this method beyond the reach of most laboratories and the simpler procedures described above still have an important role to play. The cell sorter is also very slow for large numbers of cells and antibodies coupled to magnetic beads (Section 10.3.6) are becoming the method of choice.

Centrifugation on Percoll (Pharmacia — Appendix 3) will separate cells by size (see example in Fig. 12.3).

4.4 SOLUBILIZATION OF CELLS AND MEMBRANES

Investigation of the structure of membrane proteins and their interactions with each other and with other proteins has been helped greatly by the use of detergents to solubilize membranes. When present above their 'critical micelle concentration', detergents form micelles which mimic the hydrophobic interior of the lipid bilayer of membranes. This provides a suitable environment for the individual membrane proteins without disturbing their tertiary and quaternary structure (Fig. 4.3). Under the appropriate conditions of detergent excess the membrane structure is disrupted and lipids and proteins are inserted into detergent micelles so that each protein or protein complex is present in a separate micelle. Hence, each behaves as distinct entity and can be studied using methods employed for soluble proteins with slight modification (e.g. gel filtration, polyacrylamide gel electrophoresis, isoelectric focusing, immunoelectrophoresis and immunodiffusion, immunoassays and affinity chromatography).

4.4.1 Choice of detergent

A large number of detergents are available and hundreds of them have been used in biochemical studies (Helenius & Simons, 1975; Helenius et al., 1979). Some of the chemical and physical properties of those most commonly used are presented in Tables 4.3 and 4.4. In general, commercially available detergents are chemically impure, especially non-ionic ones. They contain water or other contaminants in amounts that vary between batches. After prolonged storage of liquid detergents the composition may vary in different parts of the container. In addition, the chain length of both the hydrophobic and polyoxyethylene portions of the molecule is heterogeneous. The structure given by the

105

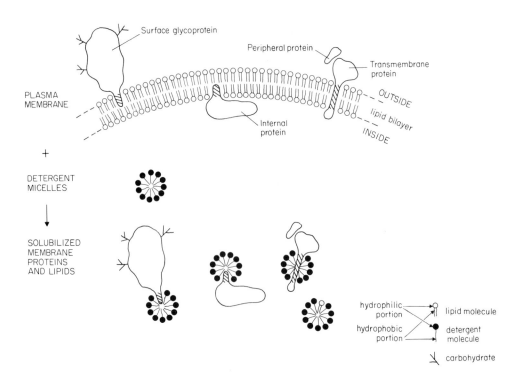

Fig. 4.3 Solubilization of plasma membrane proteins and lipids by detergent. The micelles of detergent mimic the lipid bilayer (see Singer & Nicholson, 1972, for the fluid mosaic model of membrane structure) and provide an environment suitable for the hydrophobic portions (shaded areas) of membrane proteins and lipids.

manufacturer and presented in Table 4.3 represents the majority but not all of the molecules.

Ionic detergents (e.g. sodium dodecyl sulphate, SDS) tend to denature proteins by destroying their secondary, tertiary and quaternary structure, although antibody activity is retained in low concentrations (less than 0.1% SDS). This property is useful for some applications (e.g. polyacrylamide gel electrophoresis, Section 7.3.1) but it does not help in studies of native protein structure. Non-ionic and mildly ionic detergents are less denaturing and can be used to remove a protein from a membrane whilst preserving protein–protein interactions. For example, solubilization of lymphocytes in Nonidet P40 (non-ionic) or plasma membrane in sodium deoxycholate (mildly anionic) releases histocompatibility antigens (termed HLA in humans and H-2 in mice) as two polypeptide chains still held together by non-covalent forces (see Fig. 10.8). In addition, the protein-detergent micelle is recognized by antibodies directed against the antigens (e.g. in immunoprecipitation, Section 10.4).

106

Table 4.3 Structure of some common detergents. Modified from Helenius & Simons (1975) with permission

Structural formula	Chemical name	Examples of trade names
	Anionic detergents	
	Sodium dodecylsulphate	
	Cationic detergents	
	Cetyltrimethylammonium bromide	
	Tetradecylammonium bromide	
	Non-ionic surfactants	
	Polyoxyethylene alcohol	Brij series, Lubrol W, AL series
	Polyoxyethylene isoalcohol	Sterox AJ, AP series Emulphogen BC series Renex 30 series
	Polyoxyethylene p-t-octyl phenol	Triton X series Igepal CA series Nonidet P 40
	Polyoxyethylene nonylphenol	Triton N series Igepal CO series Surfonic N series
	Polyoxyethylene esters of fatty acids	Sterox CO series Myrj series Span series
	Polyoxyethylene sorbitol esters[1]	Tween series Emasol series
	β-D-octylglucoside	
	Bile salts	
	Sodium cholate (trihydroxy bile salt)	
	Sodium deoxycholate	
	Sodium taurocholate	

[1]The formula shown is just one molecular type in a complex mixture of different possible structures, n = average number of ethylene oxide units per molecule.

107

Table 4.4 Properties of some common detergents.[1]
Modified from Helenius & Simons (1975) with permission.

Detergent	Commercial name	Aggregation number	Micellar weight ($\times 10^{-3}$)	Critical micelle concentration (mM)
Sodium dodecylsulphate (in H_2O)		62	18	8.2
Sodium dodecylsulphate (in 0.5 M NaCl)		126	36	0.52
Tetradecyltrimethyl ammonium chloride		64	19	4.5
Cetyltrimethyl ammonium bromide		169	62	0.92
POG(4,5) p-t-octylphenol[2]	Triton X–45			0.11
POG(7–8) p-t-octylphenol	Triton X–114			0.20
POG(10) stearyl alcohol	Brij 76			0.03
POG(10) oleyl alcohol	Brij 96			<0.04
POG(10) cetyl alcohol	Brij 56			0.002
POG(9) p-t-octylphenol	Nonidet P40			0.29
POG(9–10) p-t-octylphenol	Triton X–100	140	90	0.24
POG(9–10)nonylphenol	Triton N–101			0.085
POG(10) nonylphenol		100	66	0.075
POG(10) tridecyl alcohol		88	56	0.125
POG(12–13) p-t-octyl-phenol	Triton X–102			0.3–0.4
POG(14) stearyl alcohol		370	330	0.06
POG(16) p-t-octylphenol	Triton X–165			0.43
POG(17) cetyl-stearyl alcohol	Lubrol WX			0.02–0.06
POG(20) sorbitol mono-stearate	Tween 60			0.025
POG(20) sorbitol mono-oleate	Tween 80	60	50–76	0.012
POG(20) sorbitol mono-palmitate	Tween 40			0.027
POG(20) sorbitol mono-laurate	Tween 20			0.059
POG(20) cetyl alcohol	Brij 58			0.077
POG(29) oleyl alcohol	Brij 98			0.025
POG(40) p-t-octylphenol	Triton X–405			0.810
β-D-octylglucoside				25
Sodium cholate[3]		2–4	0.9–1.8	13–15
Sodium deoxycholate[3]		4–10	1.7–4.2	4–6
Sodium taurocholate[3]		4	2.2	10–15

([1]) Measured at 20–25°C
([2]) POG, polyoxyethyleneglycol
([3]) pH > 8; ionic strength < 10 mM

Several additional factors influence the choice of detergent:

1 *Material to be solubilized*
(a) An isolated membrane can be solubilized by most detergents. However, with whole nucleated cells it is desirable to keep the nucleus intact to avoid the problems associated with release of DNA. This can be accomplished by the use of some polyoxyethylene detergents (e.g. Nonidet P40, Triton X-100, Renex 30 — Table 4.3) under carefully controlled conditions (Section 4.4.2).
(b) Some proteins are not solubilized by certain detergents. A useful criterion for solubility is a high yield of the protein (measured for example by immunoassay, Chapter 11) in the supernatant after centrifugation at 100 000 g for 30 min.

2 *Detergent properties detrimental to subsequent procedures*
(a) Octyl and nonyl phenol detergents (e.g. Triton X-100 and Nonidet P40) have a high absorbance at 280 nm and hence interfere with protein monitoring (Section 1.1.1) during gel filtration or affinity chromatography. They also induce precipitation in the Folin protein assay (although the supernatant can be used to obtain values); they interfere less with the BCA modification and the Bradford assay (Sections 1.1.2 and 1.1.3).
(b) Octyl and nonyl phenol detergents are also easily iodinated and therefore should not be present during the radioiodination of proteins (Section 5.2). In addition, impurities of many other detergents can be iodinated (e.g. any unsaturated alkyl chain).
(c) Many detergents have a very high micellar weight (Table 4.4). This makes gel filtration impossible because the variation in protein size is usually insignificant compared with the size of the micelle. Also, removal of such detergents by dialysis (Section 1.3.1) is extremely slow because only the monomers can diffuse out of the dialysis sac, and the concentration of these (i.e. the critical micelle concentration) is usually very low (Table 4.4).
(d) The solubility of sodium cholate and deoxycholate decreases dramatically below pH 7.5 or above ionic strength 0.1.
(e) Ionic detergents, even sodium deoxycholate, interfere with electrophoresis and isoelectricfocusing (Chapters 6, 7 and 9).

Consideration of all these factors leads to the list of detergents recommended for various analytical procedures presented in Table 4.5. This is by no means comprehensive but should allow the reader to avoid some common pitfalls in initial experiments. Non-ionic detergents can be removed by absorption to beads in some circumstances (Drexler *et al.*, 1986).

4.4.2 Solubilization of whole lymphocytes

Under carefully controlled conditions, some non-ionic detergents solubilize the plasma membrane and most cellular organelles, releas-

Table 4.5 Detergents compatible with various immunochemical procedures

Procedure	Recommended detergents	Incompatible detergents
gel filtration	sodium deoxycholate octyl glucoside	detergents with high micellar weight affect elution; phenyl groups interfere with protein monitoring
dialysis to remove detergent	octyl glucoside cholate series	detergents with low critical micelle concentration are removed very slowly
radioiodination	sodium deoxycholate Renex 30 octyl glucoside	phenyl rings and double bonds may be iodinated
affinity chromatography	most detergents at concentrations low enough to allow binding; ionic detergents usually decrease non-specific binding	sodium deoxycholate is not compatible with acid eluting conditions or ionic strength above 0.1; phenyl groups interfere with protein monitoring
radioimmunoassay and immuno-precipitation	most detergents at concentrations low enough to allow binding	
electrophoresis, ion exchange chromatography and isoelectric focusing	most non-ionic detergents	ionic detergents; phenyl groups interfere with protein monitoring

ing the cytoplasm but leaving intact the nuclei and most of the cytoskeleton.

Materials and equipment

Lymphocytes (Section 4.2) — 10^7
Phosphate buffered saline (PBS — Appendix 2)
1% (w/v) Nonidet P40 in PBS containing 1 mM EGTA
Phenylmethylsulphonyl fluoride (PMSF)
Acetone
Ultracentrifuge

Procedure

1   Centrifuge the lymphocytes at 250 g for 5 min and resuspend the pellet in 0.5 ml PBS. Cool the cell suspension and about 1 ml of detergent solution separately on ice for 10 min.

2   Make a 0.1 M solution of PMSF in acetone. **(Warning   PMSF is very toxic.)** Add 1 μl of this protease inhibitor and 0.5 ml of cooled detergent solution to the lymphocytes. Mix *very gently* by slowly inverting the tube and incubate on ice for 30 min.

3   Centrifuge the mixture at 200 g for 10 min at 4°C. Transfer the supernatant to an ultracentrifuge tube and centrifuge at 100 000 g for 30 min at 4°C.

4   Store the supernatant at -20°C or lower.

Notes

1   Nonidet P40 and Triton X-100 are not suitable for some analytical methods (Section 4.4.1 and Table 4.5). If such procedures are planned, use Renex 30 instead. Alternatively, sodium deoxycholate may be used in the presence of DNAase II and phosphodiesterase (each 20 μg/ml/10^7 cells, 30 min at room temperature) but this is less satisfactory especially as the nucleases may contain some protease activity.

2   Larger numbers of lymphocytes can be solubilized at concentrations up to 2 $\times$ 10^8 cells/ml in the presence of 2% (w/v) detergent.

4.4.3   Solubilization of isolated membranes

Various membranes can be prepared from lymphocytes and other cells by reasonably straightforward procedures. Such methods are beyond the scope of this book. They are discussed in detail by Evans (1978). However, the preparation of mammalian erythrocyte membrane or 'ghosts' is described below as an illustration, and a general method then given for the solubilization of membranes.

Preparation of erythrocyte membrane

Materials and equipment

Mammalian erythrocytes (Section 4.2.2) — 1 ml packed volume
5 mM sodium phosphate pH 7.5
High speed centrifuge

Procedure

1   Add the erythrocytes to 40 ml of 5 mM phosphate buffer with rapid mixing and centrifuge at 20 000 g for 15 min at 4°C.

2   The supernatant is red (haemoglobin) and the membrane forms a

111

red translucent layer over a small opaque cream pellet. Aspirate the supernatant.

3   Gently tilt the centrifuge tube so that the membrane layer slides off the pellet and aspirate this pellet.

4   Wash the membrane twice in 40 ml of 5 mM phosphate buffer by resuspension and centrifugation (20 000 g, 15 min, 4°C).

The final pellet should be free from red colour. The yield is 2–5 mg membrane protein (measured as Section 1.1.2).

Solubilization of membrane

Materials and equipment

Membrane — 100 μg of protein
10 mM tris-HCl pH 8.2
1% (w/v) sodium deoxycholate in 10 mM tris buffer **(Warning   this detergent is a very fine powder. Avoid breathing the dust.)**
Phenylmethylsulphonyl fluoride (PMSF)
Acetone
Ultracentrifuge

Procedure

1   Suspend the membrane in 50 μl 10 mM tris buffer. Cool on ice.

2   Make a 0.1 M solution of PMSF in acetone. **(Warning   PMSF is very toxic.)** Add 1 μl of this protease inhibitor and 50 μl of deoxycholate solution to the membrane suspension. Mix gently and incubate on ice for 15 min.

3   Centrifuge at 100 000 g for 30 min at 4°C and store the supernatant at −20°C or lower.

Notes

1   For protein concentrations higher than 4 mg/ml increase the detergent concentration correspondingly.

2   Most of the detergents in Table 4.3 can be substituted for deoxycholate if desired (see Section 4.4.1 and Table 4.5 for choice of detergent), but assay the supernatant for solubilization yield.

5 Radiolabelling techniques

5.1 INTRODUCTION

Radioactive labelling of antibodies or target antigens is a crucial part of radioimmunoassays, immunoprecipitation and many other immunochemical techniques. Vectorial radiolabelling of cell surface molecules is used extensively in structural studies of membranes. Biosynthetic radiolabelling provides information about the synthesis and degradation of macromolecules as well as some structural data (e.g. whether a protein contains phosphate or sugar groups).

Addition of ^{125}I is usually the preferred method for labelling soluble proteins (Section 5.2) because the isotope is cheap and easily detected, and it is possible to obtain preparations of high specific activity.

Radiolabelling of cells so that the isotope is only incorporated into structures present on the outer surface is an ideal that is hard to realize in practice. Common procedures use large, highly charged or insoluble molecules (which only penetrate the plasma membrane very slowly) as mediators of radiolabelling (see Sections 5.2.2, 5.2.3, 5.3.1 and 5.3.2). However, even these widely accepted 'surface labels' result in 1–5% of the incorporated radioactivity being present in internal molecules (see for example Hubbard & Cohn, 1976). The viability of the cell preparation should be monitored throughout the labelling procedure (internal structures of dead cells will be labelled quickly) and the data obtained should always be interpreted with caution.

Biosynthetic labelling of proteins, carbohydrates and lipids is usually more easily controlled, providing the added radioactive precursors are not metabolized to form precursors of different polymers (Section 5.4). The degree of success is limited only by two factors: the difficulty of keeping cells metabolically active for long periods under the conditions necessary for labelling and the expense of the radioactive precursors.

5.1.1 Radiation safety

The half-life and emissions of commonly encountered isotopes are listed in Table 1.4. ^{125}I requires lead (or lead glass) shielding but ^{32}P may cause secondary X-rays from thin lead and Perspex is better. Most countries have legislation relating to the use and disposal of radioactive material and in the UK the Department of Employment has issued a code of practice. Additional guidance is provided by:
1 International Atomic Energy Agency Safety Series No. 1 (1973)

113

Safe Handling of Radionuclides. Available from IAEA, Wagramerstrasse 5, PO Box 100, A-1400 Vienna or in the UK from PO Box 569, London.

2 *Guide for Users of Labelled Compounds* (1979) and *Radioiodination Techniques*, review No. 18, available free from Amersham (Appendix 3).

All new experiments should be discussed with your Safety Officer.

In general, gamma emitters (^{125}I and ^{51}Cr) and 'hard' beta emitters (^{32}P) require more care than weaker isotopes but even the latter can endanger both health and other people's experiments by careless contamination. A separate area, or preferably a whole room, should be set aside exclusively for work involving large amounts (greater than 100 μCi) of ^{125}I, ^{32}P and other energetic isotopes. This area should contain an efficient fume cupboard with adequate shielding *all round* containing a large spill tray. Impermeable plastic gloves should always be worn and two layers are advisable when handling the neat isotope bottle so that the outer ones (which almost invariably become contaminated) can be discarded immediately the stock bottle is finished with.

Other precautions are simply common sense and good laboratory practice. Do not eat, drink, smoke, apply cosmetics or mouth pipette in the laboratory. Monitor the laboratory, your clothing and skin for contamination; use the appropriate Geiger counter monitors for all isotopes except the weaker ones which can be detected by liquid scintillation counting of paper wipes. Also monitor your thyroid 24 h after performing an iodination.

5.1.2 Measurement of radioactivity incorporated into protein

Not all of the total activity in a radiolabelled sample is covalently bound to protein because of the imperfections of labelling and fractionation procedures. It is usually worth while to determine the amount incorporated into protein because this is more meaningful than the total radioactivity of the sample.

Materials and equipment

Radiolabelled sample
Glassfibre filter paper (e.g. GF/A) (Whatman — Appendix 3) — 15 mm squares or circles
Rack for approximately 10 mm test tubes
10% (w/v) trichloroacetic acid
Ethanol
Test tubes approximately 12 mm × 50 mm
Radioactivity counter suitable for the isotope (Section 1.4)

Procedure

1 Place 4 pieces of glass fibre over the holes of the test tube rack so

114

that the central portions are not touching the frame. Apply an accurately measured aliquot (up to 20 μl, containing about 10 000 detectable c.p.m.) of the labelled sample to the middle of each filter and allow to dry.

2 Transfer 2 filters to test tubes and add 2 ml trichloroacetic acid solution.

3 Leave for 10 min, vortexing occasionally, and discard the liquid.

4 Add a second 2 ml of the acid solution and repeat step 3.

5 Add 2 ml of ethanol and repeat step 3.

6 Remove the filters from the tubes and allow to dry.

7 Measure the radioactivity in filters from steps 1 and 6 (Section 1.4). Calculate:

(a) Proportion of sample radioactivity bound to protein =

$$\frac{\text{mean activity after acid precipitation (step 6)}}{\text{mean activity before acid precipitation (step 1)}} \times 100\%$$

(b) Total protein-bound radioactivity in sample =

$$\frac{\text{mean activity after acid}}{\text{precipitation (step 6)}} \times \frac{\text{total volume of sample}}{\text{volume of aliquot (step 1)}}$$

Notes

1 This procedure will also precipitate nucleic acids and some lipids. To remove lipids (e.g. from detergent solubilized cells, Section 4.4) soak the filters in 2 ml of chloroform:methanol (2:1, v/v) for 10 min after step 5 before drying. Alternatively precipitate the protein in ethanol instead of the acid (Section 7.1.5).

2 For isotopes that can be detected by direct emission (e.g. ^{125}I and ^{32}P, Cherenkov) only 2 aliquots need be taken in step 1. Measure the total activity of these after drying on glassfibre and then subject the filters to steps 2–6 and determine the acid-insoluble radioactivity.

5.2 RADIOIODINATION

Na^{125}I is a cheap radioisotope that can be obtained with very high specific activity (carrier free, about 2000 Ci/matom) and used to radiolabel both soluble proteins and cells by various simple procedures. Labelling occurs by electrophilic addition of cationic iodine (I$^+$) to tyrosine residues (Fig. 5.1.) and to a lesser extent to histidine and tryptophan. The monoiodinated derivative is the major product under the conditions normally used. Alternatively, a small radioiodinated molecule can be conjugated to the protein, usually through the amino acids of lysine (Fig. 5.2).

Iodinated proteins tend to lose activity upon storage faster than dictated by the half-life of the isotope. This is attributable to several factors:

115

1 *Radiation destruction.* The products of radioactive decay of ^{125}I can cause damage to the protein with consequent loss of antibody or antigenic activity. This problem is worse for preparations labelled to a high specific activity.

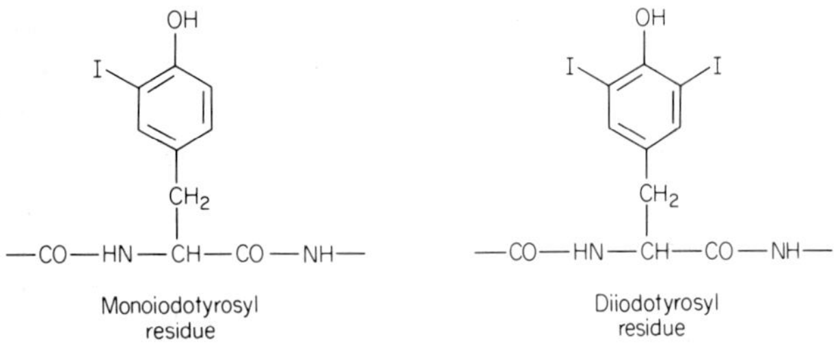

Monoiodotyrosyl residue

Diiodotyrosyl residue

Fig. 5.1 Structure of iodinated tyrosyl residues in a polypeptide. Under the conditions normally used for radioiodination the mono-iodinated derivate predominates.

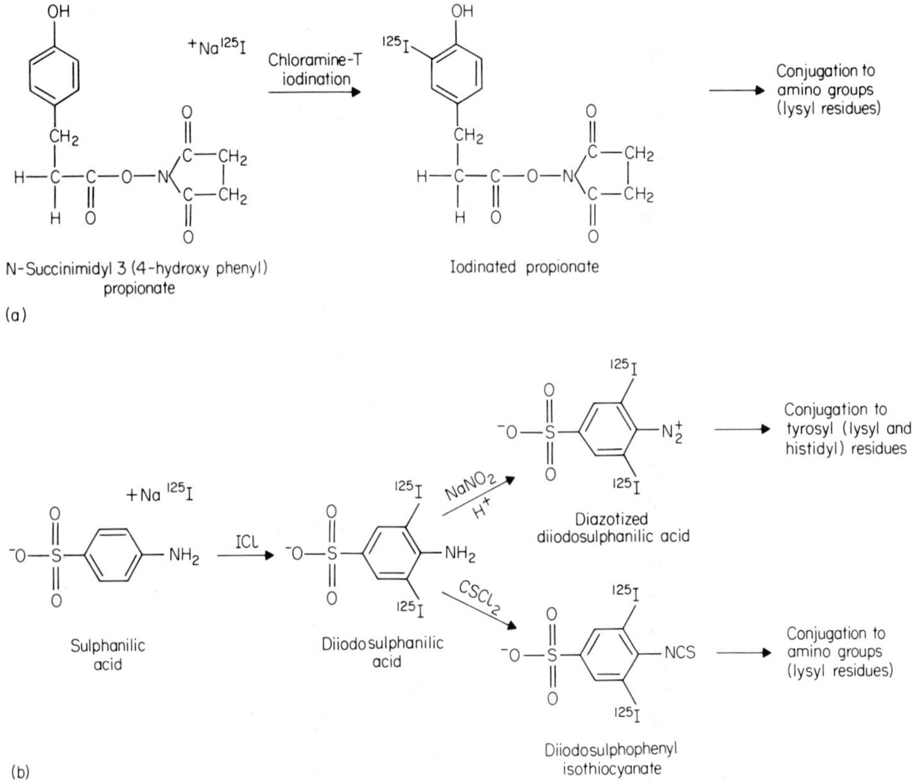

N-Succinimidyl 3 (4-hydroxy phenyl) propionate

Iodinated propionate

(a)

Conjugation to amino groups (lysyl residues)

Sulphanilic acid

Diiodo sulphanilic acid

Diazotized diiodosulphanilic acid

Conjugation to tyrosyl (lysyl and histidyl) residues

Diiodosulphophenyl isothiocyanate

Conjugation to amino groups (lysyl residues)

(b)

Fig. 5.2 Conjugation methods for radioiodinating protein (Section 5.2.4). (a) N-succinimidyl 3-(4-hydroxy 5-[^{125}I]-iodophenyl) propionate (Bolton & Hunter, 1973). (b) Diazo or isothiocyanate derivatives of iodinated sulphanilic acid or aniline (Sears *et al.*, 1971; Hayes & Goldstein, 1975).

116

2 *Loss of iodine.* Some proteins tend to break down to yield free radioiodine and unlabelled proteins.

3 *Protein deterioration.* Some proteins tend to aggregate, with loss of antibody and antigenic activities, upon iodination and during subsequent storage. Additional loss of immunochemical activity occurs for unknown reasons upon storage. These problems are probably associated with the storage of very dilute protein solutions (see Section 3.2) and are reduced somewhat by adding unlabelled carrier protein (e.g. 1 mg/ml albumin or haemoglobin), freezing aliquots rapidly, storing at $-70°C$ and thawing only once for use.

There are several established methods for radioiodination. The Chloramine T method (Section 5.2.1) is used for labelling soluble proteins to a high specific activity. If this oxidizing agent harms the protein's immunochemical activity, the solid phase reagent Iodogen can be used to produce a preparation of similar specific activity (Section 5.2.2). Lactoperoxidase will catalyse the iodination of both soluble proteins and cell surface components under very mild conditions (Section 5.2.3). Lactoperoxidase will catalyse the iodination of both soluble proteins and cell surface components under very mild conditions (Section 5.2.3), although it is difficult to produce proteins with high specific activity because of the low iodination yield. Alternative methods involve conjugation of the protein to a previously radioiodinated molecule (Section 5.2.4). Conjugation methods circumvent the problem of protein damage caused by direct contact between protein and iodination reagents and also allow derivatization of residues other than tyrosine. They are more complex than direct procedures and the consequent low iodination yield makes it difficult to prepare proteins with high specific activity.

The degree of substitution recommended for high specific activity is 1–2 atoms of iodine per molecule of protein. If carrier free $Na^{125}I$ is used, this will result in a product suitable for most radioimmunoassays and with acceptable stability: about 13–25 $\mu Ci/\mu g$ for a 150 000 molecular weight protein (IgG) and about 40–75 $\mu Ci/\mu g$ for a 50 000 molecular weight protein (Fab). Higher degrees of substitution decrease the stability of the product drastically (see above) and lower ones should be used where high specific activity is not absolutely necessary. Dilution of ^{125}I with non-radioactive iodine (^{127}I) is reported to increase the incorporation of ^{125}I by an unknown mechanism. This may be of use for preparations of low specific activity but at higher levels of substitution the extra iodine atoms incorporated will tend to reduce the protein's immunochemical activity. $Na^{125}I$ is sold in dilute sodium hydroxide (1 μM–1 mM) and a strong buffer should always be included in the mixture because the reactions are pH-dependent. Fresh solutions are advisable because $Na^{125}I$ is oxidized to molecular iodine upon storage especially if the vial is opened repeatedly. Storage at 4°C increases the rate of decomposition.

5.2.1 Chloramine T iodination

This reaction can be used to radioiodinate proteins to a very high specific activity (Greenwood *et al.*, 1963). The reaction is virtually instantaneous and the time of contact between the protein and the potentially harmful oxidizing agent should be kept to a minimum. After iodination, radioiodinated protein must be separated from free ^{125}I. Either gel filtration (method i) or ion exchange chromatography (method ii) can be used for this.

Method i

Materials and equipment

IgG (Section 3.3) — 1 mg/ml
0.25 M sodium phosphate pH 7.5
0.05 M sodium phosphate pH 7.5
Chloramine T — 1 mg/ml in 0.05 M phosphate buffer, freshly made
Sodium metabisulphite — 2.5 mg/ml in 0.05 M phosphate buffer, freshly made
Na^{125}I, carrier free (Amersham — Appendix 3) — 200 µCi
Phosphate buffered saline (PBS — Appendix 2)
1 mg/ml potassium iodide in PBS containing 0.1% (w/v) bovine serum albumin
10% (w/v) bovine serum albumin
Sephadex G-50 (fine) (Pharmacia — Appendix 3) — swollen in water
Chromatography column (0.7 cm × 15 cm) — a 5 ml graduated pipette is suitable
Polystyrene tubes 10.5 mm × 63.5 mm (Luckham — Appendix 3)
Gamma monitor (Mini-instruments — Appendix 3)

Procedure

1 Pack the Sephadex into the column (no buffer reservoir is necessary). Apply 100 µl of 10% albumin and wash through with PBS.
2 Following safety precautions (Section 5.1.1) dispense 200 µCi Na^{125}I into a polystyrene tube in a fume cupboard prepared for radioactive work.
3 Add 10 µl 0.25 M phosphate buffer and 10 µl IgG solution (10 µg) and mix.
4 Add 10 µl Chloramine T solution, mix and incubate at room temperature for 1 min.
5 Add 10 µl metabisulphite solution and mix.
6 Add 500 µl iodide and albumin solution and mix.
7 Apply the mixture to the Sephadex column, allow it to enter the gel and discard the 0.5 ml of eluant.
8 Apply 6 × 0.5 ml aliquots of PBS directly to the top of the Sephadex bed, allowing each aliquot to enter the gel before applying the next (the gel will only dry out slowly under gravity elution with a

118

narrow mouth pipette column and only 0.5 ml of eluant will be produced for each 0.5 ml PBS applied). Collect each 0.5 ml of eluant in a separate polystyrene tube.

9 The iodinated protein is normally contained in fractions 4–6. Confirm this with the gamma monitor. Discard the radioactive Sephadex (radioactive waste) and wash the column.

10 Pool the appropriate fractions, add 10 μl of 10% albumin and determine the radioactivity incorporated into protein (Section 5.1.2). This should be 120–180 μCi and comprise 70–95% of the total radioactivity in the sample.

Notes

1 The radioactive incorporation (approximately 15 μCi/μg or 2.25 mCi/nmol) is equivalent to 1 atom of iodine per molecule of protein. The product is suitable for use in most radioimmunoassays. The amount of Na^{125}I added can be increased slightly (up to 2-fold) but the product will be less stable. Decrease the amount of ^{125}I added if a high specific activity is not absolutely necessary.

2 Other proteins can be iodinated by this procedure; some are very susceptible to damage by Chloramine T and an alternative method should be used (Sections 5.2.2, 5.2.3 and 5.2.4). Adjust the amount of ^{125}I added to 3 mCi/nmol of protein.

3 This method is also applicable to membrane proteins solubilized in sodium deoxycholate (Section 4.4.3). A mixture of 50 μg protein in 100 μl of 1% deoxycholate, 10 μl of 0.25 M sodium phosphate pH 7.8, 100 μCi Na^{125}I and 10 μl 2.5 mg/ml Chloramine T gives a product suitable for immunoprecipitation analysis (Section 10.4). The subsequent separation procedure should be carried out in 0.5% deoxycholate in 10 mM tris-HCl pH 8.2.

4 More dilute protein solutions can be iodinated. Keep the final Chloramine T concentration in the reaction mixture 0.1–1.0 mg/ml.

5 The metabisulphite will reduce some disulphide bonds. This does not affect the structure of IgG but reduces F(ab′)$_2$ to Fab′ (see Sections 3.4.1 and 3.4.3) with consequent decrease in antigen binding avidity (Section 6.1.1). To avoid this problem, follow steps 1–4 and then add 500 μl of 0.1 mg/ml tyrosine in PBS, mix and follow steps 7–10.

Method ii (for IgG only)

Materials and equipment

IgG (either purified monoclonal antibody — Chapter 2 and Section 3.3.1, or affinity purified anti-F(ab′)$_2$ fragment — Chapter 3) — 2.5 mg/ml in 0.1 M sodium phosphate buffer pH 7.4

Na^{125}I (Amersham, specific activity 100 mCi/ml — Appendix 3)

0.1 M sodium phosphate buffer pH 7.4

119

0.1 M sodium phosphate buffer pH 7.4 containing 2 mg/ml BSA

Chloramine T — 5 mg/ml in water, freshly prepared

Tyrosine — 0.4 mg/ml in 0.1 M sodium phosphate buffer pH 7.4 — heat at 37°C to dissolve and store at −20°C

Dowex 1-X8 (Cl) standard grade, particle size 0.075–0.15 mm (100–200 mesh) (BDH — Appendix 3)

Pasteur pipette with glass wool plug

Plastic tubes

Bovine serum albumin (Sigma — Appendix 3)

20% w/v trichloroacetic acid (store at 4°C)

Gamma counter

Carry out iodination in a fume hood.

Procedure

1 Suspend Dowex resin in water and remove 'fines' by allowing resin to settle for 1 min and discarding supernatant. Repeat twice. Resuspend in sodium phosphate buffer containing albumin.

2 Pack resin into plugged Pasteur pipette; a column 4 cm long is suitable for one iodination. Wash through with 25–35 ml of phosphate buffer *containing 2 mg/ml BSA.*

3 Add 20–30 μl IgG solution to 180 μl sodium phosphate buffer (without BSA) — see note 1.

4 Add 100–200 μCi (see note 2) of Na^{125}I, mix and then add 10 μl chloramine T solution. Mix thoroughly.

5 Incubate for 45 sec – 1 min (see note 2) and then add 50 μl tyrosine solution and mix immediately.

6 Apply iodination mixture to the Dowex 1-X8 column and wash column through with 2.3 ml phosphate buffer containing BSA. Collect *all* effluent (this contains the ^{125}I-labelled IgG) — see note 3.

7 Check for efficient radiolabelling. For this dissolve 20 mg BSA in 200 μl phosphate buffer in a plastic conical centrifuge tube. Dilute 10 μl ^{125}I labelled IgG to 1 ml with phosphate buffer, mix and add 20 μl of this to the BSA solution in the centrifuge tube. Add 1 ml trichloroacetic acid solution, mix thoroughly (preferably vortex) and centrifuge for 5 min at about 10 000 *g*. Decant supernatant from pellet and count both separately. The percentage of counts bound to IgG is given by:

$$100 - \left(\frac{\text{c.p.m. in supernatant} \times 100}{\text{c.p.m. in pellet}} \right) \text{— see note 4}$$

Notes

1 Aliquots (20–30 μl) of IgG can be conveniently stored frozen (−20°C or −70°C) prior to radioiodination.

2 The most efficient amount of radioiodine needed and iodination

120

time vary between different antibody preparations. Monoclonal antibodies can be problematical — see note 1, method i.

3   The Dowex resin column will become very radioactive and must be
discarded with care.

4   The radioiodinated IgG should contain between 8×10^5 and 1.5×10^6 c.p.m./$10 \, \mu l$ and >92% of counts should be protein bound.

5.2.2   Iodogen iodination

Iodogen (1,3,4,6-tetrachloro-3a,6a-diphenylglycoluril), like Chloramine T, is a mild oxidising agent. However, it is practically insoluble
in aqueous solutions and the iodination proceeds by a solid phase
mechanism that damages the protein less (Fraker & Speck, 1978) but
the reaction is much slower. It has been proposed as a surface label for
cells because of its low solubility but this has not been evaluated
carefully. Even reagents which cannot traverse the plasma membrane
produce the active $^{125}I^+$ ion which can do so (see Section 5.2.3).

Materials and equipment

Iodogen (Pierce — Appendix 3)
Dichloromethane
Conical capped polypropylene tubes 10.5 mm × 39 mm (Alpha, Beck-
    man, Eppendorf — Appendix 3)
0.25 M sodium phosphate pH 7.5
IgG (Section 3.3) — 1 mg/ml
Na^{125}I, carrier free (Amersham — Appendix 3) — 200 μCi
Sephadex G-50 desalting column in phosphate buffered saline washed
    with 10 mg of albumin (Section 5.2.1, method i, step 1)
Polystyrene tubes 10.5 mm ×63.5 mm (Luckham — Appendix 3)
Gamma monitor (Mini-instruments — Appendix 3)
Heated water bath

Procedure

1   Dissolve 1 mg of Iodogen in 1 ml dichloromethane and pipette
20 μl into polystyrene tubes. Rotate the tubes in a 37°C water bath
until the solvent has evaporated leaving a film of Iodogen in the bottom
(these prepared tubes can be stored dessicated for several weeks
before use).

2   Add 10 μl of 0.25 M phosphate buffer and 10 μl IgG solution to
one Iodogen-coated tube and mix.

3   Following safety precautions (Section 5.1.1) dispense 200 μCi
Na^{125}I into the tube in a fume cupboard prepared for radioactive work.
Incubate at room temperature for 10 min, mixing every minute.

4   Remove the mixture from the tube (this terminates the production
of $^{125}I^+$) and separate the iodinated protein from free iodide as
described in Section 5.2.1, method i, steps 7–10.

121

Notes

1   The incorporation of iodine is usually a little lower than with Chloramine T but the reaction time can be extended to improve this.
2   More dilute protein solutions require a longer reaction time.
3   The procedure can be used to iodinate membrane proteins solubilized in 1% sodium deoxycholate (Section 4.4.3).
4   See Section 5.2.1, method i, notes 1 and 2.

5.2.3   Lacteroperoxidase catalysed iodination

This method is the mildest procedure available. However, it is difficult to obtain preparations with very high specific activity and its major use has been in surface labelling intact cells for structural studies (Hubbard & Cohn, 1976).

The enzyme binds all three reactants: $^{125}I^-$, H_2O_2 and tyrosine (although not necessarily simultaneously) and so, in theory, is the ideal reagent for controlled localized iodination. However, both $^{125}I^+$ and $^{125}I_2$ can be released from the enzyme and diffuse across the membrane. In addition, endogenous cytoplasmic peroxidases can catalyse the iodination of internal tyrosines by added $^{125}I^-$ and H_2O_2 both of which are permeant. Internal structures of dead cells are readily labelled and even a small proportion can lead to heavy labelling of some proteins. For surface labelling it is even more important than usual to use fresh non-oxidized $Na^{125}I$ (see above, Section 5.2) to prevent internal iodination by $^{125}I_2$. A useful modification employs glucose and glucose oxidase to generate continuously micromolar amounts of H_2O_2.

Materials and equipment

(Azide should not be present in any buffers as this inhibits lactoperoxidase.)

Lymphocytes (Section 4.2) — 2×10^7
Balanced salts solution (BSS — Appendix 2)
Lactoperoxidase — 0.2 mg/ml in PBS (this solution may be stored at
    −20°C aliquoted for single use)
Glucose oxidase — 2 i.u./ml in PBS, freshly made
β-D-glucose — 18 mg/ml (0.1 M) in PBS
$Na^{125}I$, carrier free (Amersham — Appendix 3) — 300 μCi
Gamma monitor (Mini-instruments — Appendix 3)
Polystyrene tube 10.5 mm $\times$ 63.5 mm (Luckham — Appendix 3)
Round-bottomed screw-capped polystyrene tubes 16 mm $\times$ 100 mm
    (Sterilin — Appendix 3)
Hepes buffered BMEE medium (Table 4.1)

122

Procedure

1 Wash the lymphocytes twice with 10 ml BSS by repeated suspension and centrifugation (250 g, 5 min) in a 16 mm × 100 mm tube.

2 Resuspend the final cell pellet in BSS to a total volume of 200 μl. Determine cell viability and total cell number (Section 4.1.1).

3 Following safety precautions (Section 5.1.1) dispense 300 μCi Na^{125}I into a 10.5 mm × 63.5 mm tube in a fume cupboard prepared for radioactive work.

4 Add 100 μl of the cell suspension (10^7 cells), 10 μl of lactoperoxidase solution (2 μg), 10 μl of glucose oxidase solution (0.02 i.u.) and 10 μl of glucose (180 μg). Mix gently and incubate on ice for 10 min.

5 Add 1 ml of BMEE to the tube, mix and transfer the mixture to a fresh 16 mm × 100 mm tube. Add 9 ml BMEE and centrifuge at 250 g for 5 min.

6 Discard the supernatant (radioactive waste), resuspend the pellet in 10 ml BMEE and centrifuge at 250 g for 5 min.

7 Discard the supernatant, resuspend the pellet in 10 ml BMEE and incubate at room temperature for 5 min.

8 Centrifuge at 250 g for 5 min, discard the supernatant and resuspend the pellet in 0.5 ml BMEE. Determine cell viability and total cell number (Section 4.1.1) and also radioactive incorporation into protein (Section 5.1.2).

Notes

1 Approximately 10% of added ^{125}I is associated with cells. Only 10–40% of this is incorporated into protein, the remainder being mostly free ^{125}I with a very small proportion bound to lipid.

2 The vectorial nature of cell labelling cannot simply be assumed. It is important that cell viability is high both before and after iodination. The cell surface localization of the label can be tested by proteolytic removal of external proteins (Section 4.1.3) combined with polyacrylamide gel analysis (Section 7.3.1). Alternatively the cells can be homogenized and centrifuged at 100 000 g for 30 min; less than 5% of the total trichloroacetic acid insoluble radioactivity (Section 5.1.2) should be present in the supernatant.

3 The labelled cells can be solubilized in detergents (Section 4.4.2) for subsequent analysis (e.g. see Figs. 10.7 and 10.8).

4 Soluble proteins are best iodinated by insolubilized enzyme to facilitate the separation of substrate and enzyme (both radioiodinated) after the reaction. A mixture of lactoperoxidase and glucose oxidase bound to small beads is commercially available (Bio-Rad — Appendix 3). Alternatively, couple 5 mg of enzyme to 10 ml of Sepharose 4B (Section 10.2.1). Mix 10 μl of 10% suspension of lactoperoxidase-Sepharose in PBS (0.5 μg enzyme), 50 μl of 1 mg/ml protein in PBS (50 μg protein), 500 μCi Na^{125}I (carrier free) and 1 μl of 1/10 000 dilution of 100 vols hydrogen peroxide (10^{-5} M) in PBS. Incubate for

123

10 min at room temperature with constant gentle mixing. Add 10 μl of 10% sodium azide and centrifuge at 500 g for 1 min. Dialyse or desalt (Section 5.2.1) the supernatant to remove free ^{125}I. This procedure can also be used to label membrane proteins solubilized in detergents (Section 4.4.3); the enzyme is active in 1% (w/v) solutions of sodium deoxycholate and Nonidet P40.

5.2.4 Other iodination techniques

The original method for direct protein iodination involved the addition of iodine monochloride. This procedure can be used for high specific activity preparations under carefully controlled conditions (Glover *et al.*, 1967), although some non-radioactive iodine is invariably incorporated. The procedure is not used widely.

There are several reagents that can be iodinated and subsequently conjugated to protein through various amino acid residues. The most common is the Bolton-Hunter reagent — N-succinimidyl 3-(4-hydroxy 5-[^{125}I]-iodophenyl) propionate — although derivatives of sulphanilic acid and aniline have also been used. Figure 5.2 shows the protocol for their preparation; the radioiodinated Bolton-Hunter reagent is commercially available (Amersham — Appendix 3). Although these reagents are technically difficult to make or expensive to buy, they obviate direct contact between protein and oxidizing and reducing agents and radioiodide. They should also be used when direct iodination of tyrosine is undesirable or impossible.

5.3 RADIOLABELLING GLYCOPROTEINS AND GLYCOLIPIDS

Cell surface carbohydrate residues can be oxidized under mild conditions to form aldehyde groups which can then be radioactively labelled (Fig. 5.3). The first step involves periodate oxidation of sialic acid (Section 5.3.1) or oxidation of terminal galactose or N-acetylgalactosamine residues with galactose oxidase (Section 5.3.2). The second step is usually reduction of the aldehyde back to an alcohol using NaB[^{3}H]$_4$ to incorporate a tritium label, but alternative reagents are available (see Section 5.3.1, note 4).

Some proteins are labelled by NaB[^{3}H]$_4$ alone without prior oxidation and a non-oxidized sample should always be reduced in parallel with the test sample to control for this.

The choice of method is mostly empirical but in addition several theoretical and practical considerations influence the decision. Oxidation by an enzyme is, in theory, more likely to restrict labelling to the cell surface, although the current consensus of opinion places the vast majority of carbohydrate on the outside of the plasma membrane anyway. However, galactose oxidase may contain protease contaminants, and the neuraminidase treatment used in conjunction with it

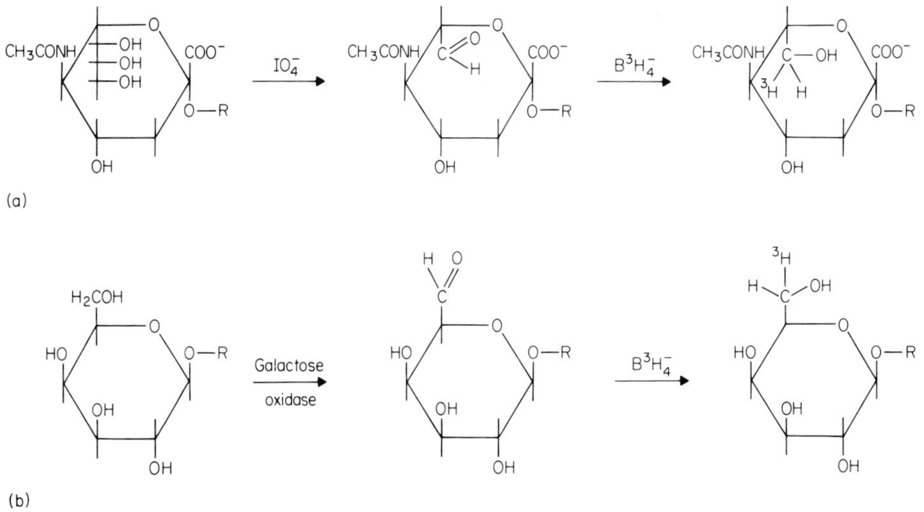

(a)

(b)

Fig. 5.3 Radiolabelling carbohydrate by oxidation of (a) N-acetylneuraminic acid (sialic acid), Section 5.3.1, or (b) galactose, Section 5.3.2, followed by reduction with tritiated sodium borohydride.

changes the mobility of some proteins in subsequent electrophoretic analyses. Sodium periodate is considerably cheaper than galactose oxidase.

5.3.1 Periodate oxidation (from Gahmberg & Andersson, 1977)

Low concentrations of sodium periodate at neutral pH cleave the alkyl chain of sialic acid between vicinal hydroxyls to generate an aldehyde group which can then be reductively radiolabelled (Fig. 5.3a). The reaction appears to be specific for sialic acid; a higher concentration of periodate ion (45 mM) at a lower pH (in 7% acetic acid) will cleave between vicinal hydroxyls in other sugar groups.

Materials and equipment

Lymphocytes (Section 4.2) — 2×10^7
Balanced salts solution (BSS — Appendix 2)
10 mM sodium periodate in BSS, freshly made
0.1 M glycerol in BSS
Sodium borohydride, tritium labelled (NaB[^{3}H]$_4$) — specific activity 10 Ci/mmol (Amersham — Appendix 3)
Polystyrene screw-capped tubes 16 mm × 100 mm (Sterilin — Appendix 3)

Procedure

1   In a fume cupboard prepared for radioactive work, dissolve the

125

NaB[^{3}H]$_4$ in 0.01 M sodium hydroxide to a final concentration of 0.5 mCi/μl and store in 5 μl aliquots at $-70°$C. This preparation can be used for up to 1 year.

2 Cool BSS on ice for steps 5–8. Wash the lymphocytes twice with 10 ml BSS by repeated suspension and centrifugation (250 **g**, 5 min) in a 16 mm × 100 mm tube.

3 Resuspend the final cell pellet in 200 μl BSS, divide into 2 equal volumes and cool on ice.

4 Add 10 μl of sodium periodate solution to one cell aliquot, mix gently and incubate on ice for 10 min (final periodate concentration 1 mM).

5 Add 10 μl of glycerol solution and 10 ml cold BSS to the periodate treated aliquot. Mix gently and centrifuge at 250 **g** for 5 min at 4°C.

6 Discard the supernatant, resuspend the cell pellet in 10 ml cold BSS and centrifuge as in step 5.

7 Discard the supernatant and resuspend the cell pellet in 100 μl cold BSS.

8 In a fume cupboard prepared for radioactive work add 1 μl NaB[^{3}H]$_4$ (0.5 mCi) to each sample (steps 3 and 7). Mix gently and incubate on ice for 20 min.

9 Wash the lymphocytes three times with 10 ml cold BSS by repeated suspension and centrifugation (250 **g**, 5 min). Discard the supernatants (radioactive waste).

10 Resuspend the final cell pellets in 250 μl BSS and determine the radioactivity incorporated into protein (Section 5.1.2) for both samples.

Notes

1 Tris buffers interfere with the periodate oxidation.

2 0.1–0.5 μCi should be incorporated into the protein of 10^7 lymphocytes. Some glycolipids are also labelled. The added NaB[^{3}H]$_4$ is a vast excess over aldehyde groups (greater than 100-fold) and the incorporation is determined by the amount of sialic acid in the preparation. It is pointless to add more radioactivity.

3 If restricting labelling to the cell surface is important, the vectorial nature of the label should be investigated as described in Section 5.2.3, note 2.

4 Other isotopes can be introduced by conjugating the aldehyde groups with the hydrazide of an amino acid containing the required label.

5 The labelled cells can be solubilized in detergents (Section 4.4.2) for subsequent analyses (e.g. immunoprecipitation or polyacrylamide gel electrophoresis).

6 Soluble glycoproteins can also be radiolabelled by this procedure. Add 25 μl of 0.1 M periodate to 1 mg of glycoproteins in 0.5 ml PBS. Incubate on ice for 10 min and remove excess reagent by desalting on a 1.0 cm × 20 cm column of Sephadex G-25 (medium) in PBS. Add

126

10 mCi NaB[^{3}H]$_4$ (1 μmol) to the protein pool and incubate for 30 min on ice and remove excess reagents by desalting or dialysis.

5.3.2 Galactose oxidase oxidation (from Gahmberg, 1976)

Galactose oxidase catalyses the oxidation of the primary hydroxyl group of terminal galactose and N-acetylgalactosaminyl residues to generate an aldehyde group which can then be reductively radiolabelled (Fig. 5.3b). Neuraminidase is usually also added to remove sialic acid and generate extra terminal galactose residues from the common carbohydrate structure: -Gal-NANA (Fig. 10.5).

Materials and equipment

Lymphocytes (Section 4.2) — 2×10^7
Galactose oxidase, protease free, 1000 i.u/ml (Kabi — Appendix 3)
Neuraminidase, protease free, 500 i.u/ml (Behringwerke — Appendix 3)
Balanced salts solution (BSS — Appendix 2)
Sodium borohydride, tritium labelled (NaB[^{3}H]$_4$) — specific activity 10 Ci/mmol (Amersham — Appendix 3)
Screw-capped polystyrene tubes 16 mm $\times$ 100 mm (Sterilin — Appendix 3)

Procedure

1 Dissolve and aliquot the NaB[^{3}H]$_4$ as described in Section 5.3.1, step 1. Place BSS to cool on ice for steps 6 and 7.
2 Wash the lymphocytes twice with 10 ml BSS by repeated suspension and centrifugation (250 g, 5 min) in a 16 mm $\times$ 100 mm tube.
3 Resuspend the final cell pellet in 200 μl BSS and divide into 2 equal aliquots.
4 Add 10 μl of neuraminidase (5 i.u.) and 5 μl of galactose oxidase (5 i.u.) to one sample only, mix gently and incubate at room temperature for 30 min.
5 Add 10 ml BSS to the oxidized sample, mix and centrifuge at 250 g for 5 min. Discard the supernatant.
6 Resuspend the cell pellet in 100 μl cold BSS. In a fume cupboard prepared for radioactive work add 1 μl NaB[^{3}H]$_4$ (0.5 mCi) to each sample (steps 3 and 6). Mix gently and incubate on ice for 20 min.
7 Follow steps 9 and 10, Section 5.3.1 to remove excess reagents.

Notes

1 Approximately 0.5 μCi should be incorporated into the protein of 10^7 lymphocytes. A similar amount is also incorporated into glycolipids.
2 See notes 2–5, Section 5.3.1.

127

3 Soluble glycoproteins can also be labelled by this procedure. Add 10 i.u. neuraminidase (20 μg) and 5 i.u. galactose oxidase (30 μg) to 1 mg of glycoprotein in 0.5 ml PBS and incubate at room temperature for 30 min. Add 10 mCi NaB[^{3}H]$_4$ and incubate for a further 30 min on ice. Remove excess reagents by desalting (Section 5.2.1 or 5.3.1, note 6) or dialysis.

5.4 BIOSYNTHETIC LABELLING

Viable cells in culture will incorporate added radiolabelled precursors into the macromolecules that they synthesize. This technique is useful in various metabolic studies, in confirming that a molecule of interest is manufactured by the cell and not passively acquired and in labelling many cellular constituents which are not easily labelled by other procedures (e.g. lipids, internal proteins). Some radioactive precursors are metabolized during long term cultures to form labelled products which may then be incorporated into macromolecules different from those synthesized directly from the original precursor. Hence the possible metabolism of the precursor should be considered when interpreting incorporation data. Unfortunately the specific activities of the products are usually low and the radioactive precursors and special media required are expensive. Labelling of phosphoproteins and phospholipids by addition of [^{32}P]P$_i$ (Section 5.4.2) is an exception to both of these drawbacks.

Added [^{14}C]acetate and [^{14}C]glucose will label many different macromolecules. Free fatty acids and glycerol are incorporated into lipids and some nucleoside diphosphate sugars (e.g. UDP-L-fucose) specifically into complex carbohydrates. [^{3}H]inositol can be used to label inositol phospholipids so that their subsequent cleavage can be monitored during signal transmission. Added amino acids will be incorporated into proteins; essential amino acids for cells from higher animals (i.e. leucine, isoleucine, valine, lysine, phenylalanine, tryptophan, threonine, arginine and methionine) are incorporated to a greater extent.

Cells that are growing and dividing (e.g. lymphoblasts and lymphoblastoid cell lines) will incorporate more precursor than quiescent cells (e.g. small lymphocytes). A special medium deficient in the appropriate precursor should be used to keep the specific activity of the added label as high as possible. However, the shortage of an essential nutrient can cause a decrease in growth rate and even cell death and so the addition of a small amount of unlabelled precursor is recommended in some cases.

5.4.1 Biosynthetic labelling of proteins

Materials and equipment

Human peripheral blood lymphocytes (Section 4.2) — 10^7

128

Methionine-free minimal essential medium (Flow — Appendix 3)
Fetal calf serum, heat inactivated (Section 4.1)
200 mM glutamine
Hepes buffered BMEE medium (Table 4.1)
L-[^{35}S]methionine, specific activity 100–500 mCi/mmol (Amersham — Appendix 3) — 200 μCi
Polystyrene round-bottomed screw-capped tubes 16 mm × 100 mm — (Sterilin — Appendix 3)
Culture flask 25 mm^2 (50 ml)
Incubator with 5% carbon dioxide atmosphere, 37°C

Procedure

1 Wash the lymphocytes twice with 10 ml methionine-free medium by repeated suspension and centrifugation (250 *g*, 5 min) in a 16 mm × 100 mm tube.

2 Resuspend the final cell pellet in 10 ml methionine-free medium containing 10% (v/v) fetal calf serum and 1/100 dilution of glutamine solution and transfer to a culture flask.

3 Add 200 μCi [^{35}S]methionine to the cells. Mix gently and incubate at 37°C in 5% carbon dioxide for 16–24 h.

4 Transfer the cell suspension to a 16 mm × 100 mm tube and centrifuge at 250 *g* for 5 min.

5 Discard the supernatant (radioactive waste), resuspend the pellet in 10 ml BMEE medium and incubate for 10 min at room temperature. Centrifuge as in step 4.

6 Repeat step 5. Resuspend the final cell pellet in 500 μl BMEE medium and determine the radioactivity incorporated into protein (Section 5.1.2).

Notes

1 The serum contains some methionine and this lowers the overall specific activity of the [^{35}S]methionine. However, this small amount of 'carrier' methionine helps to maintain the cell viability and it should not normally be removed.

2 The plasma membrane and culture supernatant from biosynthetically labelled lymphocytes are analysed in Figs. 2.1 and 7.10.

3 A similar procedure can be used to label proteins with other amino acids, carbohydrates with sugars and lipids with fatty acids.

4 The labelled cells can be solubilized in detergents (Section 4.4.2) for subsequent analysis.

5.4.2 Biosynthetic labelling of phosphoproteins and phospholipids

Materials and equipment

Human peripheral blood lymphocytes (Section 4.2) — 3 × 10^7

Phosphate-free minimal essential medium (Flow — Appendix 3)
Fetal calf serum, heat-inactivated (Section 4.1)
200 mM glutamine
0.9% (w/v) sodium chloride (isotonic saline)
Hepes buffered BMEE medium (Table 4.1)
[^{32}P]inorganic phosphate, carrier free (9000 Ci/mmol) (Amersham —
   Appendix 3) — 500 μCi
Polystyrene screw-capped round-bottomed tubes 16 mm $\times$ 100 mm
   (Sterilin — Appendix 3)
Beta monitor (Mini-instruments — Appendix 3)

Procedure

Warning ^{32}P requires different shielding from gamma emitters (Section 5.1.1).

1 Dialyse 1 ml serum against 2 changes of 500 ml saline at 4°C.
2 Wash the lymphocytes twice with 10 ml phosphate-free medium by repeated suspension and centrifugation (250 g, 5 min) in a 16 mm $\times$ 100 mm tube.
3 Resuspend the final cell pellet in 5 ml phosphate-free medium containing 10% (v/v) dialysed serum (step 1) and 1/100 dilution of glutamine solution.
4 Following safety precautions (Section 5.1.1) add 500 μCi [^{32}P]P$_i$ to the cells in a fume cupboard prepared for radioactive work and behind Perspex shielding. Mix gently and incubate at room temperature in a sealed tube for 16–24 h.
5 Add 5 ml BMEE, mix and centrifuge at 250 g for 5 min.
6 Discard the supernatant (radioactive waste), resuspend the cell pellet in 10 ml BMEE and incubate at room temperature for 10 min. Centrifuge as in step 5.
7 Repeat step 6. Resuspend the final cell pellet in 500 μl BMEE and determine the radioactivity incorporated into protein (Section 5.1.2).

Notes

1 Dividing cells (e.g. lymphoblastoid) should be incubated with [^{32}P]P$_i$ at 37°C for 2–4 h (step 4).
2 0.5–5.0 μCi is incorporated into the protein of 10^7 quiescent lymphocytes. A similar amount is also incorporated into lipid. The figure is 10–50-fold higher for rapidly growing cells.
3 Cell viability drops by 10–15% during the incubation, presumably because of the lack of inorganic phosphate. Non-dialysed serum may be used to provide some phosphate if this is important.
4 The labelled cells can be solubilized in detergents (Section 4.4.2) for subsequent analysis.

130

6 Precipitation techniques in agar and agarose

6.1 INTRODUCTION

The ability of antibodies to precipitate antigens from solution is one of their best known properties. This process involves the formation of a lattice of cross-linked antibody–antigen which is too large to remain in solution.

It should be emphasized that an immunoprecipitate will not always form when antibody encounters antigen. Concentration of both antibody and antigen are very important and the limited range of their relative concentration over which immunoprecipitation will occur is normally referred to as 'equivalence'. Outside of this range conditions of either antibody or antigen excess exist and only small (soluble) complexes of antigen–antibody are formed. For further explanation of this see Roitt (1984, Chapter 5).

In some cases (e.g. with monovalent antigen and some monoclonal or even oligoclonal antibodies) immunoprecipitation never occurs because the cross-links necessary for construction of the immuno-precipitation lattice cannot form.

6.1.1 Affinity and avidity

The affinity of antibody for antigen is important in immuno-precipitation techniques; usually only high affinity antibodies give good precipitation (see Chapter 2 for production of antisera). Affinity is defined as the equilibrium constant when a monovalent antibody reacts with a monovalent antigenic determinant. Even more important is the avidity of the antibody for the multivalent antigen. Avidity can be considered as a combination of the individual affinities of each anti-body binding site — antigenic determinant interaction. For high affin-ity polyclonal antibodies, e.g. from a hyperimmune animal, the avidity may be ten thousand times the affinity. For further information see Roitt (1987, Chapter 4). The terms affinity and avidity are sometimes replaced by 'intrinsic affinity' and 'functional affinity' respectively.

6.2 AGAR AND AGAROSE GEL TECHNIQUES: BASIC CONSIDERATIONS

Agar is a high molecular weight complex polysaccharide derived from seaweeds. It will dissolve in aqueous solutions at high temperature (around 90°C) and forms a gel on cooling to 30–45°C. A gel formed from 1–2% (w/v) agar is robust and has a large pore size. Agarose is a more highly purified form of agar, which in some cases has been chemically modified.

Most proteins will readily diffuse through an agar or agarose gel and, if precipitating antibody contacts the appropriate antigen whilst migrating in such a gel, an immunoprecipitate will form at the point at which they reach equivalence concentration. The use of agar precipitation techniques is one of the simplest methods for detecting precipitating antibody and can be made quantitative (Section 6.3.2).

Many modifications to the basic techniques (especially immunoelectrophoresis) have been developed and the most commonly used of these are described in this chapter. The system of albumin/anti-albumin is used throughout as an example but all techniques can be modified for most antigen/antibody systems.

6.2.1 Precoating glass plates with agar

It is advantageous to precoat glass plates and microscope slides which are to be used as supports for agar and agarose gels. This provides an adhesive surface for supporting the analytical gel and prevents it from floating away during washing and staining procedures. The procedure involves setting a low porosity agar gel onto the plate and then allowing it to dry onto the glass surface.

Materials and equipment

Agar
Levelling table
Boiling water bath
Glass plates or microscope slides (26 mm × 76 mm)

Procedure

1   Boil 0.5 g agar in 100 ml water until it dissolves (15–20 min).
2   Allow agar solution to cool to 50°C and then pipette 2 ml onto each microscope slide (for plates, use 0.2 ml/cm^2) placed on a levelling table.
3   Allow the agar to gel and then leave overnight at room temperature (or 4–6 h at 40°C) until *completely dry*. Protect precoated slides from moisture.

6.2.2 Staining precipitin lines

Although immunoprecipitin lines produced in agar are often visible, intensification and visualization of weaker lines can be achieved by staining with Coomassie brilliant blue. This will also aid photography. If staining is to be carried out it is essential to use precoated slides or plates to support the gel. Excess protein left in solution after precipitin formation must be completely removed by washing, except for rocket and crossed immunoelectrophoreses (Sections 6.4.4 and 6.4.5), in which excess protein is electrophoresed into the electrode chambers.

Materials and equipment

Agar gel containing immunoprecipitate
Phosphate buffered saline containing 0.02% w/v sodium azide (PBS-azide — Appendix 2)
Whatman 3 MM filter paper
Stain: 0.5% w/v Coomassie brilliant blue R in ethanol: water: acetic acid 50:45:5 by volume
Destain: water: acetic acid: methanol 87:8:5 by volume

Procedure

1   Wash gel in 5 changes of 100 ml PBS-azide over 48 h.
2   Dry by covering with a sheet of filter paper and leaving for 16 h at room temperature or 2–6 h at 40°C.
3   Immerse gel in stain for 5–10 min until stained bands are visible.
4   Destain in 3–4 changes of destain solution until background is clear.
5   Dry in air at room temperature.

6.3   DIFFUSION TECHNIQUES

These are techniques in which antibody is allowed to encounter antigen by diffusion alone. Many variations of the basic techniques have been developed (see Ouchterlony & Nilsson, 1986) and two of the most commonly used methods are described below.

6.3.1   Double immunodiffusion

This technique is one of the simplest and yet most informative of immunochemical methods. A buffered agar gel is prepared and antigen and antibody loaded into separate wells bored in the agar about 0.5–2 cm apart. After incubation for 12–48 hours antibody–antigen recognition is detected by the formation of an immunoprecipitin line between the wells. An advantage of this technique is that concentration gradients of antigen and antibody are automatically formed by the diffusion process. Immunoprecipitation will occur somewhere between the wells providing that equivalence concentration is obtained at some point in the overlapping antigen and antibody gradients.

Materials and equipment

Precoated microscope slide (Section 6.2.1)

133

Agar (Difco — Appendix 3)
Levelling table
Humid chamber (see note 1)
Phosphate buffered saline containing 0.02% w/v sodium azide (PBS-azide)
Gel punches or cork borer
Whatman no.1 filter paper
Vacuum line
Human serum albumin (HSA) 1 mg/ml in PBS-azide
Anti-human serum or anti-human serum albumin
Control pre-immune serum
Boiling water bath

Procedure

1 Level table and place the required number of slides on it. Each 26 mm × 76 mm slide can be used for up to 3 experiments.
2 Prepare 1% (w/v) agar solution by heating 1 g agar in 100 ml PBS-azide in the boiling water bath until completely dissolved.
3 Allow agar solution to cool to 45°C and carefully pipette 3.5 ml onto each slide (use a large bore 10 ml pipette). Allow to solidify.

Fig. 6.1 Templates for double diffusion. (a) is the most commonly used pattern, but (b) can be useful in some cases.

4 Place a slide over one of the templates shown in Fig. 6.1 and carefully punch holes in the agar using the cork borer or gel punch. The precise pattern used depends on the nature of the experiment.
5 Remove the plugs of agar from the wells using a Pasteur pipette attached to the vacuum line. Adjust pressure so that the plugs are quickly and evenly removed.
6 Prepare dilutions of antiserum, control serum and antigen in PBS-azide. Appropriate dilutions for most systems are neat, 1/2, 1/4, 1/8, 1/16, 1/32.
7 Pipette 20 μl neat antiserum into the centre well of the pattern shown in Fig. 6.1a and pipette the dilutions of HSA (20 μl/well) in order of concentration in the surrounding wells. Repeat with control serum.
8 Pipette 20 μl neat (1 mg/ml) HSA into the centre well of another set of wells bored in the same pattern and pipette the dilutions of antisera (20 μl/well) in order of dilution in the surrounding wells.

134

Incubate overnight at room temperature in the humid chamber.
9 Examine slides for immunoprecipitin lines. If necessary stain as described in Section 6.2.2.

Notes

1 A humid chamber can be easily constructed using a sandwich box lined at the bottom with moist tissue or plastic foam.
2 The presence of one immunoprecipitin line shows that the antiserum contains antibodies specific for the antigen. If more than one line is produced this indicates heterogeneity of *both* antigen and antiserum.
3 The distance of the precipitin line from the wells depends on concentration of reagents and their molecular weight (which governs their rate of diffusion).
4 Absence of a precipitin line indicates:
(a) There are no antibodies present with specificity for the antigen.
or
(b) There are antibodies present but they are not able to precipitate antigen.
or
(c) There are antibodies present but the concentrations of antigen and/or antiserum were not correct, i.e. equivalence was not obtained.
   These possibilities can be investigated by trying other concentrations of reagents or using a technique which will detect non-precipitating antibodies, e.g. immunocytochemistry (Chapter 12), immunoassay (Chapter 11), affinity chromatography (Chapter 10), or immunoblotting (Section 8.4).
5 Control experiments in which serum obtained from the animal prior to immunization ('pre-immune serum') is substituted for antiserum should always be carried out in parallel to test experiments (see Section 2.2).
6 A particularly useful aspect of this technique is its ability to demonstrate antigenic identity or non-identity. These terms refer to the ability of an antiserum to recognize antigens as identical or different, with the implication that the antigens are structurally similar or different. Degrees of identity as notated by double diffusion are shown in Fig. 6.2.
7 Large scale preparative double diffusion can also be carried out (see Section 9.1).
8 Inclusion of 3% w/v polyethylene glycol 6000 in the gel enhances precipitation of large molecular complexes and this may increase the sensitivity. This may be particularly advantageous when using monoclonal antibodies.

6.3.2 Single (radial) immunodiffusion

In this technique antigen is loaded into wells bored in an agar gel

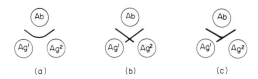

Fig. 6.2 Interpretation of double immunodiffusion. Fusion of immunoprecipitin lines (a) infers immunochemical identity of antigens 1 and 2, whereas crossing of the lines (b) shows their non-identity. Partial fusion or spur formation (c) suggests partial identity, i.e. antigen 2 has some determinants which are not shared by antigen 1, but all the determinants recognized by these antibodies that are present on antigen 1 are also present on antigen 2.

which contains a fixed concentration of antibody. The antigen diffuses into the gel and combines with antibody until equivalence is reached. At this point an immunoprecipitin 'halo' is formed round the well, and Mancini showed that the diameter of the 'halo' at equivalence is related to the antigen concentration. This quantitative aspect is the major advantage of the technique.

Materials and equipment

As for double diffusion (Section 6.3.1)
Rule, micrometer scale, or calibrated lens (Bio-Rad — Appendix 3)

Procedure

1   Prepare dilutions of antiserum and control pre-immune serum in PBS-azide. The right dilution varies between sera and can only be determined by experiment. Initially try 1/10, 1/20, 1/50. 1 ml of diluted antiserum is required per slide.
2   Level table and place required number of precoated slides on it (each slide can be used for 5 samples).
3   Prepare 2% w/v agar solution by dissolving 1 g agar in 50 ml PBS-azide (heat at 100°C until it dissolves). Allow to cool to 56°C.
4   Mix thoroughly equal volumes of diluted antiserum (or control serum) with agar solution and then pour 2 ml of this mixture onto each slide. Allow to solidify.
5   Punch 5 wells in the agar 5–6 mm apart using the cork borer or gel punch. Ensure that the walls of the well are vertical and smooth.
6   Remove the plugs of agar from the wells using a Pasteur pipette attached to the vacuum line. Adjust pressure so that the plugs are quickly and evenly removed. Place slide in the humid chamber.
7   Prepare dilutions of antigen in PBS-azide. Initially try 0.5, 0.25, 0.125, 0.0625, 0.03125 mg/ml HSA.
8   Pipette 20 μl of each antigen dilution into separate wells in both the antiserum and control slide. Incubate for at least 24 h at room temperature (see note 1 below).

136

9   Measure the diameter of the 'halo' with the rule or micrometer scale or calibrated lens. Direct measurement of the immunoprecipitin rings with a rule may not be sufficiently accurate, but the rings can be enlarged using a photographic enlarger and the measurements made from the projected image. Alternatively dividers may be used or fine rules obtained commercially (also see note 2).

10   Plot halo diameter against $\log_{10}$ concentration of antigen to give a standard curve. This should be linear. The antigen concentration in unknown samples can be found by reference to this curve.

Notes

1   It is essential to allow complete equilibration to occur. This will take at least 24 h (or 6 h at 37°C) and 48 h is preferable. If the antiserum contains considerable amounts of IgM then longer incubation time is necessary. Use of purified IgG or antibody (Sections 3.3.1 and 10.3.1) may improve results in some cases.

2   Staining the halos with Coomassie blue may give better definition especially for small or faint immunoprecipitates (Section 6.2.2).

3   It is *essential* to include control sera obtained from the animal prior to immunization in all experiments. Radial immunodiffusion is especially prone to artefactual precipitation.

4   See note 8, Section 6.3.1.

5   Equipment is available for automatic readout of single immunodiffusion plates (Autodata, Dynatech — Appendix 3).

6.3.3   Modifications for insoluble proteins

It is possible to adapt diffusion techniques for use with detergent solubilized proteins. This is of use when the proteins under investigation are insoluble in physiological solutions (e.g. cytoskeletal and membrane proteins).

Most non-ionic detergents (e.g. Triton X-100, Nonidet P40, Lubrol PX; see Tables 4.3 and 4.4) do not affect antigen–antibody precipitation reactions and so these detergents can be incorporated into the gel and the detergent solubilized proteins treated as normal samples. However, some proteins are not solubilized by non-ionic detergents and they require more drastic treatment with 2% (w/v) sodium dodecylsulphate (SDS) and disulphide bridge reduction with 2-mercaptoethanol before solubilization is achieved (e.g. some cytoskeletal and viral proteins). These reagents affect immunoprecipitin reactions in the following ways: (a) antigenic determinants may be destroyed, and so immunoprecipitation does not occur. There is little or nothing that can be done to avoid this. However, many antigens do retain sufficient functional determinants after such treatment to enable immunoprecipitation to occur. (b) 2-mercaptoethanol in the gel will partially denature antibodies (low concentrations of SDS do not do this). Usually 2-mercaptoethanol can be used in the sample but omit-

137

ted from the gel without precipitating the antigen. If insolubility does result, alkylate the antigen with iodoacetamide after 2-mercapto-ethanol reduction to prevent re-oxidation of thiols (see Section 3.4.1 for further information). (c) Inclusion of SDS in antigen samples and gels often leads to non-specific precipitation of proteins present in either antiserum or antigen, and under certain circumstances SDS itself can form a precipitate. This can be avoided by also including a non-ionic detergent (e.g. Triton X-100) in the gel. This forms mixed micelles with the SDS which seems to prevent protein and self pre-cipitation. Normally 0.1% (w/v) SDS in gels is sufficient to prevent precipitation of most proteins and 1% (w/v) Triton X-100 prevents non-specific precipitation.

6.4 ELECTROPHORETIC TECHNIQUES

Agar may be used as a solid support for electrophoresis. At concentra-tions normally used (around 1% w/v) molecular sieving of nearly all proteins is minimal, and separation of proteins is almost entirely due to charge differences.

6.4.1 Electroendosmosis

The phenomenon of electroendosmosis is especially pronounced when agar is used for electrophoresis. This effect is attributable to the large number of negatively charged groups present on the agar. When a potential difference is applied across an agar gel, the positively charged ions, which normally ensure electrical neutrality of the gel are free to move in the electrical field, whereas the negative counter ions are covalently bound to the gel matrix, and are thus immobile. The overall effect is the tendency for positive ions to migrate to the cathode, which cannot be balanced by a migration of negative ions to the anode. Therefore the ionic concentration at the cathode becomes greater than at the anode and water moves to the cathode to overcome this concen-tration imbalance. Proteins present in the agar during this process experience an osmotic effect, due to the variable amount of water present in different parts of the gel, and this force, together with the bulk movement of liquid, tends to cause the proteins to move towards the cathode.

Thus, during electrophoresis in agar, proteins experience two forces:
(a) An electrophoretic force, due to the applied potential difference. At pH values normally used for agar electrophoresis (above pH 8) most proteins are negatively charged, and so the electrophoretic force causes them to migrate towards the anode.
(b) An electroendosmotic force, which causes the proteins to move towards the cathode.

The overall direction of movement of a protein will be determined by whether the electrophoretic or electroendosmotic force is greater.

138

For most proteins the electrophoretic force is considerably the larger and so most proteins migrate to the anode. However, there are exceptions to this and most immunoglobulins are notable for their cathodal migration in agar electrophoresis.

Although electroendosmosis of agar gels can be advantageous in some techniques (e.g. crossover immunoelectrophoresis, Section 6.4.2), there are disadvantages associated with too high electroendosmosis. These are: (i) high voltages cannot be applied to agar gels as the gel itself will move in the electrical field; (ii) the medium is unsuitable for isoelectric focusing as the gel molecules 'focus' themselves. The ideal nature of agar gels for supporting immunoprecipitin reactions has led to development of agar derivatives with low electroendosmosis. The outcome of this is the availability commercially of highly purified agar derivatives known as agarose. This material is less heterogeneous than agar and is preferable for carrying out electrophoretic techniques. Agarose is also now available in which charged groups have been chemically neutralized and thus little or no electroendosmosis is shown. A range of agaroses is available with different degrees of charge neutralization and therefore different electroendosmotic properties (LKB, Pharmacia, Sigma — Appendix 3).

6.4.2 Crossover immunoelectrophoresis

This technique is like double diffusion (Section 6.3.1) except an electrophoretic force is used to drive antigen and antibody together instead of simple diffusion. Advantages over double diffusion are that a result can be obtained in about 1 h and that less antigen and antibody are needed as the electrophoretic force drives all the antigen and antibody together whereas diffusion occurs in every direction.

The method relies upon the cathodal migration of IgG and IgM, and so agarose of high electroendosmosis or electrophoretic grade agar is essential (Section 6.4.1).

Materials and equipment

Level table
Precoated microscope slides (Section 6.2.1)
Electrophoretic grade agar or agarose showing high electroendosmosis
Small gel punch, blunt hypodermic needle or Pasteur pipette, about
    1.5 mm diameter
Barbitone buffer pH 8.2 (Appendix 2)
3 MM filter paper
Electrophoresis tank (Shandon — Appendix 3)
Power pack (Shandon — Appendix 3)
Human serum albumin
Rabbit anti-human serum albumin
Vacuum line

139

Procedure

1 Prepare a layer of 1% w/v agar or agarose on precoated micro-scope slides as described in Section 6.3.1, steps 1–3, *except* dissolve the agar/agarose in barbitone buffer.

2 Bore two wells 1 cm apart along the long axis of the slide using the gel punch, needle or Pasteur pipette. Remove the plugs of agar from the wells using a Pasteur pipette attached to a vacuum line.

3 Transfer the slide to the electrophoresis tank containing the barbi-tone buffer as electrode solutions. Soak filter paper strips in this buffer and use a triple thickness of these to connect the ends of the slide with the electrode compartments (Fig, 6.3).

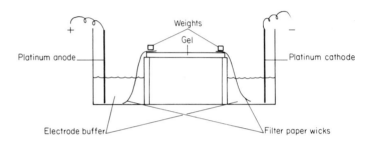

Fig. 6.3 Electrophoresis tank suitable for immunoelectrophoretic techniques. Similar tanks are available commercially (Shandon — Appendix 3).

4 Fill the well closest to the cathode with antigen and the other well with antiserum (use an automatic pipette, a drawn out Pasteur or a Hamilton syringe for this). Carry out electrophoresis at 8 V/cm for 30 min.

5 An immunoprecipitate may be visible directly, but intensification of weak lines or detection of 'invisible' precipitates can be achieved by staining for protein (Section 6.2.2).

Notes

1 For interpretation of results see Section 6.3.1.

2 If no immunoprecipitate is formed under the conditions described above it may be due to the slow migration of the antigen. This can be overcome by increasing the period used for electrophoresis.

3 See note 8, Section 6.3.1.

6.4.3 Immunoelectrophoresis

In this technique proteins in the antigen are first separated by elec-trophoresis in agar or agarose. Antiserum is then allowed to diffuse from a trough cut in the gel parallel to the direction of electrophoresis.

Immunoprecipitin arcs are observed where antigen–antibody interaction occurs (see Fig. 6.4).

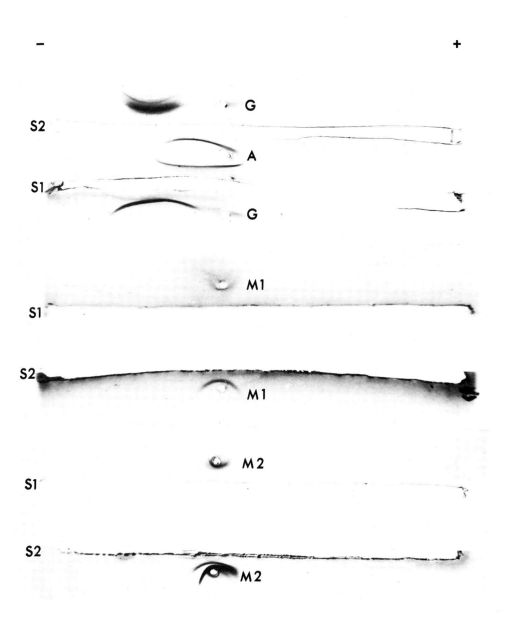

Fig. 6.4 Analysis of human immunoglobulin preparations by immunoelectrophoresis (Section 6.4.3). G, normal pooled IgG (Sections 3.3.1); A, normal pooled secretory IgA (Section 3.7.2); M1, myeloma IgM_{κ} (Section 3.5); M2, normal pooled IgM (Section 3.5); S1, goat anti-(human immunoglobulin, all classes); S2, goat anti-(whole human serum). These preparations are also analysed in Figs. 7.6 and 11.5.

The major limitation of this technique is the relatively low resolution obtained with most antigen mixtures using agar electrophoresis. Electroendosmosis may either hinder or help separation of proteins depending upon the antigen under investigation. Normally high or medium electroendosmosis agarose is used. The migration of serum proteins in immunoelectrophoresis is shown diagrammatically in Fig. 6.5.

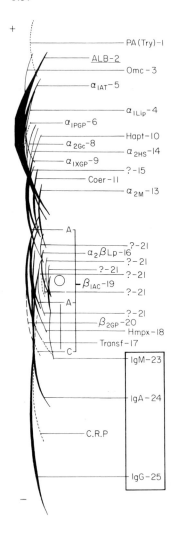

Fig. 6.5 Migration of human serum proteins in immunoelectrophoresis (Section 6.4.3). Reproduced from Heremans (1974) with permission. (1) PA (Try), tryptophan-rich prealbumin; (2) Alb, albumin; (3) Omc, orosomucoid; (4) α_{1Lip}, α1-lipoprotein; (5) α_{1AT}, α1-antitrypsin; (6) α_{1PGP}, α1-precipitable globulin; (8) α_{2Gc}, α2-Gc-globulin; (9) α_{1XGP}, α1-X-glycoprotein; (10) Hapt, haptoglobulin; (11) Coer, ceruloplasmin; (13) α_{2M}, α2-macroglobulin; (14) α_{2HS}, α2-HS-glycoprotein; (16) $\alpha_{2}\beta Lp$, low-density lipoproteins; (17) Transf, transferrin; (18) Hmpx, hemopexin; (19) β_{1AC}, C3; (20) β_{2GP}, β2-glycoprotein-I; CRP, C-reactive protein; (23) IgM; (24) IgA; (25) IgG.

As for crossover electrophoresis (Section 6.4.2) except medium
   electroendosmosis agarose can be used
Gel cutters for immunoelectrophoresis (Shandon — Appendix 3)
Human serum
Humid chamber (Section 6.3.1, note 1)

Procedure

1   As for Section 6.4.2, step 1.
2   Using the immunoelectrophoresis gel cutter, stamp out wells and
troughs in the gel, and remove the agar plugs from the *wells only* using
a Pasteur pipette attached to a vacuum line. The pattern of wells and
troughs normally used for immunoelectrophoresis can be seen in the
top of Fig. 6.4.
3   Place the slide in the electrophoresis tank and set up an electrical
connection between the ends of the slide and the electrode chambers
(Section 6.4.2, step 3). The wells should be nearest the cathode.
4   Load 2 μl of human serum and 1 μl of human serum albumin
(1 mg/ml) into wells on either side of a trough, and carry out electrophoresis for 1 h at 6 V/cm.
5   Carefully remove the agar from the trough using a Pasteur pipette
attached to the vacuum line, and transfer the slide to the humid
chamber.
6   Fill the trough with antiserum, and incubate overnight. The
strongest immunoprecipitin arcs will be visible, but weaker components will require staining for visualization (see Section 6.2.2).

Notes

1   The progress of the electrophoretic stage of the procedure can be
monitored by inclusion of 0.02% w/v bromophenol blue in the sample. The dye binds to albumin which is normally the fastest moving
protein present in serum. Any unbound dye will run faster than
albumin.
2   The heterogeneity of antiserum and antigen is reflected in the
number of immunoprecipitin arcs observed. The precise position of an
arc may enable identification of the antigen usually by comparison with
known standards (see Fig. 6.5).
3   See note 8, Section 6.3.1.

6.4.4   Rocket immunoelectrophoresis

This technique, first introduced by Laurell, enables quantitation of the
antigen and for this reason is occasionally referred to as electro-
immunoassay. Antigen is loaded into wells bored in antibody-containing agar or agarose gel and is then driven into the gel by elec-

trophoresis. When equivalence is reached (see Section 6.1) immuno-precipitation occurs giving a rocket shaped line. The area under the rocket is proportional to the antigen concentration, and if the wells are small and the process allowed to go to completion, the antigen concentration is proportional to the height of the rocket. The technique may be regarded as an electrophoretic adaption of single (radial) immuno-diffusion (Section 6.3.2) but it is less prone to artefactual precipitation.

Materials and equipment

As for crossover immunoelectrophoresis (Section 6.4.2) except use medium or low electroendosmosis agarose.

Procedure

1   Prepare slides coated with antibody-containing agar or agarose gel described in Section 6.3.2, steps 1–4 *except* use barbitone buffer (Appendix 2) instead of PBS. Each 26 mm × 76 mm slide can be used for 2 samples; it is more convenient to use larger glass plates for large numbers of samples.
2   Bore wells 1 cm apart, 1.5 cm from one end of the slide using the gel punch, needle or Pasteur pipette. Remove the agar plugs from the wells using a Pasteur pipette attached to the vacuum line.
3   Place slides in the electrophoresis tank and set up electrical contact using filter paper as described in Section 6.4.2 (antigen wells at cathodal end). Load dilutions of human serum albumin (Section 6.3.2, step 7) into the wells and carry out electrophoresis at 5 V/cm for at least 6 h or better overnight.
4   Immunoprecipitin rockets may be visible, but are shown better by staining (Section 6.2.2; it is not necessary to wash the slides before drying).
5   Measure the height of the rockets using a rule or by superimposing the slide on a sheet of 1 cm square graph paper. Antigen concentration in 'unknown' samples can be determined by reference to a standard curve constructed using known concentrations of antigen.

Notes

1   If the antigen and antiserum are heterogeneous the rockets may be composite and difficult to analyse easily. This problem may be re-solved using a modification of the technique known as line im-munoelectrophoresis. For this antigen is loaded into a trough (instead of a well) cut in the antibody-containing agar gel. After electrophoresis at 90° to the trough, straight immunoprecipitin lines are produced instead of rockets.
2   The immunochemical relationship between different samples can be investigated by the rocket technique. For this the wells are bored close together (2–4 mm apart). Fusion or overlapping of the rockets

144

suggests immunochemical identity or non-identity respectively. Partial identity is revealed by one-sided fusion (cf. double diffusion, Section 6.3.1 and Fig. 6.2).

3   See note 8, Section 6.3.1.

6.4.5   Crossed immunoelectrophoresis

This technique is a combination of immunoelectrophoresis with the rocket procedure. Proteins in the antigen are first separated by agarose gel electrophoresis, after which they are electrophoresed into an antibody-containing agarose gel at right angles to the direction of the first electrophoretic separation. Proteins recognized by the antibody immunoprecipitate as rockets, the distance from the sample application well reflecting the electrophoretic mobility of the protein. The technique can be used to show heterogeneity of antigen and antibody, immunochemical identity of the various components of the antigen, and concentration of antigen components in different samples of antigen.

Materials and equipment

As for rocket immunoelectrophoresis (Section 6.4.4) except use pre-
   coated 5 × 7.5 cm slides
Non-precoated 5 × 7.5 cm slides
Strip razor blade (Dako — Appendix 3)

Procedure

1   Prepare a layer of 1% w/v agarose in barbitone buffer on a *non-precoated* slide (Section 6.4.2, step 1). Use 4 ml agar/slide.

2   Cut the agarose into 5 strips, 5 cm × 1.2 cm, (Fig. 6.6) using the razor blade. Discard the remaining agarose and separate the strips from each other.

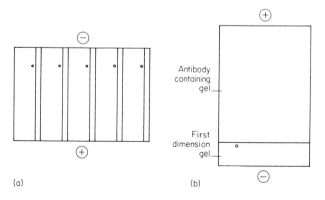

Fig. 6.6   Gel arrangement for crossed immunoelectrophoresis (Section 6.4.5). Gels for the first dimension are prepared as in (a), and for the second dimension as in (b).

145

3   Bore a small well using the gel cutter, needle or Pasteur pipette about 1 cm from one end of each strip and as close as possible (1–1.5 mm) to one side (Fig. 6.6). Transfer the slide to the electrophoresis chamber (well at cathodal end) and set up electrical contact between the ends of the gels and the electrophoresis chambers (Section 6.4.2, step 3).

4   Load 2–5 μl sample antigen into each well (for trial use human serum albumin and human serum in duplicate gels). Carry out electrophoresis at 6 V/cm for 1–2 h (if necessary use bromophenol blue to judge electrophoresis time; Section 6.4.3, note 1).

5   Transfer each strip to the end of a *precoated* slide using the razor blade (Fig. 6.6). Prepare antibody-containing agarose gel in barbitone buffer (Section 6.4.4, step 1) and, with the slides on the level table, pour onto the remaining area of each slide. Use 3–3.5 ml/slide.

6   When the gel has solidified transfer the slides to the electrophoresis chamber, set up electrical contact as before, and electrophorese at 2 V/cm overnight. Rockets may be visible but are best shown by staining (Section 6.2.2).

7   Heterogeneity of antigen and antiserum is reflected in the number of rockets produced. Immunochemical identity or non-identity is deduced from fusion or overlapping of rockets (e.g. Fig. 6.7). Concentration of any component of the antigen in different antigen preparations can be determined by measuring the height of the rocket as described in Section 6.4.4.

Note

See note 8, Section 6.3.1.

6.4.6   Modifications of crossed immunoelectrophoresis techniques

Many modifications and adaptions of the crossed immunoelectrophoresis technique have been devised, such as tandem comparison of two antigens in the first dimension, incorporation of an intermediate gel containing different antibody between the first and second dimension gels, and using lectins instead of antibodies. The agar enthusiast will find these and other similar techniques described in Axelsen (1983).

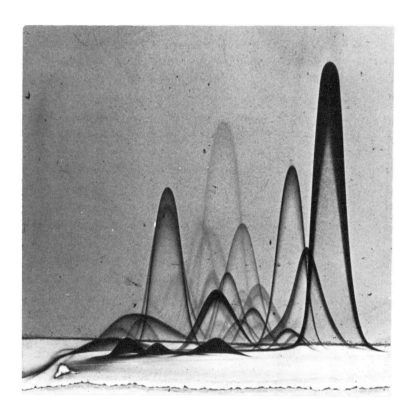

Fig. 6.7 Crossed immunoelectrophoresis of whole human serum. The second dimension contained anti-(whole human serum). Courtesy of Mrs M. Brasher.

147

7 Polyacrylamide gel techniques

Electrophoresis of proteins in polyacrylamide gel has proved to be one of the most useful analytical and preparative techniques. A gel is formed by polymerizing acrylamide ($CH_2=CH-CO-NH_2$) and a suitable bifunctional cross-linking reagent, normally N,N'-methylene bisacrylamide (polymerization of acrylamide alone produces only linear polymers which do not form a rigid gel). The polymerization occurs rapidly at room temperature in the presence of an initiator and catalyst and porosity of the gel can be adjusted by varying the acrylamide concentration and degree of cross-linking. Normally gels contain between 3 and 30% w/v total acrylamide — gels containing less than this disintegrate easily whereas those containing more are excessively brittle. Polyacrylamide gels have relatively low porosity and most large molecules experience sieving effects (cf. agarose gel electrophoresis, Chapter 6). Hence proteins are separated on the basis of both size and charge.

Polyacrylamide gel electrophoretic techniques have the advantages of high resolution and sensitivity, and they are simple to carry out. The gel is robust and relatively inert compared with the available alternatives (e.g. agar and starch). Numerous adaptions of the basic technique have been developed.

7.1 PREPARATION AND MANIPULATION OF POLYACRYLAMIDE GELS

Polyacrylamide gels are normally prepared as slabs, polymerized in a mould made from two sheets of glass separated by plastic spacers, or as rods which are polymerized in glass tubes. In the latter case the protein bands migrate as discs and so this procedure is often called disc polyacrylamide gel electrophoresis.

Normally N,N,N',N'-tetramethylethylene diamine (TEMED) is used as the catalyst for polymerization, and ammonium persulphate or a combination of riboflavin and UV light as the initiator. Both acrylamide and N,N'-methylene bisacrylamide are *neurotoxins* which can be absorbed through the skin, and so great care should be taken when using them (polyacrylamide is *not* neurotoxic). Acrylamide–bisacrylamide solutions are normally prepared and stored as a concentrated stock solution. These may polymerize explosively if heated and so they should be stored at 4°C. If the acrylamide crystallizes the solution should be warmed at 40°C *but no higher* until it redissolves.

After electrophoresis gels can be stained for protein (Section 7.1.1) or carbohydrate (Section 7.1.2), treated for autoradiography (Section 1.5) or used for immunochemical studies (Chapter 8).

7.1.1 Staining for protein

Coomassie blue stain

Coomassie brilliant blue R is a sensitive protein stain which can be used to locate protein bands after electrophoresis in polyacrylamide gel. Although many other protein stains can be used the authors consider this dye to be the best for most purposes.

Materials and equipment

Polyacrylamide electrophoretogram
Sandwich box
0.025% w/v Coomassie brilliant blue R (Sigma — Appendix 3) in 50% v/v methanol, 5% v/v acetic acid (see note 1)
Destain solution: 7.5% v/v acetic acid, 5% v/v methanol
Plastic foam (optional)
Orbital shaker (optional; Luckham — Appendix 3)

Procedure

1 Incubate polyacrylamide gel in 3–5 volumes of Coomassie blue stain solution overnight at room temperature (or for 5–6 h on orbital shaker).
2 Discard stain solution, rinse gel quickly in water and place gel in destain solution. Place on orbital shaker (see note 2) and destain until a clear background is obtained. Changing destain frequently and placing a piece of plastic foam in the solution speeds up this process (the foam adsorbs stain).

Notes

1 Dissolve the Coomassie blue in the methanol before making up to volume with acetic acid and water. The stain solution will keep for about 3 months at room temperature. Each portion of stain solution should be used only once (especially for SDS-polyacrylamide gel electrophoresis, Section 7.3.1).
2 Destaining can be carried out without shaking but this takes longer.
3 Do not store gels in destain as the bands will eventually disappear — see Section 7.1.3.
4 The sensitivity of this protein stain varies between proteins but usually 0.5 μg/band is detectable.

149

Silver staining

Although many dyes like Coomassie brilliant blue are sensitive protein stains, a much more sensitive method relies on the production of silver atoms from silver salts (usually silver nitrate) by groups present on proteins. These procedures have the disadvantages of being prone to artefacts, often produce unacceptably high background staining, and are more complex than dye staining. There are many variations of the basic methodology and it is possible to buy the reagents in kit form (Bio-Rad, National Diagnostics — Appendix 3). The following procedure is usually successful; it is fairly simple and can be used after Coomassie blue staining. See Wray *et al.* (1981) for a more detailed discussion.

Materials and equipment

It is essential to use pure, preferably deionized, water. Most single distilled water will cause high non-specific background staining.

Polyacrylamide electrophoretogram
Sandwich boxes or glass dishes (see note 1)
Orbital shaker (Luckham — Appendix 3)
50% (v/v) methanol (see note 2)
Silver nitrate solution, *freshly prepared*: 0.8 g dissolved in 4 ml water
14.8 M ammonium hydroxide
0.36% sodium hydroxide
1% (w/v) citric acid
38% (w/v) formaldehyde solution
45% (v/v) methanol, 5% (v/v) acetic acid

Procedure

1   Agitate the gel in 50% methanol on the orbital shaker for at least 1 h (see note 3). If the gel has been stained with Coomassie blue, wash for at least 3 h in 3 changes.
2   Just prior to use, prepare staining solution: mix 21 ml sodium hydroxide with 1.4 ml ammonium hydroxide and then add the silver nitrate solution drop-wise (4 ml) whilst vortexing or stirring very vigorously (see note 4). Make up to 100 ml with distilled water.
3   Add the staining solution to the gel and leave on the orbital shaker for 15 min.
4   Wash the gel for 30 min in 3–4 changes of water on the orbital shaker.
5   Just before use, prepare developing solution: mix 2.5 ml citric acid with 0.25 ml formaldehyde and make up to 500 ml with water. Develop the staining by agitating the gel in developing solution until bands appear (about 10 min).

150

6   When the bands reach the desired intensity, immediately rinse the gel briefly with water and then stop the staining reaction by agitating the gel in the methanol/acetic acid solution. Store the stained gel in this solution in the dark.

Notes

1   The containers must be washed thoroughly before use and it is best to reserve a set exclusively for this technique.
2   Analar or reagent grade methanol is suitable. Ultrapure methanol is not recommended.
3   If possible wash in 50% methanol for longer than 1 h before staining — overnight is recommended.
4   The staining solution should be used within 15 min of preparation. Care should be taken with ammoniacal silver solutions — they can be explosive. The staining solution should just cover the gel; prepare sufficient solution according to gel size.
5   An overstained gel can be destained by washing with photographic fixative. However, care must be taken with this as it is fairly drastic and will eventually remove all staining. Adding 10–15% methanol to the fixative makes the destaining more controllable. When the gel has destained sufficiently, wash it immediately with water and then with fixer clearing agent. Finally store in the methanol/acetic acid solution.
6   Wedrychowski *et al.* (1986) report that high backgrounds caused by nucleic acid contamination or lack of staining caused by the presence of metal ions can be overcome by exhaustive washing of the gel with acetic acid and methanol before staining. For this, wash sequentially with 10% acetic acid (3 changes over at least 12 h); water (3 changes over 30 min); 50% methanol (3 changes over 3 h); water (3 changes over 30 min); 50% methanol (3 changes over 3 h); water (3 changes over 30 min); 50% methanol (3 changes over 3 h); water (up to 2 min). Then stain immediately as in steps 2–6.

7.1.2   Staining for carbohydrate

Periodic acid reacts with vicinal hydroxyl groups commonly found in sugar molecules to generate aldehydes which can be detected by their colour reaction with reduced Schiff's reagent (cf. Section 5.3.1).

Materials and equipment

Electrophoresed polyacrylamide gel
Sandwich box
Destain solution: methanol: acetic acid: water 40:7:53 by volume
Periodic acid
7% (v/v) acetic acid cooled to 0–4°C
Schiff's reagent (BDH — Appendix 3) cooled to 0–4°C
1% sodium metabisulphite in 0.1 M HCl

Procedure

1 Fix the electrophoresed gel with 5 × its volume of destain in the sandwich box overnight at room temperature.
2 Discard the liquid and equilibrate the gel with 5 × its volume of cold 7% acetic acid for 1 h at 4°C.
3 Discard the liquid and add 5 × volume of freshly prepared 1% (w/v) periodic acid in cold 7% acetic acid. Incubate for 1 h at 4°C in the dark.
4 Discard the liquid (care — powerful oxidizing agent) and wash the gel for 24 h at 4°C in the dark with several changes of 5 × volume of 7% acetic acid.
5 Discard the liquid and incubate the gel with 5 × volume of cold Schiff's reagent for 1 h at 4°C in the dark.
6 The red bands of glycoproteins should be visible. To preserve the staining pattern, wash out excess reagent with the acidic metabisulphite solution.

Notes

1 This procedure will not work after Coomassie blue staining and so samples should be electrophoresed in duplicate if a comparison with the total protein pattern is required.
2 Heavily glycosylated proteins (e.g. fetuin, stomach mucins) can be detected at the 5–10 μg level. However, 20–100 μg is required for glycoproteins containing less carbohydrate.
3 Immunoblotting (Section 8.4) using lectins is usually much more sensitive for detecting glycoproteins and it can also provide some structural information on the carbohydrate portion of such molecules.

7.1.3 Storage and drying polyacrylamide gels

Most protein stains are soluble in organic solvents and are bleached by light. Therefore if the gels are to be kept for reference purposes they should be stored in the dark in 10% (v/v) acetic acid (*not* destain as this contains methanol). If a gel fades, it can be restored by restaining (Section 7.1.1).

It is often convenient to dry down gels onto filter paper as such dried gels can be stored indefinitely. This procedure is essential for autoradiography (Section 1.5). Simply allowing gels to dry out at room temperature usually results in cracking and distortion of the gel. However, gels can be quickly and easily dried by application of heat and a vacuum. Gel driers are available commercially (Bio-Rad, Miles, Pharmacia — Appendix 3), but a cheap and efficient apparatus can easily be made in the lab.

Construction of gel drier

Materials and equipment

2 silicone rubber sheets 20 × 20 cm (ESCO — Appendix 3)
1 silicone rubber bung, 4–5 cm diameter
Cork borer (no. 4)
Stainless steel tubing 8 cm long, 1 cm diameter
Dow-Corning Silastic 732 RTV adhesive sealant (Hopkin and Williams — Appendix 3)

Procedure

1   Bore a hole through the bung slightly narrower than the outside diameter of the steel tube. Insert the steel tube through the bung until it is flush with the large diameter bung surface (Fig. 7.1).
2   Bore a hole in the centre of *one* of the rubber sheets using the cork borer.
3   Cement the bung and tubing to the pierced rubber sheet, aligning the hole in the sheet with the steel tubing (Fig. 7.1). Allow to dry overnight.

Drying gels

Materials and equipment

Gel drier assembly (see above)
Boiling water bath
Vacuum pump
Pressure tubing
1 litre side-arm vacuum flask fitted with bung and glass tubing as liquid trap
Whatman 3 MM filter paper

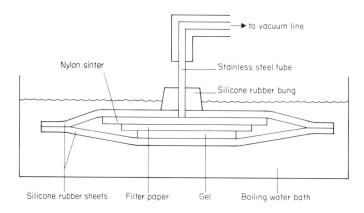

Fig. 7.1   Assembly for drying polyacrylamide gels (Section 7.1.3). Courtesy of Dr P. Minor.

153

Plastic sinter sheet (Vyon) larger than gel to be dried (Porvair — Appendix 3)
Molykote III compound silicone grease (Hopkin and Williams — Appendix 3) — see note 3.
Polyacrylamide gel

Procedure

1 Heat water bath to boiling.
2 Place unpierced rubber sheet on a level surface and position gel in the centre of the sheet (see note 2).
3 Overlay the gel with a piece of filter paper just larger than the gel, and cover this with the sintered sheet.
4 Apply a thin layer of silicone grease 3 cm wide around the edges of the rubber sheet, and place the pierced rubber sheet and bung on top. Press round the edges of the sheet to form a seal.
5 Attach the vacuum line through the liquid trap to the protruding piece of steel tubing (Fig. 7.1) and turn on the pump (full pressure). Check that the rubber sheets have sealed together completely.
6 Submerge the assembled drier in the boiling bath, and leave for 30–60 min (see note 4). Drying is complete when the gel outline is no longer visible.
7 When gel is dry remove drier from the water bath, disconnect the vacuum and separate the rubber sheets. Carefully peel the dried gel and filter paper from the rubber sheet.

Notes

1 For all gel driers (including commercial ones) it is important to use a good vacuum pump. A water pump is suitable if the water pressure is high. If an oil pump is used it should be protected from the acidic vapour by a solid CO_2 trap.
2 If gels containing radioactive proteins are dried, it is advisable to cover the bottom (unpierced) rubber sheet with plastic food-wrapping film to avoid contaminating the sheet.
3 The silicone grease must not liquefy at 100°C. Molykote III does not.
4 Drying time depends on size of gel, acrylamide concentration used, strength of the vacuum and temperature of the water bath.
5 Soaking the gel in destain containing glycerol (0.1–0.5% w/v) for 30 min before drying makes it more supple and easier to store, but increases the drying time.

7.1.4 Slicing polyacrylamide gels for determining their radioactive profile

This procedure is an alternative to autoradioagraphy (Section 1.5). It gives quantitative information but is less sensitive. It works best for

154

isotopes that can be detected by direct emission (e.g. ^{125}I, ^{32}P Cherenkov) but it is applicable to scintillation counting if the slices are eluted first to circumvent the quenching attributable to the solid gel and paper (see note below). The results of slicing and counting one gel is presented in Fig. 7.2; this can be compared with the autoradiograph of the same gel in Fig. 10.8.

Materials and equipment

Polyacrylamide slab gel electrophoretogram
Graph paper with 1 mm divisions
Clear adhesive tape — 3/4" wide
Sharp scissors — straight 5"
Equipment for measurement of the isotope (Section 1.4)

Procedure

1   Stain, destain and dry the gel (including 0.1% glycerol) as described in Section 7.1.3.
2   Cut out the tracks to be counted keeping the sides of the tracks parallel to each other. Label each track.
3   Stick each track to the graph paper using the adhesive tape and aligning the direction of electrophoresis with one axis of the paper.
4   Cut each track into 1 mm slices following the ruling of the graph paper. Cut right through the adhesive tape-gel-graph paper sandwich. The first 1 mm slice should contain the sample application point.
5   Place the slices in sequence into appropriate containers and measure their radioactive content.

Note

Isotopes that are detected by β radiation (e.g. ^{14}C, ^{35}S, ^{3}H) are measured most efficiently by eluting polypeptides from the gel. Add 0.5 ml of 90% (v/v) NCS solubilizer (Amersham — Appendix 3) to each slice in a vial. Stopper and incubate at 50°C for 2 h. Cool, neutralize with acetic acid and add a toluene based scintillant (Section 1.4).

7.1.5   Concentration of samples for polyacrylamide gel electrophoresis

This procedure is used if the sample is too dilute to be loaded directly or if it contains a high level of salt or detergent which might interfere with the electrophoresis. If removal of contaminants is required rather than simple concentration of protein, the precipitate in step 4 should be resuspended in 10 volumes of ethanol at −20°C and the centrifugation in step 3 repeated. The method can also be used before many other procedures but does cause some aggregation of protein

155

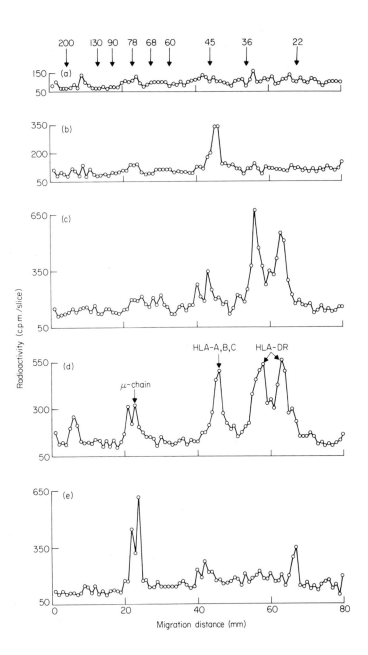

Fig. 7.2 Radioactivity profile of polyacrylamide gel (Section 7.1.4). Specific immuno-precipitates were analysed by SDS-polyacrylamide electrophoresis (Laemmli system, 10% gels, Section 7.3.1) as described in Section 10.4 and Fig. 10.8. Each track was then cut into 1 mm slices and the radioactivity of each slice measured. The positions of standard proteins of known molecular weight ($\times\ 10^{-3}$) are indicated. Compare the information obtained with that provided by the autoradiograph of the same gel (Fig. 10.8).

156

(see Sections 1.3.2, 2.3.2 and 3.3.1 for alternative concentration procedures).

Materials and equipment

Sample to be concentrated
Ethanol, 95% (v/v)
Sodium acetate, saturated solution
Refrigerated centrifuge
Conical centrifuge tubes

Procedure

1   Add 9 volumes of ethanol and 1/50 volume of sodium acetate
solution (to improve flocculation of precipitate) to 1 volume of sample.
2   Mix and incubate at $-20°C$ for 48 h.
3   Cool the centrifuge and rotor to $-10°C$ and centrifuge at 1800 *g*
for 30 min at $-10°C$.
4   Discard the supernatant and dry the pellet by inverting the tube
and leaving to drain.
5   The pellet can be stored at $-20°C$ and redissolved in appropriate
sample buffer before analysis.

Notes

1   If the sample (step 1) contains less then 10 μg of protein/ml, a
carrier protein (e.g. 20 μg of haemoglobin or albumin) should be
added to facilitate precipitation providing this does not interfere with
the subsequent analysis.
2   The quantity of ethanol can be reduced to 4 volumes (with only a
small decrease in the recovery of most proteins) if required (for
example, if the total volume is unwieldy or if the salt or detergent is
also precipitated by the ethanol concentration used in the standard
procedure).
3   This method can be used for concentrating samples for non-
denaturing polyacrylamide gel electrophoresis (Section 7.4). However,
the dehydrating effect of the reagents used can lead to denaturation of
some proteins, and so the result should be interpreted with caution.

7.2   POLYACRYLAMIDE GEL ELECTROPHORESIS
(PAGE): GENERAL PRINCIPLES

Many different buffers have been used for PAGE. It is usually advisable to use a discontinuous system (buffer in the gel is different from
the electrode buffer) and that of Ornstein (1964) and Davis (1964) is
suitable for most purposes. This system consists of a relatively high
molarity (0.37 M) tris-HCl buffer pH 8.8 in the gel and a low molarity
tris-glycine buffer pH 8.3 in the electrode compartments. Resolution

157

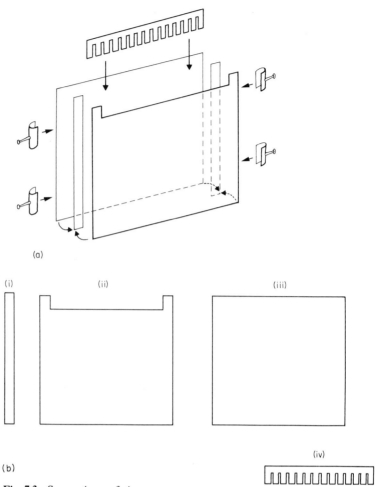

(a)

(i)   (ii)   (iii)

                                                    (iv)
(b)

Fig. 7.3 See caption on facing page.

is increased considerably by a 'stacking gel' (a low porosity gel polymerized above the separating gel) containing a pH 6.8 low molarity tris-HCl buffer. This system will cope with fairly large sample volumes and it allows a rapid separation and good resolution of proteins.

Proteins in the sample rapidly migrate into the stacking gel (they are virtually all negatively charged at pH 8.3 and the sieving effect of the stacking gel is minimal), but concentrate into a narrow band in this gel as the neutral stacking gel buffer reduces their electrophoretic mobility. The concentrated band of protein migrates through the stacking gel and enters the pH 8.8 separating gel. Once again the proteins become more highly charged and they separate according to their charge as they migrate through this gel (this is a simplified explanation — for a more thorough description see Ornstein (1964) and references contained therein). Although this system was originally described for use with rod gels (Section 7.3.4) it is usually more convenient to use slab gels (Section 7.2.1).

158

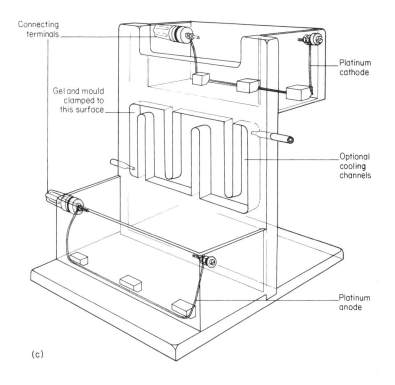

Connecting terminals

Platinum cathode

Gel and mould clamped to this surface

Optional cooling channels

Platinum anode

(c)

Fig. 7.3 Apparatus for slab polyacrylamide gel electrophoresis (Section 7.2.1.). (a — *facing page*) Exploded view of gel mould. (b — *facing page*) Components of the mould (i) Perspex spacers (2 required per mould) (ii) front glass plate (iii) back glass plate (iv) Perspex comb, 14 slot variety. A similar mould can be used to prepare gels for isoelectric focusing (Section 7.5), except omit the 'ears' on the front plate, use thinner spacers (1 mm) and the comb is not required. (c) Electrophoresis tank — the gel mould is clamped to the front of the tank using bulldog clips.

PAGE techniques can be divided into denaturing and non-denaturing systems. In the former, proteins are treated with reagents such as sodium dodecyl sulphate (SDS) and/or urea and the denatured proteins electrophoresed in the presence of the denaturing agent; in the latter, proteins are not subjected to any pre-electrophoresis treatment. Denaturing PAGE (particularly SDS-PAGE) is by far the most widely used now and so it will be considered first.

7.2.1 Apparatus for PAGE

Apparatus for moulding gels and carrying out slab PAGE is available commercially (Bio-Rad, Genetic Research, Shandon — Appendix 3). Alternatively the apparatus can be constructed in a laboratory workshop using glass plates (soak in chromic acid — Appendix 2 — before use), Perspex (Lucite) sheets, platinum wire and electrical connectors (Fig. 7.3). Slabs of any dimensions can be made, but the gel thickness

159

is usually less than 3 mm to avoid uneven heating effects. A gel size of 18 cm × 13 cm × 1.5 mm thick is suitable for most analytical purposes; this can accommodate up to 30 samples (see Section 9.2.1 for preparative polyacrylamide gel electrophoresis). Samples are loaded into slots formed in the stacking gel by inserting a Perspex comb into the gel solution before it polymerizes. Combs can be designed to accommodate the required number of samples. They should be cut from the same sheet of Perspex as the spacers and milled if necessary so that they are all the same thickness.

Apparatus for disc PAGE is best purchased (Shandon — Appendix 3). This technique differs from slab gel electrophoresis in that the gels are polymerized in tubes and hence are cylindrical in shape. The gels are often referred to as 'rods' or 'sticks'. The technique seems to have little or no advantage over slab gel electrophoresis (except for 2-dimensional electrophoresis, Section 7.6) and suffers from the disadvantage that each sample is electrophoresed in a separate gel making comparison of different samples difficult.

7.3 POLYACRYLAMIDE GEL ELECTROPHORESIS UNDER DENATURING CONDITIONS

The robust nature of polyacrylamide gel makes it an ideal support for electrophoresis in the presence of denaturing agents. Such techniques have the following advantages:

(a) Insoluble materials such as membranes and cytoskeletal structures can be solubilized and analysed in dissociating agents or detergents.

(b) Macromolecular complexes, such as enzymes and viral particles can be disrupted into their component polypeptides by a dissociating agent (especially if the disulphide bonds are broken) and then analysed by electrophoresis.

(c) If a strongly ionic detergent (usually sodium dodecyl sulphate — SDS; Tables 4.3 and 4.4) is used, then proteins are denatured and combine with a constant ratio (w/w) of SDS. The overwhelming negative charge provided by the SDS coating makes any charge contributed by the protein negligible, and so separation of such protein-SDS complexes by polyacrylamide gel electrophoresis is almost entirely due to sieving, and is therefore dependent on the molecular size of the protein. Thus a reasonably accurate value for the molecular weight of most proteins can be obtained by comparison of their electrophoretic mobility with those of standard proteins of known molecular weight. A high degree of glycosylation or gross deviation from 'normal' globular structure makes this determination inaccurate.

7.3.1 Sodium dodecyl sulphate (SDS) polacrylamide gel electrophoresis

This is probably the most widely used electrophoretic technique in biochemistry. Advantages are that almost all proteins are solubilized by

160

heating with 2% SDS w/v plus a reducing agent (splits any disulphide bonds), and that the protein separation is usually dependent upon molecular weight (see Section 7.3).

Most proteins bind a constant amount of SDS (w/w) but there are exceptions to this which cause anomalous migration. For example, carbohydrate residues do not bind the detergent and so heavily glycosylated proteins migrate more slowly than non-glycosylated proteins of the same molecular weight. Also some proteins (e.g. J chain) are not fully unfolded by the SDS treatment and so migrate more slowly than expected (Fig. 7.4).

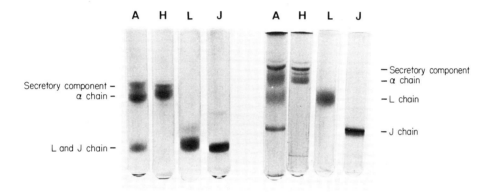

Fig. 7.4 Disc polyacrylamide gel electrophoresis in the presence of urea (right) or SDS (left) (Sections 7.3.1 and 7.3.3). A, reduced and alkylated rabbit secretory IgA; H, and J, fractions from the separation of reduced and alkylated secretory IgA (see Fig. 3.11). Note that J chain is only resolved from L chain by the urea gel. This gel (separating proteins on the basis of charge rather than size) also demonstrates the heterogeneity of the α and L chains (due to their variable regions) compared with J chain and secretory component.

Many buffer systems have been developed for SDS-polyacrylamide gel electrophoresis, and two of these are described in this section. Method i is Laemmli's modification of the Ornstein-Davis buffer system described in Section 7.2. Method ii is simpler and covers a wider molecular weight range. Examples of SDS-polyacrylamide gel electrophoresis of standard proteins using the two systems are shown in Fig. 7.5.

Method i (Laemmli, 1970)

Materials and equipment

Power pack (Shandon, LKB — Appendix 3)
Electrophoresis tank and gel mould (Section 7.2.1)

161

Bulldog clips

Petroleum jelly (Vaseline)

48.75% (w/v) acrylamide, 1.25% (w/v) N,N'-methylene bisacrylamide (store in the dark at 4°C) — this is 50% total acrylamide

Isobutanol (2-methyl propan-1-ol) saturated with water

1 M tris-HCl pH 8.8

1 M tris-HCl pH 6.8

TEMED

1.5% (w/v) ammonium persulphate solution (freshly prepared)

Stock (10 × concentrated) electrode buffer — 1.92 M glycine, 0.25 M
  tris (pH should be about 8.3)

Samples for electrophoresis (see note 2)

50 ml syringe

10% SDS

Sample buffer: 6% SDS, 6% (v/v) 2-mercaptoethanol, 40% (w/v)
  sucrose, 0.02% bromophenol blue in 0.125 M tris-HCl pH 6.8

Standard protein mix: home-made (Fig. 7.5) or Sigma (Appendix 3,
  Fig. 7.8)

Procedure

1   Assemble the gel mould according to the manufacturer's instructions or see Fig. 7.3 (coat spacers with petroleum jelly prior to
assembly).

2   Seal the bottom of the gel mould either with molten 1% agar or
with acrylamide. For the latter, clamp the gel apparatus upright in a
plastic trough, make up 10 ml of separating gel solution (Table 7.1),
add 100–200 μl TEMED and immediately pour this into the trough.
Allow to polymerize (5–15 min).

3   Prepare separating solution (40 ml is sufficient for a gel 18 × 13 ×
0.15 cm) according to Table 7.1. For choice of acrylamide concentration, see note 1 below. Add 0.025 ml TEMED.

4   Pour the separating gel into the mould leaving a 3.5–4 cm space at
the top of the mould. Overlay at once with isobutanol and leave to
polymerize — this is complete when a sharp interface is visible between gel and alcohol layer.

5   Polymerize a stacking gel on top of the separating gel. For this,
make up the solution according to Table 7.1 and add 10–20 μl
TEMED. Wash the isobutanol from the polymerized separating gel,
rinse with about 2 ml stacking gel solution and fill the remaining space
in the mould with this solution. Push the plastic comb into the solution, ensuring that no air bubbles are trapped and leave to polymerize
(10–20 min). Remove comb carefully.

6   Fill the syringe with petroleum jelly, and squeeze a line of jelly
along the top of the electrophoresis tank (running from one 'ear' to the
other). Squeeze another line 4–5 cm below this (the jelly forms a
water-tight seal between the tank and the gel mould). Clamp the gel

162

Table 7.1 Composition of SDS-polyacrylamide gels — (Laemmli system)

Separating gel — volume (ml) to make 40 ml

| | Final polyacrylamide concentration | | | | |
	5%	7.5%	10%	12.5%	15%
Acrylamide stock (50% w/v total)	4.0	6.0	8.0	10.0	12.0
1 M tris-HCl pH 8.8	15.0	15.0	15.0	15.0	15.0
water	19.7	17.7	15.7	13.7	11.7
			degas and add		
10% w/v SDS	0.4	0.4	0.4	0.4	0.4
1.5% w/v ammonium persulphate	0.9	0.9	0.9	0.9	0.9

Stacking gel — volume (ml) to make 10 ml

| | Final polyacrylamide concentration | |
	3%[1]	5%[2]
acrylamide stock (50% w/v total)	0.6	1.0
1 M tris-HCl pH 6.8	1.25	1.25
water	7.55	7.15
10% w/v SDS	0.1	0.1
1.5% w/v ammonium persulphate	0.5	0.5

([1]) for 5–7.5% separating gel.
([2]) for 7.5% and higher separating gel.

mould containing the polymerized gel to the electrophoresis tank using bulldog clips.

7 Prepare electrode buffer from the 10 × stock, add SDS to give a final 0.1% concentration and pour into electrode reservoirs. The apparatus shown in Fig. 7.3 requires 700 ml.

8 Dilute samples with sample buffer (2 + 1), mix and heat at 100°C for 2–4 min. Allow to cool.

9 Load samples carefully into the slots in the stacking gel (capacity normally 50–100 μl) using an automatic pipette or Hamilton syringe (see note 6).

10 Connect the electrodes to the power pack (lower electrode is positive) and electrophorese at 20–50 mA (constant current) until the bromophenol blue reaches the bottom of the gel (usually 3.5 – 5 h).

11 Turn off the power, remove the gel from the mould and stain it (Sections 7.1.1 and 7.1.2).

Notes

1 The molecular sieving of the gel depends on the concentration of polyacrylamide (Fig. 7.5). High porosity gels (5% w/v total acrylamide concentration) are suitable for analysis of large molecular weight proteins (above 10^5 daltons), whereas low porosity (15% total acrylamide) should be used for small proteins (less than 5×10^4 daltons). 7.5 or 10% w/v total acrylamide gels are suitable compromises for most

163

(a)

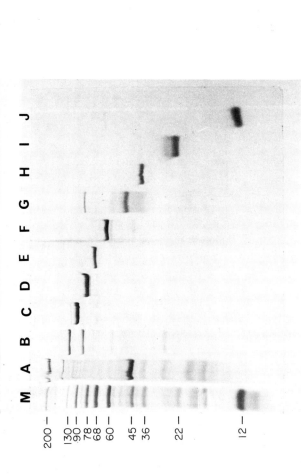

(b)

Fig. 7.5 Molecular weight distribution on SDS-polyacrylamide gel electrophoresis using various systems (Section 7.3.1). (a) shows the components of a molecular weight standard mixture (M) made by mixing (A) crude myosin (200 000) and actin (45 000) (extracted from rabbit muscle) 10 μg; (B) β-galactosidase (130 000) (Boehringer — Appendix 3) 10 μg; (C) phosphorylase (90 000) 10 μg; (D) transferrin (78 000) 5 μg; (E) bovine serum albumin (68 000) 5 μg; (F) catalase (60 000) 10 μg; (G) ovalbumin (45 000) 15 μg; (H) glyceraldehyde-3-phosphate dehydrogenase (36 000) 5 μg; (I) cytochrome C (12 000) 5 μg. (b) shows the migration of this mixture using (A) tris-bicine system, 5% acrylamide; (B) tris-bicine system, 7.5% acrylamide; (C) tris-bicine system, 10% acrylamide; (D) Laemmli system, 7.5% acrylamide; (E) Laemmli system, 10% acrylamide. S indicates the stacking gel in the Laemmli system. In (D) and (E) polypeptides of molecular weight less than 25 000 and 15 000 respectively migrate with the marker dye.

purposes (but see Section 7.3.2). Table 7.1 shows the composition of various percentage gels.

2 If samples contain a high concentration of salt (above 0.1 M), dialyse against 0.125 M tris-HCl pH 6.8 (one change of 100 volumes). For removal of other contaminants see Section 7.1.5.

3 Quantity of sample to be loaded depends on protein concentration, heterogeneity of sample and the ability of the individual proteins to bind stain — see Sections 7.1.1 and 7.1.2.

4 SDS-polyacrylamide gel electrophoresis cannot be carried out in the cold as SDS precipitates at low temperatures. Gels can be prevented from overheating (with consequent band distortion and loss of resolution) by cooling with a fan.

5 Samples can be electrophoresed without reducing their disulphide bonds to allow investigation of a multi-chain complex (see example Fig. 7.6). For this, substitute 10 mM iodoacetamide or iodoacetate for mercaptoethanol in the sample buffer. If both reduced and unreduced samples are electrophoresed in the same slab, add 1/10 volume 1.5 M iodoacetate to the reduced samples after boiling to destroy excess reducing agent.

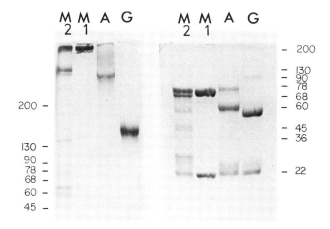

Fig. 7.6 Analysis of human immunoglobulin preparations by SDS-polyacrylamide gel electrophoresis (Section 7.3.1). M2, pooled normal IgM (Section 3.5); M1, myeloma IgM$_\kappa$ (Section 3.5); A, pooled normal dimeric secretory IgA (Section 3.7.2); G, pooled normal IgG (Section 3.3.1). For the left-hand gel (tris-bicine system, 5% acrylamide) samples were not reduced but were alkylated with 0.01 M iodoacetate. For the right-hand gel (tris-bicine system, 10% acrylamide) the samples were reduced with 0.05 M dithiothreitol and then alkylated with 0.105 M iodoacetate. Note the relative impurity of M2 compared with M1. These immunoglobulin preparations are also analysed by immunoelectrophoresis (Fig. 6.4) and radioimmunoassay (Fig. 11.5).

165

6   Special automatic pipettes are available for loading viscous samples such as whole cell lysates (Gilson — Appendix 3).

7   The glass plates should be soaked in chromic acid (Appendix 2), rinsed with water and ethanol and dried thoroughly before use.

8   It is possible to use a combination of urea and SDS for solubilizing very difficult samples. For this include 2–4 M urea in all solutions.

Method ii — tris-bicine system

This system is faster running than Laemmli (method i) and does not require a stacking gel. It is particularly suited for use with short gels and apparatus for this is available commercially (Inotech — Appendix 3). However, resolution is not as good as Laemmli, particularly with long gels.

Materials and equipment

As for method i above but substitute a solution containing 1 M tris and 1 M bicine for the stock gel and electrode buffers.

Procedure

1   Assemble the gel mould and prepare gel solution (Table 7.2; degas before adding the SDS, TEMED and persulphate). For choice of acrylamide concentration see Fig. 7.5. If polyacrylamide is to be used to seal the bottom of the gel, follow instruction in method i, step 2.

2   Fill the mould completely with gel solution and insert comb in the top of the mould (there is no stacking gel in this system).

3   When the gel has polymerized, remove the comb and clamp the gel to the electrophoresis tank (method i above, step 6).

4   Prepare electrode buffer (7 ml 10% w/v SDS plus 14 ml tris-bicine stock made up to 700 ml) and fill electrode reservoirs. Prepare and load samples as described in method i, steps 8 and 9, and carry out electrophoresis at 10–15 V/cm until bromophenol blue reaches the bottom of the gel.

Table 7.2 Composition of SDS-polyacrylamide gels — (tris-bicine system). Volume (ml) to make 40 ml separating gel (no stacking gel is required)

	Final polyacrylamide concentration			
	5%	7.5%	10%	12.5%
acrylamide stock (50% w/v total)	4.0	6.0	8.0	10.0
1 M tris, 1 M bicine	4.0	4.0	4.0	4.0
water	30.7	28.7	26.7	24.7
		degas and add		
10% w/v SDS	0.4	0.4	0.4	0.4
1.5% w/v ammonium persulphate	0.9	0.9	0.9	0.9
TEMED	0.025	0.025	0.025	0.025

166

5   Turn off power, remove gel from mould and stain (Sections 7.1.1 and 7.1.2).

Notes

1   This system is ideally suited for short gels to give a rapid analysis of column fractions, immunoglobulin preparations and fractionations, etc. If staining is carried out on an orbital shaker, bands are visible after 15–45 min.
2   See notes 1–8, method i, above.
3   Analysis of immunoglobulin preparations by SDS-polyacrylamide gel electrophoresis is presented in Figs. 7.6 and 7.7.

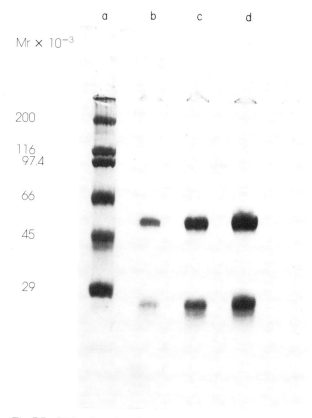

Fig. 7.7   SDS-polyacrylamide gel electrophoresis analysis (Section 7.3.1, method ii) of a mouse monoclonal antibody purified by HPLC (Clezardin *et al.*, 1985 and Section 1.2.4). (a) Molecular weight markers; (b)–(d) purified antibody applied at three different loadings.

7.3.2   Gradient SDS–polyacrylamide gel electrophoresis

Resolution can be improved in some cases by the use of a gradient of increasing polyacrylamide concentration in the separating gel (for example, see Fig. 7.8). Proteins undergo increasing molecular sieving as they migrate through the gel and this allows analysis of proteins over a wide molecular weight range. 5–15% (w/v) acrylamide gradients are suitable for most purposes.

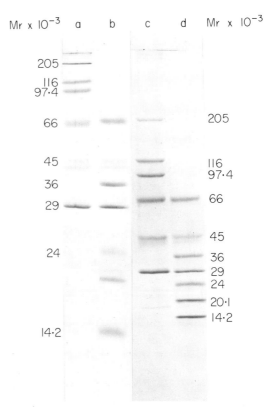

Fig. 7.8 SDS–polyacrylamide gel electrophoresis of commercially available molecular weight marker proteins (Sigma — Appendix 3). Tracks a and c high Mr range, b and d low Mr range. Tracks a and b analysed using a 12.5% total acrylamide slab gel (Section 7.3.1, method i); (c) and (d) analysed using a 5–15% total acrylamide linear gradient gel (Section 7.3.2). The gradient gel shows a compaction of the molecular weight range and produces tighter bands, particularly in the low Mr range.

Materials and equipment

As for Section 7.3.1, method i
2 chambered linear gradient maker (Section 1.2.2; Fig. 1.3) or better a
   3 channel pump (Shuco — Appendix 3)
Sucrose
Magnetic stirrer

Procedure

The procedure differs from Section 7.3.1 only in the preparation of the separating gel.

168

1 Prepare heavy gel solution (15% w/v total acrylamide). For this add 4.5 g sucrose to 11.25 ml 1 M tris-HCl pH 8.8, 9.0 ml stock acrylamide, 0.7 ml ammonium persulphate solution and 0.3 ml 10% w/v SDS solution and make up to 30 ml with water. Mix thoroughly until all the sucrose dissolves. Use 10 ml of this solution to seal the gel trough (if required) — see Section 7.3.1, step 2.

2 Prepare light gel solution (5% w/v total acrylamide). For this mix 7.5 ml tris-HCl pH 8.8 with 2 ml stock acrylamide, 0.47 ml ammonium persulphate solution, 0.2 ml 10% w/v SDS solution and make up to 20 ml with water.

3 Add 5 μl TEMED to each gel solution mix and pipette 12 ml (see note 1) of each into separate chambers of the gradient maker. Stir the heavy solution and prepare the gradient (Fig. 1.3) by pumping from the heavy side slowly into the top of the gel mould (should take about 5–10 min). Alternatively, if a 3 channel pump is available, place the gel solutions in 25 ml beakers and stir the heavy one. Use *two* channels to pump from the heavy solution to the gel mould and *one* channel to pump light solution into the heavy solution. All channels must pump at the same rate.

4 Overlay with isobutanol saturated with water and leave to polymerize.

5 Prepare the stacking gel (Section 7.3.1, method i, step 5) and continue as for Section 7.3.1, method i, steps 6–11.

Notes

1 For apparatus different from that shown in Fig. 7.3 use equal volumes of heavy and light solutions to give the total volume required to fill the mould to 3.0–4.0 cm from the top.

2 If gradients other than 5–15% are required, adjust the light and heavy solutions to give initial and final acrylamide concentrations respectively.

7.3.3 Urea polyacrylamide gel electrophoresis

Most 'insoluble' proteins can be solubilized and electrophoresed in urea. Proteins which consist of disulphide-linked subunits can be split into constituent chains by reduction with dithiothreitol.

Materials and equipment

As for Section 7.3.1 but substitute solutions:

Stock acrylamide solution — 7% (w/v) acrylamide, 0.35% (w/v) N,N'-methylene bisacrylamide, 45% (w/v) urea (7.5 M) made up to volume with 0.37 M tris-HCl pH 8.8

169

TEMED

Electrode buffer — 0.05 M boric acid adjusted to pH 9.2 with sodium hydroxide (700 ml per run)

Sample buffer —

with reduction: 8 M urea containing 2% w/v dithiothreitol

without reduction: 8 M urea containing 0.004 M iodoacetamide prepared with 0.37 M tris-HCl pH 8.8

Procedure

1　Assemble gel mould (Section 7.3.1, steps 1 and 2).

2　Prepare gel solution by mixing 32 ml of stock acrylamide solution, 7.2 ml of water and 0.8 ml of ammonium persulphate solution and degas under vacuum. Add 10 μl TEMED, mix and completely fill the mould with gel solution. Insert plastic comb into the top of the gel to form slots and leave to polymerize.

3　Remove comb carefully, wash slots with electrode buffer and clamp gel to electrophoresis tank (Secion 7.3.1, step 6). Fill reservoirs with electrode buffer.

4　Prepare samples for electrophoresis by mixing with an equal volume of sample buffer and boiling for 1 min. Load samples onto gel as described in Section 7.3.1, step 9, and electrophorese (Section 7.3.1, step 10) for 2–3 h at 10 V/cm length of gel.

5　Turn off power, remove gel from mould and stain (Section 7.1.1 and 7.1.2).

Notes

1　If both reduced and unreduced samples are electrophoresed in the same slab, add 1/10 volume of 1.5 M iodoacetate to the reduced samples after boiling to destroy excess reducing agent.

2　Bromophenol blue (0.02%) can be added to the sample buffer to monitor the progress of the electrophoresis. The free dye migrates faster than any protein. If albumin (normally one of the faster moving proteins) is present, some of the dye will bind to this and show its position. To separate slow moving proteins, continue electrophoresis for 1–2 h after the dye has run off the bottom of the gel.

3　Quantity of sample to be loaded depends on protein concentration, heterogeneity of the sample and the ability of the individual proteins to bind stain — see Section 7.1.1 and 7.1.2.

4　If heating effects cause distortion of bands, cool the apparatus with a fan (carrying out electrophoresis at 4–8°C might precipitate the urea).

5　See note 8, Section 7.3.1.

7.3.4　Disc PAGE under denaturing conditions

All of the procedures in Sections 7.3.1 to 7.3.3 can be carried out in polyacrylamide rods using disc gel apparatus and adjusting the buffer volume appropriately.

Materials and equipment

As for slab polyacrylamide gel electrophoresis (Section 7.3.1) except an electrophoresis tank suitable for disc gel electrophoresis is required (Shandon — Appendix 3).
Glass tubes, about 10 cm × 0.6 cm (lab-made or Shandon — Appendix 3)
Rubber bungs for sealing the bottoms of the tubes
10 ml syringe with long hypodermic needle

Procedure

1   Seal the base of the glass tubes with rubber bungs (see note) and a layer of parafilm (or use commercially available 'sealing bungs'). Place sealed tubes *vertically* in a test tube rack.
2   Prepare separating gel solution (Section 7.3.1, step 3); 2 ml is required per rod. Pipette gel solution into each mould leaving a 3 cm gap at the top of each tube. Overlay with isobutanol and leave to polymerize (see Section 7.3.1, step 4).
3   Just before electrophoresis is to be carried out prepare the stacking gel solution (0.3 ml per gel rod — see Section 7.3.1, step 5). Wash the isobutanol from the gel surface and overlay the separating gel with stacking gel solution (1.0–1.5 cm high). Overlay *carefully* with isobutanol and leave to polymerize (10–20 min).
4   Rinse off the isobutanol from the stacking gel surface and position the rods in the electrophoresis tank. Fill electrode reservoirs with electrode buffer (Section 7.3.1, step 7) and remove any air bubbles lodged at the top and bottom of the gels by displacement with electrode buffer forced from the syringe.
5   Load samples (Section 7.3.1, step 9 and note 3) onto the surface of the gels, connect the tank to the power pack (lower compartment positive) and electrophorese at 1.5 mA/tube for 20 min followed by 3.0–3.5 h at 2 mA/tube.
6   Turn off power and remove rods from the tank. Remove gels from the glass tubes by 'rimming' with the hypodermic syringe and needle. Fill the syringe with water and insert the needle in between the gel and the glass tube. Hold the tube over a test tube and rotate it whilst expelling water from the syringe. The gel will fall into the test tube. Stain and destain the gel (Sections 7.1.1 or 7.1.2).

Note

The glass tubes should be soaked in chromic acid (Appendix 2) and rinsed and dried thoroughly before use.

171

7.4 POLYACRYLAMIDE GEL ELECTROPHORESIS UNDER NON-DENATURING CONDITIONS

In non-denaturing PAGE, proteins in the sample are neither disrupted nor denatured, and migration is largely due to the inherent charge of the components. Usually low concentrations of polyacrylamide are used (4–8%) because the molecular sieving effect of higher concentrations effects the charge-dependent separation. As the proteins are electrophoresed unaltered, the technique is sometimes called native PAGE. Many different buffer systems have been described for this technique, but many lack resolution or are only suitable for a particular class of proteins.

Probably the most widely used native PAGE system is that described by Ornstein (1964) and this may be carried out as described for SDS-PAGE in Section 7.3.1, method i, by omitting SDS from all solutions. The samples should be dialysed against electrode buffer and then sucrose (final 10% w/v) and bromophenol blue (final 0.005%) added before loading; they should not be heated. The stock electrode buffer should be diluted 40- or 80-fold rather than the 10-fold used for SDS-PAGE. Carry out electrophoresis at 4–8°C to avoid uneven heating effects.

Native disc PAGE can be carried out using the same modifications to Section 7.3.4.

7.5 ISOELECTRIC FOCUSING IN POLYACRYLAMIDE GELS

7.5.1 Introduction

This technique is capable of the greatest resolution of a protein mixture. The components are separated according to their isoelectric point (pI) which is the pH at which they possess no net electric charge.

A pH gradient is formed in a gel between cathode and anode, and proteins migrate (due to the attraction of their charged groups for anode or cathode) until they reach their pI. As the protein is not charged in this position it remains stationary. Isoelectric focusing is therefore a steady state process (components should theoretically never run off the end of a gel containing the correct pH gradient).

A pH gradient will form automatically if a potential difference is applied to an H^+ containing ionizable solvent (H^+ ions will be displaced towards the cathode). However, such gradients are unstable and so gradient stabilizing molecules are added. These are normally purpose-made amphoteric compounds known as 'carrier ampholytes'. These zwitterions have sharply defined pIs and the mixture is chosen to have pI values evenly distributed over the desired pH range. Such mixtures are commercially available.

Polyacrylamide gel is an ideal anticonvention medium for isoelectric focusing because it is robust, permeable to most proteins, easy to

172

prepare and shows very little electroendosmosis (Section 6.4.1). This latter property is very important in isoelectric focusing as electroendosmosis will cause the whole pH gradient to move toward the cathode and thus disrupt the steady state process. However, polyacrylamide is not sufficiently permeable to very large proteins (e.g. pentameric IgM, Section 3.5) and special agarose is available for isoelectric focusing of such proteins (LKB, Pharmacia — Appendix 3).

7.5.2 Focusing in slab gels

Isoelectric focusing can be carried out in rods or slabs of polyacrylamide. Slabs are usually preferred, as several samples can be compared on one gel and uneven heating effects can be avoided more easily. Samples can be applied to the gel away from the strong acid or alkaline electrode solutions, hence avoiding denaturation of the protein components. It is advisable to use riboflavin as the initiator of polymerization rather than ammonium persulphate, because the latter reagent oxidizes proteins and ampholytes and can lead to artefactual results.

All the equipment necessary for isoelectric focusing in polyacrylamide gel including electrophoresis chamber, cooling plate, power pack and even ready-made ampholyte containing polyacrylamide gels are available commercially (LKB, Pharmacia — Appendix 3). Such set-ups are expensive but it is usually impractical to synthesize one's own ampholytes and a high voltage power pack and complex chamber with safety cut-outs are necessary.

Materials and equipment

Ampholytes (LKB, Pharmacia — Appendix 3)

High voltage (preferably constant power) power pack (LKB, Pharmacia — Appendix 3)

Commercially available gel mould, or lab-made mould consisting of 2 glass plates 15 × 10 cm, 2 Perspex spacers 16 cm long × 1 cm wide × 0.1 cm thick and 4 bulldog clips — see Fig. 7.3, (a) and (b)

Petroleum jelly (e.g. Vaseline)

Electrophoresis tank suitable for isoelectric focusing equipped with platinum electrodes (LKB, Pharmacia — Appendix 3) (see note 1)

Riboflavin solution: 4 mg/100 ml water freshly prepared

Stock acrylamide solution: 28.5% (w/v) acrylamide, 1.5% (w/v) N,N'-methylene bisacrylamide (store at 4°C — see note 2)

TEMED

UV lamp (wavelength of emitted light = 350 nm) or fluorescent strip light

Electrode solution (Table 7.3)

Whatman 3 MM filter paper

Fixing solution: 3.5% (w/v) sulphosalicylic acid, 11.5% (w/v) trichloroacetic acid

173

Table 7.3 Electrode solution for isoelectric focusing

pH range	Anode	Cathode
2.5–4	1 M H$_3$PO$_4$	2% w/v ampholine pH 6–8
3.5–5.2	1 M H$_3$PO$_4$	2% w/v ampholine pH 5–7
4.5–7	1 M H$_3$PO$_4$	1 M NaOH
5.5–7.7	2% w/v ampholine pH 4–6	1 M NaOH
6–8.5	2% w/v ampholine pH 4–6	1 M NaOH
7.8–10.0	2% w/v ampholine pH 6–8	1 M NaOH
3.5–9.5	1 M H$_3$PO$_4$	1 M NaOH

Reproduced from LKB application note 250, with permission.

Stain and destain (see Section 7.1.1)
Samples for analysis (for a trial run use serum)
0.05% (w/v) glycine
Vacuum line

Procedure

1 Dialyse samples against 2 changes of 100 volumes of glycine solution overnight.
2 Assemble gel mould and seal either according to the manufacturer's instructions or see Section 7.3.1, method i, step 2.
3 Prepare gel solution. For each 10 ml mix 1.8 ml stock acrylamide solution with 0.25 ml of ampholyte solution (see note 3). Make up to volume with water and degas for 2 min under vacuum. Add 0.1 ml riboflavin, pour into the gel mould and irradiate with the UV lamp about 50–70 cm from the gel. Polymerization takes about 1.5–2.5 h.
4 Turn off the lamp, remove mould from trough and pour off residual fluid from the top of the gel. Cool the assembly in ice for 30 min and remove plastic spacers and *carefully* prise the top glass plate from the gel using a spatula (see note 4). Place gel on cooling plate of electrophoresis tank (or place whole apparatus in cold room) and allow to cool.
5 Prepare two electrode wicks (0.5 cm × width of the gel) from the filter paper and soak one in anode solution and the other in cathode solution. Place on gel surface (see note 1).
6 Apply samples to gel. For this soak samples onto rectangular pieces of filter paper (3 mm × 5 mm hold 10–15 μl). Blot off excess liquid and position them on the surface of the gel 0.5–1 cm from the cathodal wick and 2–5 mm apart. Samples should contain about 5–20 μg protein.

174

7 Set up chamber for isoelectric focusing (platinum electrodes should press onto the wicks — see Fig. 7.9 and note 1). Connect electrodes to the power pack and carry out focusing. If available, set 25 W constant power. For wide pH ranges (e.g. 3.5–9.5) focusing will be complete in 1.5–2 h, but for narrower pH ranges focusing should be continued for 3–3.5 hours. If constant power is not available start at 200 V and increase up to 750–1500 V over 2 h. Alternatively focus overnight at 150 V.

8 Turn off power, remove gel from tank and submerge gel in fixing solution for 0.5–1.0 h (agitation on an orbital shaker speeds up this process). Stain and destain (Section 7.1.1). An example of isoelectric focusing of a complex protein mixture is shown in Fig. 7.9.

+

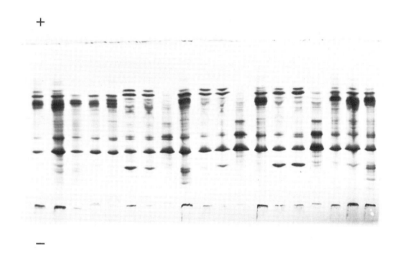

−

Fig. 7.9 The protein composition of human saliva samples from different individuals compared by isoelectric focusing (Section 7.5.2). The samples were applied to filter paper squares at the cathodal end of a pH 3–10 gel. Courtesy of Ms S. Peach.

Notes

1 The tank should be of the flat bed type. Platinum wire electrodes are expensive and carbon rods can be substituted. These should be soaked for 10 min in the electrode solutions prior to use then placed directly on the gel surface and held in position by a glass plate placed on top of them. Samples should be applied at least 1 cm from the anode or cathode rod.

2 Electrophoretic grade acrylamide and bisacrylamide must be used. If poor results are obtained, use a new batch of acrylamide or deionize the stock solution using Amberlite MB-1 resin (BDH — Appendix 3).

175

3 Ampholytes are supplied as 40% (w/v) solutions and they should be used at 1–2% (w/v) final concentration in the gel. Try a 1% concentration first; if poor results are obtained, increase the concentration to 2% w/v.

4 If the plates are difficult to separate after polymerization (step 4), siliconize the top one before use.

7.5.3 Isoelectric focusing in the presence of urea or detergents

Polyacrylamide gel isoelectric focusing can be carried out in the presence of urea or non-ionic detergents (Tables 4.3 and 4.4), thus enabling analysis of proteins which are insoluble in physiological solution (e.g. immunoglobulin heavy chains, membrane proteins, cytoskeletal proteins, some viral proteins). Inclusion of urea or detergent also stops precipitation of proteins at or near their pI values, which can limit the resolution in some cases.

Materials and equipment

As for Section 7.5.2
9 M urea or 2% (w/v) Nonidet P40

Procedure

1 Add 2 vol 9 M urea or 2% Nonidet P40 to 1 vol of dialysed sample.
2 Proceed as for Section 7.5.2 except make up focusing gel solution with urea or Nonidet P40 solution instead of water (step 3).

Note

Pure urea must be used for isoelectric focusing. If poor results are obtained, deionize the urea solution prior to use with Amberlite MB-1 ion exchange resin (BDH — Appendix 3).

7.6 TWO-DIMENSIONAL ISOELECTRIC FOCUSING AND SDS–POLYACRYLAMIDE GEL ELECTROPHORESIS

In this technique proteins are first separated by isoelectric focusing in a rod gel and then by SDS–polyacrylamide slab gel electrophoresis at right angles to the focusing dimension. Thus the resolving powers of two polyacrylamide gel techniques are combined and information about molecular weight and pI can be obtained for each protein of a mixture. O'Farrell (1975) first used this technique to study the proteins of *E. coli* and could clearly resolve 1100 proteins from this organism on a single gel. A two-dimensional gel of membrane proteins is shown in Fig. 7.10.

Urea and a non-ionic detergent are usually included in the focus-

176

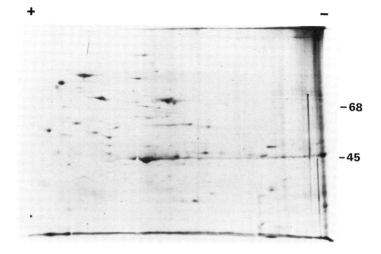

+   −

−68

−45

Fig. 7.10 Two-dimensional electrophoretic analysis of the polypeptide composition of lymphocyte plasma membrane (Section 7.6). The membrane was isolated from lymphocytes that had been biosynthetically labelled with [^{35}S]methionine (Section 5.4.1), separated by isoelectric focusing in the horizontal dimension followed by SDS–polyacrylamide gel electrophoresis (Laemmli system, 10% acrylamide) in the vertical dimension. The labelled spots were visualized by fluorography (Section 1.5.2).

ing gel to ensure solubility of all the proteins of a mixture, and to avoid precipitation of proteins at their pI positions.

Materials and equipment

High voltage power pack (LKB, Pharmacia — Appendix 3)

Electrophoresis tank and glass tubes as described for disc gel electrophoresis except internal diameter of tubes should be 0.25 cm (Section 7.3.4).

Equipment and solutions for gradient SDS–polyacrylamide gel electrophoresis (Section 7.3.2) — see note 1

Dialysis tubing

Urea

Focusing sample buffer: 9.5 M urea, 5% (v/v) 2-mercaptoethanol 2% (w/v) ampholytes (LKB — Appendix 3) — see note 2. Store this solution frozen in aliquots

Focusing acrylamide solution: as for isoelectric focusing (Section 7.5.2)

10% (w/v) Nonidet P40

8 M urea

10% (w/v) ammonium persulphate (freshly prepared)

Overlay solution: 9 M urea, 1% (w/v) ampholytes (store frozen in aliquots)

0.02 M sodium hydroxide

0.01 M orthophosphoric acid

SDS-sample buffer: 10% (w/v) glycerol, 5% (v/v), 2-mercaptoethanol, 2.3% (w/v) SDS, 0.0625 M tris-HCl pH 6.8

Rod gel sealing solution: 1% (w/v) agarose prepared in SDS sample buffer

Procedure

1   Seal the bases of the glass tubes with bungs or parafilm and clamp upright. Prepare a 5–15% gradient slab-SDS polyacrylamide gel (Section 7.3.2) but do not polymerize stacking gel.

2   Prepare focusing gel solution: 0.25 cm diameter tube requires about 0.5 ml (see note 2). For 10 ml place 5.5 g urea, 1.33 ml stock focusing acrylamide solution, 2 ml Nonidet P40 solution, 0.4 ml ampholytes and 1.978 ml water in a 100–150 ml side arm flask and swirl until the urea has dissolved. Add 10 μl ammonium persulphate solution and degas for 1–2 min.

3   Prepare focusing gels: add 7 μl TEMED to the 10 ml of gel solution and load into glass tubes using a syringe with a long hypodermic needle leaving about 0.5 cm gap at the top. Overlay carefully with 8 M urea. After 1 or 2 hours remove the urea solution and replace it with sample buffer. Leave gels for a further 1–2 h.

4   Soak dialysis membrane in water. Remove rubber bungs or parafilm from the polymerized focusing gels and cover the ends of the tubes with knotted dialysis tubing and hold this in place with a rubber band.

5   Place gels in the disc gel electrophoresis chamber, remove fluid from gel surface and overlay gels with sample buffer. Fill the remaining space in the glass tubes (above the sample solution) and the upper electrode reservoir with 0.02 M sodium hydroxide, and the lower reservoir with 0.01 M orthophosphoric acid. Connect to power pack (upper reservoir negative) and pre-run gels for 15 min at 200 V, 15 min at 300 V and then 30 min at 400 V (see note 3). Turn off power.

6   Treat sample with focusing sample buffer (add at least 4 vol sample buffer to 1 vol sample) — see note 4.

7   Pour away upper electrode buffer and aspirate fluid from the surface of the gels. Load samples onto gel surfaces (5–25 μl sample/gel) using a Hamilton syringe or automatic pipette. Overlay each gel with 10 μl overlay solution and fill remaining space in the tube and upper electrode reservoir with 0.02 M sodium hydroxide. Carry out isoelectric focusing at 400 V for 12 h followed by 800 V for 1 h (see note 5).

8   Turn off power and remove gels from tubes by 'rimming' (Section 7.3.4, step 6). Place each gel in a stoppered test tube half filled with SDS-sample buffer, and agitate for 0.5–1.0 h at room temperature (see note 6).

9   Polymerize the stacking gel above the SDS-slab gel (Section 7.3.1) *but do not use the comb*. Fill the space above the separating gel with

178

stacking gel solution leaving a 1 cm space at the top of the mould. Overlay with isobutanol saturated with water, and allow gel to polymerize (10–15 min).

10   Prepare 2 ml molten rod sealing solution and keep at 56°C. Wash isobutanol from stacking gel surface and rinse with SDS-gel electrode buffer.

11   Remove equilibrated focusing gel from SDS-sample buffer. Quickly pipette warm rod sealing solution into the space above the stacking gel and *immediately* push the rod gel into the molten solution using a spatula and allow agarose to set (5 min). The rod should be completely embedded in the agarose gel when it sets, and should be perpendicular to the stacking gel surface (Fig. 7.11).

12   Carry out SDS-slab polyacrylamide gel electrophoresis as described in Section 7.3.1, method i, steps 6–10 (except no samples to load) — see note 7.

13   Turn off power, remove gel from mould and stain (Sections 7.1.1 and 7.1.2).

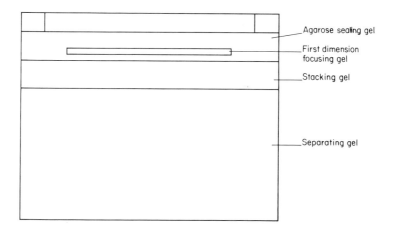

Fig. 7.11 Arrangement of polyacrylamide gels for two-dimensional electrophoresis (Section 7.6).

Notes

1   A non-gradient slab-SDS gel can be used instead of a gradient gel, but this limits the molecular weight range resolved by the gel.

2   Ampholyte pH range should be selected for each experiment. O'Farrell used 4 vol pH 5–7 to 1 vol pH 3–10.

3   Pre-running is essential. It removes residual ammonium persulphate from the gels.

4   Better results may be obtained with cells if they are freeze-thawed 3 or 4 times, sonicated or solubilized in non-ionic detergent (Section 4.4.2) before adding the sample buffer.

179

5   The focusing schedule can be varied. The product of time and voltage should be about 8000 volt-hours and the final voltage should be at least 400 V.

6   Equilibrated gels can be frozen if it is more convenient to run the second dimension later. For some samples good results can be obtained even if equilibration is omitted.

7   Molecular weight markers, or non-focused sample, can be run in the second dimension for reference purposes, by forming a slot at one end of the rod sealing gel using a Perspex spacer pushed about 0.5 cm into the agarose before it sets. Just prior to electrophoresis the spacer is removed, and the sample loaded into the slot using an automatic pipette or Hamilton syringe.

8   This technique can be particularly useful when combined with immunoblotting (Section 8.4).

7.7   PEPTIDE MAPPING USING PROTEOLYTIC ENZYMES AND SDS–POLYACRYLAMIDE GEL ELECTROPHORESIS

This technique enables the primary structure of proteins to be compared. The proteins are partially digested with a proteolytic enzyme and the products analysed by SDS–polyacrylamide gel electrophoresis (Cleveland *et al.*, 1977). The technique is especially useful for showing similarities between proteins of different molecular weight, and for distinguishing between proteins in different samples which happen to have the same electrophoretic mobility.

Proteins for investigation are prepared by preparative SDS–polyacrylamide gel electrophoresis (Section 9.2.1), and the strips of acrylamide containing proteins are cut into short lengths and loaded together with enzyme onto a second analytical (normally gradient) polyacrylamide gel. Electrophoresis is carried out and enzyme and protein under investigation mix together in the stacking gel, where proteolysis occurs. The fragments produced are then separated by the separating gel and the digestion patterns obtained from the proteins under investigation compared. By using a panel of enzymes, differences and similarities between proteins are easily established. It is advisable to use a range of enzyme concentrations on one gel, loading the two proteins to be compared in adjacent tracks (see Fig. 7.12 for a typical example).

Materials and equipment

Equipment and solutions for preparative SDS–polyacrylamide gel electrophoresis (Section 9.2.1)

Equipment and solutions for gradient SDS–polyacrylamide gel electrophoresis (Section 7.3.2)

Proteolytic enzymes — see Table 7.4

180

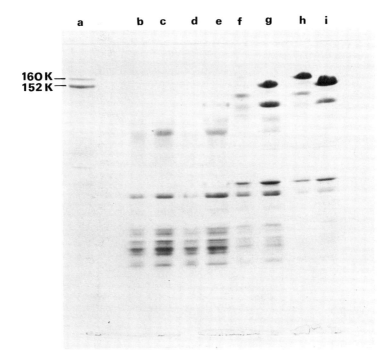

Fig. 7.12 Comparison of the two *Myxicola infundibulum* neurofilament polypeptides by polyacrylamide gel peptide mapping (Section 7.7). Track (a) contains undigested polypeptides (molecular weights 160 000 and 152 000). Tracks (b), (d), (f) and (h) contain the 160 000 molecular weight polypeptide digested with 5 μl of 5, 1.67, 0.5 and 0.167 μg/ml papain respectively. Tracks (c), (e), (g) and (i) contain the 152 000 molecular weight polypeptide digested similarly. Note that although the mobilities of the larger fragments differ for the two polypeptides, the overall digestion pattern, and the migration of the smaller fragments are the same, suggesting considerable structural similarity of the two polypeptides. The gel contained a gradient of 7.5–17.5% (w/v) polyacrylamide.

Equilibration solution: 0.125 M tris-HCl pH 6.8 containing 0.5% (w/v) SDS

Enzyme diluent: 0.125 M tris-HCl pH 6.8 containing 10% (w/v) glycerol, 0.1% SDS and 0.01% bromophenol blue

Glass Universal containers

Procedure

1   Isolate proteins for investigation by preparative SDS–polyacrylamide gel electrophoresis (Section 9.2.1) *except* use 1.5 mm thick gels (i.e. normal analytical gel thickness). Cut bands for investigation from gels after quick staining and place in Universals containing 15 ml equilibration solution. Mix for 20–30 min at room temperature. Discard the liquid and store at −20°C or use immediately.

181

2   Prepare a gradient SDS–polyacrylamide gel as described in Section 7.3.2 *except* use only 11 ml of each separating gel solution (the stacking gel should be longer than for ordinary gels). A 7.5–17.5% (w/v) acrylamide gradient gel is suitable for most proteins.

Table 7.4   Enzyme concentrations for use in partial proteolytic cleavage peptide mapping

Enzyme[1]	Concentration range [2](μg/ml)
papain	0.167–5
pronase (protease VI)	0.033–1
subtilisin BPN' (protease VII)	3.3–100
chymotrypsin	20–600

([1]) All enzymes obtained from Sigma (Appendix 3).
([2]) Load 5 μl of this solution/1 cm wide gel slot.

3   Prepare a range of 4 enzyme concentrations in enzyme diluent (Table 7.4).
4   Load enzyme solutions through the electrode buffer into the slots in the stacking gel. See Fig. 7.12 for suggested loading pattern.
5   Cut 0.9 cm long section from the protein bands (step 1). Load these into the enzyme containing slots in the stacking gel using forceps, and push them into position 2 mm above the enzyme solution with a thin spatula — see Fig. 7.12 for loading pattern.
6   Carry out electrophoresis as described in Section 7.3.1, method i, but turn off the power for 20–30 min when the bromophenol blue has travelled 1.5–2 cm into the stacking gel.
7   Continue electrophoresis until the bromophenol blue reaches the bottom of the gel. Turn off power, remove gel from mould and stain (Sections 7.1.1 and 7.1.2). The interpretation of the results from one such comparison is presented in Fig. 7.12.

Notes

1   Prepare fresh enzyme solutions for each run.
2   Conditions should be such that only partial proteolysis occurs, and large fragments are produced (above 4000 molecular weight). If only very small fragments are produced, reduce the enzyme concentration.
3   Cleveland *et al.* (1977) include 1 mM EDTA in all solutions. The authors have not found this to be advantageous.
4   Chemical cleavage, for example by cyanogen bromide, can be used in place of enzymatic cleavage.

8 Specific detection of antigens separated by polyacrylamide gel electrophoresis

8.1 INTRODUCTION

Combination of the high resolving power of polyacrylamide gel techniques (Chapter 7) with the specificity of antibodies can provide a considerable amount of information on both antigens and antibodies. The small pore size of polyacrylamide gels limits their use in such techniques as double diffusion (Section 6.3.1) and immunoelectrophoresis (Section 6.4.3) but alternative strategies have been developed. The different approaches can be classified under the following headings:

1   Electrophoresis in polyacrylamide gel followed by crossed immunoelectrophoresis (at right angles to the first dimension) into an agarose gel containing antibody (Section 8.2). This technique is fundamentally similar to agarose crossed immunoelectrophoresis (Section 6.4.5), but has to be modified to allow for the different physical characteristics of polyacrylamide gel and for the presence of detergent in the case of SDS-polyacrylamide gel electrophoresis (Section 7.3.1).

2   Polyacrylamide gel electrophoresis followed by fixation of the separated proteins and then direct application of a labelled antibody system to the gel (Section 8.3).

3   Transfer of proteins separated by polyacrylamide gel electrophoresis to a sheet of porous material (e.g. nitrocellulose or diazotized filter paper) which can then be stained with labelled antibodies, as in 2 above (Section 8.4). Such transfer can be carried out by diffusion but as this is inefficient, time consuming, usually requires the construction of composite agar/acrylamide gels and can result in a loss of resolution, electrophoretic transfer is now almost always used (but see Section 8.4).

4   Coupling antibody to a porous material (e.g. diazotized filter paper) and 'blotting' radiolabelled antigens separated by polyacrylamide gel electrophoresis onto this (Section 8.5). This technique is known as filter affinity transfer.

The last few years have seen a rapid increase in the use of this technology, and approach 3 (now known as immunoblotting or Western blotting) has been favoured because of its simplicity and speed (Towbin *et al.*, 1979; Towbin and Gordon, 1984). The authors particularly recommend immunoblotting using nitrocellulose filters

183

(Section 8.4.3). However, the other approaches are occasionally used and may be advantageous in some circumstances.

8.2 CROSSED IMMUNOELECTROPHORESIS USING POLYACRYLAMIDE GEL ELECTROPHORESIS IN THE FIRST DIMENSION

This procedure is a modification of crossed immunoelectrophoresis (Section 6.4.5). It has the advantage that immunological relationships between the components of a mixture separated by polyacrylamide gel electrophoresis can be established by the fusing or crossing of rockets, but the technique requires a precipitating antibody (see Section 6.1).

The main application of this technique is with SDS-polyacrylamide gel electrophoresis (Section 7.3.1) to enable the immunochemical characterization of insoluble proteins (e.g. membranes, cytoskeletal proteins, viral particles). Unfortunately the presence of SDS often leads to precipitation artefacts in the second dimension antibody containing gel (see Section 6.3.3). These artefacts can be eliminated by including an intermediate gel containing other detergents which form mixed micelles with the SDS and prevent artefactual precipitation.

The method is technically difficult and several different versions have been published. With care the procedure below is usually successful, but in general the techniques described in the remainder of the chapter, particularly immunoblotting (Section 8.4.3), are better alternatives.

Materials and equipment

Apparatus and solutions for SDS-polyacrylamide gel electrophoresis (Section 7.3.1)
Electrophoresis tank and power pack for crossed immunoelectrophoresis (Section 6.4.5)
Glass plate (see Fig. 8.1 for size)
Brass rod, square cross-section approx $10 \times 1 \times 1$ cm
Levelling table
Whatman 3 MM filter paper
Heated water bath
Strip blade (Dako — Appendix 3)
Agarose (medium electroendosmosis; see Section 6.4.1)
Electrophoresis buffer: 80 mM tris, 40 mM sodium acetate, 1 mM EDTA adjusted to pH 8.6 with acetic acid
Phosphate buffered saline (PBS — Appendix 2)
50% w/v polyethylene glycol (PEG) molecular weight 6000 (BDH — Appendix 3) prepared in electrophoresis buffer
20% w/v Lubrol PX (BDH — Appendix 3) prepared in water
10% w/v sodium deoxycholate (BDH — Appendix 3) prepared in water
Antigen and antibody (for a trial run use serum and anti-albumin)

184

Procedure

1 Electrophorese the antigen mixture on an SDS-polyacrylamide gel (Section 7.3.1).

2 About 1 hour before the electrophoresis is complete, prepare molten 1.2% w/v agarose in electrophoresis buffer (Section 6.3.1).

3 Prepare the following gel solutions and keep them at 50°C in the water bath:

Cathodal gel: 1 ml sodium deoxycholate solution + 9 ml agarose solution.

Anodal and intermediate gel: 2.9 ml Lubrol solution + 35.1 ml agarose solution.

Antibody gel: 1.3 ml PEG solution + 18.7 ml agarose solution + 1 ml antibody solution (see note 1).

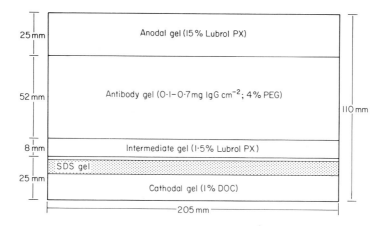

Fig. 8.1 Arrangement of gels for crossed immunoelectrophoresis using polyacrylamide gel in the first dimension. Reproduced from Chua & Blomberg (1979) with permission.

4 Level the glass plate. Allow the anodal/intermediate gel solution to cool to about 35°C and pour it onto the glass plate covering the entire surface. Allow to solidify (10 min).

5 Use the strip blade to remove the gel from the areas marked 'antibody gel', 'cathodal gel' and 'SDS gel' in Fig. 8.1.

6 Allow the antibody gel solution to cool to 35°C and pour it into the antibody gel space on the glass plate. The gel thickness should be about 1.8 mm. Allow to solidify.

7 When SDS-gel electrophoresis is complete, turn off power and remove the gel from the mould. Using the strip blade cut out a strip of gel corresponding to one sample track. Trim the edges of the strip parallel (final width should be about 8 mm) and transfer it to the glass plate (Fig. 8.1).

8 Allow the cathodal gel solution to cool to 35°C and pour it onto the glass plate in the space reserved for the cathodal gel (Fig. 8.1). This gel

185

should be 1.6 mm thick and must entirely enclose the polyacrylamide gel.

9   Place the assembled gel system in the electrophoresis tank, fill the electrode compartments with electrophoresis buffer and set up electrical contact between the electrodes and the electrode gels using a triple thickness of filter paper soaked in electrode buffer (see Fig. 6.3). Carry out electrophoresis for 20 h at 100 V.

10   Turn off the power and remove the gel from the electrophoresis chamber. Remove the polyacrylamide gel using the strip blade and discard. Soak the agarose gel for 36 h in 4 changes of 500 ml PBS.

11   Soak for 4 h in water. Dry, stain and destain as described in Section 6.2.2.

Notes

1   It is advisable to purify the antibody or at least the immunoglobulin fraction from the antiserum for this technique (Sections 10.3.1 and 3.3.1). The final immunoglobulin concentration should be 0.1–0.8 mg/cm^2 of gel.

2   Completion of SDS-polyacrylamide gel electrophoresis and the preparation of the second dimension agarose gel should coincide. If the agarose gel is prepared too soon it can be stored for a short time in a humid chamber.

3   The technique can be adapted for use with lectins instead of antibodies (see Section 6.4.6).

8.3   DIRECT APPLICATION OF ANTIBODIES TO POLYACRYLAMIDE GELS

In this technique antigens separated by polyacrylamide gel electrophoresis are fixed, and antibody is applied directly to the gel surface. Antibody–antigen interaction is detected either by prior labelling of the antibody (normally with ^{125}I) or by application of a labelled anti-immunoglobulin antibody: this latter procedure considerably increases sensitivity (cf. solid-phase radiobinding assays, Section 11.1.1).

The procedure has now been almost completely superseded by immunoblotting techniques (Section 8.4) because it is more time consuming and requires the use of fixatives whilst offering no apparent advantages. For these reasons we do not recommend this approach and the reader is referred to Burridge (1978) for the methodology if required.

8.4   TRANSFER OF PROTEINS FROM GELS TO POROUS MEMBRANES (IMMUNOBLOTTING)

This technique has three considerable advantages over alternatives such as the direct application technique (Section 8.3):

186

1 The procedure is considerably quicker.

2 No fixation of proteins is necessary, thus avoiding the possible destruction of antigenic determinants by chemicals such as glutaraldehyde.

3 Antibodies of all classes (including IgM) easily penetrate the porous membrane.

A possible disadvantage is that it is not possible to stain antibody-processed blots for protein; however, with nitrocellulose membranes a duplicate track can be cut off and stained separately (Section 8.4.3, note 6) which allows a direct comparison of antibody binding paterns with the total number of protein components.

Porous membranes suitable for immunoblotting are chemically derivatized (usually diazotized) paper, nitrocellulose filters or, more recently, nylon membranes. Derivatized paper has the posible advantages that proteins are covalently bound and it can have a higher capacity. Nitrocellulose filters bind proteins by physical forces and have the considerable advantages of being stable and ready for use as supplied but some proteins bind poorly to nitrocellulose. Nylon membranes are physically stronger and hence easier to handle and may have a higher capacity for some proteins.

Electrophoretic transfer is now almost always preferred for immunoblotting. A possible exception to this is in transfer from isoelectric focusing gels (Section 7.5), where the proteins are at their isoelectric points and therefore uncharged. Hence with electrophoretic transfer there is a considerable delay before the proteins start to migrate, they can migrate in different directions and their rate of transfer can differ considerably. For these reasons, transfer from isoelectric focusing gels by diffusion may be preferable particularly if very thin gels are used (to minimize spreading of bands and increase transfer efficiency).

Methods for the preparation of diazotized paper are given followed by procedures for transfer by diffusion and electrophoresis.

8.4.1 Preparation of diazotized paper

Diazotized paper can be used for immunoblotting and is necessary if the blot is to be used more than once (Section 8.4.4). It is also necessary for filter affinity transfer (Section 8.5) and if proteins of interest do not bind efficiently to nitrocellulose filters. The diazotized paper can be either the diazobenzyloxymethyl (DBM) or diazophenyl-thioethyl derivative. The chemical properties of the two seem similar (the active group is the same) but the latter is easier to prepare.

Preparation of DBM paper

DBM paper is produced by diazotizing aminobenzyloxymethyl (ABM) paper. This material is available commercially (Schleicher and Schull — Appendix 3) but it is expensive and has a limited reactive life. Synthesis of ABM paper is relatively simple and it can be carried out in most laboratories equipped with a good fume cupboard.

187

Materials and equipment

(a) Preparation of ABM paper
1-[(m-nitrobenzyloxy)methyl] pyridinium chloride (BDH — Appendix
   3, see note 1)
Whatman 540 filter paper
Benzene
Sodium acetate
Sodium dithionite
30% v/v acetic acid
Oven
Plastic or enamelled tray

(b) Diazotization of ABM paper (see notes 2 and 3)
1.8 M hydrochloric acid
10 mg/ml sodium nitrite (freshly prepared)
Ice cold water
Ice cold 50 mM borate buffer pH 8.0

Procedure

(a) Preparation of ABM paper
1   Dissolve 1.6 g of 1-[(m-nitrobenzyloxy)methyl] pyridinium chloride and 0.5 g sodium acetate in 20 ml of water and pour into the tray.
2   Soak 3–4 sheets of filter paper in the above solution for about 1
min. Ensure that no air bubbles are trapped beneath the sheets.
3   Dry the sheets at 60°C.
4   Heat the sheets at 135°C for 35 minutes and then wash twice with
500–750 ml of water.
5   Dry and then wash twice with 500 ml benzene. Allow to dry.
6   Submerge sheets in 500–700 ml 20% w/v sodium dithionite
(freshly prepared) and incubate at 60°C for 30 min. Agitate occasionally.
7   Wash at room temperature with water for 20 min (2 changes,
750 ml each), with 30% v/v acetic acid for 20 min (2 changes, 750 ml
each) and then with water until there is no odour of hydrogen sulphide
(about 30 min).
8   Dry and store desiccated at 4°C.

(b) Diazotization of ABM paper (see note 2)
1   Cool all solutions on ice.
2   Prepare diazotizing solution by mixing 80 ml of 1.8 M hydrochloric
acid with 40 ml of water and 3.2 ml sodium nitrite solution.
3   Cool on ice and then soak the ABM paper in this solution for 30
min on ice.
4   Wash the paper with ice cold water for 30 min (5 changes; 400–
500 ml each) and then 10–12 min with ice cold borate buffer (2
changes; 400–500 ml each). The paper should become yellow-orange
during this procedure.

188

5   Keep on ice until needed (see note 2).

Notes

1   1[(m-nitrobenzyloxy)methyl] pyridinium chloride can be synthesized in the laboratory, but some knowledge of, and equipment for organic chemistry is required (Alwine *et al.*, 1977).
2   DBM paper is unstable and should be prepared as it is needed. Diazotize the ABM paper so that the reaction is complete 10–15 min before it is needed.
3   It is *essential* to cool all reagents on ice.

Preparation of diazophenylthioethyl paper

Diazophenylthioethyl paper is produced by diazotizing aminophenylthioethyl paper. Like DBM paper the diazo derivative is unstable and must be prepared immediately before use. A good fume cupboard is required.

Materials and equipment

(*a*) *Preparation of aminophenylthioethyl paper*
1,4-butanediol diglycidyl ether (Aldrich — Appendix 3)
2-aminothiophenol (Aldrich — Appendix 3)
Acetone
0.1 M hydrochloric acid
Whatman 50 filter paper 14 × 25 cm
0.5 M sodium hydroxide containing 2 mg/ml sodium borohydride *(freshly prepared)*
Plastic tray with tight fitting lid or sealable (waterproof) plastic bag — *resistant to acetone*
Orbital shaker

(*b*) *Diazotization of aminophenylthioethyl paper*
As for diazotization of ABM paper (see above)

Procedure

(*a*) *Preparation of aminophenylthioethyl paper*
1   Place seven sheets of Whatman 50 paper in the tray or bag and add 70 ml borohydride solution and 30 ml of 1,4-butanediol diglycidyl ether. Seal and agitate briskly for 16 h at room temperature.
2   Discard the liquid and add 40 ml acetone and 10 ml 2-aminothiophenol. Reseal and agitate for a further 10 h.
3   Wash twice with acetone (500 ml), twice with 0.1 M hydrochloric acid (500 ml) and then 5–6 times with water (500 ml each). Wash once more with HCl and water and then air dry.
4   Store desiccated at 4°C.

189

(*b*) *Diazotization of aminophenylthioethyl paper*
As described for DBM paper (see above).

8.4.2 Transfer by diffusion

Transfer by diffusion is hardly ever used for immunoblotting SDS or native polyacrylamide gels as electrophoretic transfer is almost always better. The procedure below is suitable for diffusion transfer from thin isoelectric focusing gels and is one of the most simple versions.

Materials and equipment

Isoelectric focusing gel about 0.5 mm thick (Section 7.5.2).
Nitrocellulose filter, 0.45 μm pore size (Schleicher and Schull —
    Appendix 3) or freshly prepared diazotized paper (Section 8.4.1)
Whatman 3 MM filter paper
Glass plate larger than the gel
Phosphate buffered saline containing azide (PBS — Appendix 2)

Procedure

1 Place gel on glass plate and overlay with the diazotized paper or nitrocellulose filter soaked in PBS.
2 Cut 5 pieces of filter paper just larger than the gel. Soak in PBS, drain and use to cover diazotized paper or nitrocellulose. Leave for 1–4 h at room temperature (see note).
3 Remove filter paper and process blot with antibodies as for electrophoretic transfer (Section 8.4.3).

Note

Optimal transfer time depends on gel thickness, percentage acrylamide and the molecular size of the proteins. This can only be determined empirically. If weak or diffuse blots are obtained try electrophoretic transfer (Section 8.4.3).

8.4.3 Electrophoretic transfer

Proteins can be easily transferred to nitrocellulose or diazotized paper by electrophoresis. This technique has the advantages that transfer takes only 1–4 h and lateral diffusion of proteins (which causes diffuse bands) is minimized (see for example Fig. 8.2).

A suitable electrophoretic transfer chamber and power pack are required and these are available commercially (E–C, Bio-Rad — Appendix 3) or can be made in a laboratory workshop (see Fig. 8.3).

In general nitrocellulose filters are recommended. However, if the antigens of interest do not bind efficiently or if the blot is to be re-used

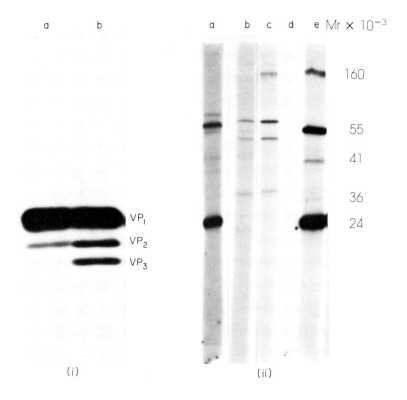

Fig. 8.2 Autoradiographs of immunoblots (Section 8.4.3).

(i) Poliovirus proteins, either unlabelled (a) or biosynthetically radiolabelled with ^{35}S methionine (b), were separated by SDS-polyacrylamide gel electrophoresis and then electrophoretically transferred to a nitrocellulose sheet. After processing with a rabbit anti-poliovirus serum the antigen–antibody complexes were detected using a ^{125}I label-led anti-rabbit immunoglobulin. Comparison of the two tracks shows that the antiserum strongly recognizes VP_1, also binds to VP_2 but does not recognize VP_3.

(ii) Lymphoblastoid cells infected with human immunodeficiency virus (HIV) were lysed and the proteins separated by SDS-polyacrylamide gel electrophoresis. After elec-trophoretic transfer to nitrocellulose sheets the strips were processed with sera from individuals suffering with AIDS (tracks A, B, C and E) or an individual seronegative for HIV (D). Antigen–antibody complexes were detected by further processing with a ^{125}I labelled monoclonal antibody specific for human IgG. Note the different pattern obtained with sera from different seropositive individuals and the complete lack of reactivity in the negative control. Immunoblotting is ideal for comparing the antigen specificity of different sera or monoclonal antibodies.

(Section 8.4.4) then diazotized paper, or possibly nylon membranes, must be used.

The nylon membranes introduced recently, e.g. Zeta-Probe, Hybond–N (Bio-Rad, Amersham — Appendix 3), are ready to use and may have a higher capacity for some proteins than nitrocellulose. They are also less fragile, more expensive and may have a greater retention allowing re-use (Section 8.4.4).

Procedures for electrophoretic transfer of proteins from polyacryl-amide gels to nitrocellulose or diazotizcd paper are described separ-

191

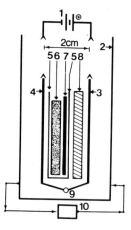

Fig. 8.3 Diagram of electrophoretic transfer system. Power source (1); tank (2); palladium anode (3); stainless steel cathode (4); filter paper (5); gel (6); nitrocellulose sheet or diazotized paper (7); scouring pads (8); cassette (9); buffer recirculating pump (10). It is possible to attach the electrodes (platinum wire can also be used) onto the walls of the tank rather than in the cassette.

ately in this section. Transfer to nylon membranes is similar to that given for nitrocellulose, but see individual manufacturers' literature.

Transfer to nitrocellulose sheets

Materials and equipment

SDS slab polyacrylamide electrophoretogram (Section 7.3.1) (see note 1 below)

Electrophoretic transfer system (E–C, Bio-Rad — Appendix 3; or lab-made equivalent)

Orbital shaker (Luckham — Appendix 3)

Scouring pads

Nitrocellulose sheet, 0.45 μm pore size, large enough to cover the gel (Schleicher and Schull — Appendix 3)

Plastic box large enough to accommodate the blot and allow movement on shaking

Whatman 3MM paper

Transfer buffer: 4 vols 0.192 M glycine, 0.025 M tris + 1 vol methanol — enough to fill the transfer chamber (see note 1)

Phosphate buffered saline containing azide (PBS — Appendix 2)

Hb-PBS: PBS containing 3% (w/v) bovine haemoglobin (BDH — Appendix 3; see note 2)

Antibody and ^{125}I labelled anti-immunoglobulin (see note 3)

Procedure

1 Fill the tank with transfer buffer (see notes 1 and 4). Fold a piece

of filter paper twice the size of the internal cassette in half, soak in transfer buffer and place on the cathodal side of the cassette.

2 Unfold the filter paper and place the gel on the half of the filter paper covering the cathode (or on the cathodal side of the cassette). Immediately soak the nitrocellulose sheet in transfer buffer and place it on the gel, expelling any trapped air bubbles. Do not move the nitrocellulose once it has been positioned.

3 Fold over the other half of the filter paper and overlay with another sheet of filter paper soaked in transfer buffer. Fill the remaining space in the cassette with scouring pads soaked in transfer buffer, ensuring that the gel is pressed firmly against the nitrocellulose. Secure the cassette tightly.

4 Place the cassette in the tank and fit the lid. If apparatus has the facility for buffer recirculation (e.g. E–C system), turn on the recirculating pump (see note 4). If not (e.g. Bio-Rad system), use a magnetic stirrer to agitate the transfer buffer (see note 3).

5 Electrophorese for 1–4 h at 0.45 A (see note 5).

6 Turn off power and remove nitrocellulose sheet and gel from the cassette. The gel can be stained if required (Section 7.1.1; see note 6 below).

7 Shake nitrocellulose sheet for 30 min (see note 7) in 50–200 ml of Hb-PBS at room temperature.

8 Shake sheet for 2–16 h with 20–40 ml Hb-PBS containing antibody (see note 8).

9 Wash for 0.5–1 h (6 to 7 changes, 20–200 ml each) with Hb-PBS. Use brisk agitation on the orbital shaker for this.

10 Shake for 2–6 h with 20–50 ml Hb-PBS containing ^{125}I labelled anti-immunoglobulin. Use $5 \times 10^5 - 10^6$ c.p.m./track or 5×10^6 c.p.m./gel (see note 3).

11 Wash for 0.5–1 h (6 to 8 changes, 20–200 ml each) with PBS.

12 Pin blots to a suitable support so that they hang freely in air. Dry at room temperature in an oven at 56°C or using a hair-dryer. When *completely dry*, carry out autoradiography (Section 1.5).

Notes

1 This buffer is suitable for use with SDS gels and the buffer system described in Section 7.3.1, method i; methanol can be omitted in some cases with no adverse effects. Methanol is not necessary for non-SDS gels (Section 7.4) or isoelectric focusing gels (Section 7.5). If a buffer system other than that described in Section 7.3.1, method i, is used, then use the electrode buffer of the system as transfer buffer. For gels containing urea (Section 7.3.3), use 0.7% acetic acid as transfer solution and reverse the position of the gel and nitrocellulose sheet (i.e. place the gel on the anode or anodic side of the cassette).

2 Bovine haemoglobin is an efficient blocking agent and is very cheap. However, many other blocking agents can be used — e.g. ovalbumin, serum albumin. In general haemoglobin is recommended

over albumin, and the use of detergents such as Tween 20 is not recommended.

3 It is possible to radioiodinate the first antibody, but this will require purification and ^{125}I-labelling of every antibody of interest as well as being less sensitive. It is therefore usually better to use a labelled anti-immunoglobulin — affinity purified polyclonal or purified monoclonal. It is possible to use an enzyme labelled antibody for immunoblotting (cf. ELISA and immunohistochemistry — Sections 11.4 and 12.3) but high backgrounds and/or false positives are often problems with these.

4 It is best to cool the transfer buffer to 8–15°C during transfer to avoid heating effects. The method of cooling depends on the design of the transfer tank. If a buffer re-circulating system is used, pre-cool the transfer buffer to 8°C and place the recirculating tubing in an ice bath (use sufficient tubing to maintain the temperature below 16°C). If recirculation is not used, then use a cooling coil coupled to a cooling system (controlled chiller or ice bath).

5 Higher current can be used, but may result in uneven heating effects and blurred or distorted blots. The use of lower currents is not recommended as transfer efficiency is reduced and poor blots obtained. Overnight transfer can be used, but it is generally not recommended. The time required for efficient transfer depends on the acrylamide concentration, gel thickness, gel buffer system and the molecular size and shape of the proteins. Most proteins will pass through the nitrocellulose sheet if transfer is continued for too long. Proteins migrate fastest from SDS gels (they are coated with SDS and highly charged) and transfer from non-SDS gels takes longer (around 4–5 h). Electrophoretic transfer of proteins from isoelectric focusing gels can be problematical (see Section 8.4.2); transfer takes 4–6 h.

6 The gel sometimes contains enough residual protein afer transfer to produce visible bands on staining. The nitrocellulose sheet cannot be stained with Coomassie blue, but amido black will work as an alternative to processing with antibody. For this immerse for 3–5 min in 0.5% (w/v) amido black prepared in 50% (v/v) methanol, 5% (v/v) acetic acid. Then wash for about 1 min with water and destain in 50% methanol, 5% acetic acid until an acceptable background is obtained. This procedure is fairly insensitive and more sensitive stains suitable for nitrocellulose blots are now commercially available — Ferridye, Aurodye (Janssen — Appendix 3).

7 30 min incubation with blocking protein is sufficient to saturate all the protein binding sites on the blot. However, longer times, up to overnight, can be used if this is more convenient. Unprocessed blots can be stored frozen after blocking for long periods. For this, block the blot for 30 min (as in step 7), drain and remove excess blocking agent and store at −20°C or −70°C. When required for processing with antibody, wash with blocking agent for 10 min and then continue as in steps 8–12.

8   The amount of antibody required varies enormously, depending on its source, avidity, concentration and the amount of antigen present on the blot. Usually 1–100 μl of antiserum or ascites fluid, or 0.1–5 ml of hybridoma culture supernatant is required. It is emphasized that this is only a rough guide.

Transfer to diazotized paper

Materials and equipment

As for transfer to nitrocellulose sheets (see above) but substitute *freshly prepared* DBM paper or diazophenylthioethyl paper (Section 8.4.1) for nitrocellulose sheets and use different buffers (below).

Transfer buffer: for DBM paper, 25 mM sodium phosphate pH 5.5; for diazophenylthioethyl paper, 10 mM sodium borate pH 9.2

50 mM sodium borate pH 9.2 (for diazophenylthioethyl paper only)

Solutions for antibody processing of the blot (as for nitrocellulose sheets; see above)

Procedure

1   Cool transfer buffer to 4°C. Wash gel for 0.5–1.0 h in 2 changes of 500 ml of transfer buffer (DBM paper) or 50 mM sodium borate pH 9.2 (diazophenylthioethyl paper).

2   Assemble the cassette using diazotized paper as described for transfer to nitrocellulose sheets (see above, steps 2 and 3).

3   Place transfer buffer and cassette in tank, fit lid and turn on circulating pump.

4   Electrophorese at 36 V for 1–4 h (see note 1).

5   Turn off power and remove gel and diazotized paper from cassette.

6   Stain the gel (Section 7.1.1) and process diazotized paper with antibody as described for nitrocellulose sheets (see above, steps 7–12).

Notes

1   The voltage should be adjusted so that excessive bubble formation and heating are avoided (the diazo groups are stable only at low temperature).

2   See Section 8.4.4.

3   It is not possible to stain diazotized paper for protein.

4   See note 4 above.

8.4.4   Removal of antibody from diazotized paper blots

Antibody bound to antigen on a diazotized paper blot can be removed by treatment with urea and 2-mercaptoethanol. When these reagents are removed, most (but not all) of the bound protein antigens refold to their original conformation and the blot can then be processed with a second antibody. Caution should be taken when interpreting the repeat blots in case the first antibody is not removed completely.

Materials and equipment

Processed diazotized paper blot (Sections 8.4.2 and 8.4.3)
Phosphate buffered saline containing azide (PBS-azide — Appendix 2)
PBS-Hb-NP40: PBS-azide containing 0.1% w/v haemoglobin and 0.05% v/v Nonidet P40 (BDH — Appendix 3)
10 M urea, 0.1 M 2-mercaptoethanol, 50 mM sodium phosphate pH 5.5
Plastic box large enough for the blot
Orbital shaker

Procedure

1 Shake the processed blot in 250–500 ml urea-mercaptoethanol buffer for 30 min (see note below).
2 Rinse thoroughly with PBS-azide.
3 Shake for 30 min with PBS-Hb-NP40 (3 changes of 250 ml).
4 Process with a second antibody as described in Section 8.4.3, steps 7–12.

Note

Some antibodies are not displaced by this treatment (try incubating at 60°C).

8.5 FILTER AFFINITY TRANSFER (FAT)

In this technique antibody is coupled covalently to diazotized paper and this is used to blot a polyacrylamide gel electrophoretogram. Antigens specifically recognized by the antibody bind to the paper and are detected either by prior radiolabelling (direct FAT, Section 8.5.1) or by processing the blot with radiolabelled second antibody (FAT sandwich, Section 8.5.2).

8.5.1 Direct FAT

The main advantage of this technique is speed (no washing is required) but the antigens must be radiolabelled before electrophoresis.

Materials and equipment

Radiolabelled antigens (Chapter 5) electrophoresed on a slab polyacrylamide gel (Section 7.4) or a SDS-polyacrylamide gel (Section 7.3.1) or a 2-dimensional gel (Section 7.6)

Freshly prepared DBM paper or diazophenylthioethyl paper (Section 8.4.1)

25 mM sodium phosphate pH 6.5

NP40-PBS: 0.5% (v/v) Nonidet P40 (BDH — Appendix 3) prepared in PBS-azide (Appendix 2)

Blocking buffer: 0.1 M tris-HCl pH 9.0 containing 10% (v/v) ethanolamine and 0.25% (w/v) haemoglobin (BDH — Appendix 3)

Whatman 3 MM filter paper

Humid chamber

Plastic box large enough for the blot

Orbital shaker (Luckham — Appendix 3)

Appropriate antibody dissolved in 10–20 ml PBS (see note)

Equipment for autoradiography (Section 1.5)

Procedure

1   Shake the diazotized paper with antibody solution for 12–16 h at 4°C.

2   Block remaining diazo groups on the blot by shaking for 2 h with 250 ml blocking buffer at 37°C.

3   Soak the paper for 10 min in 250 ml NP40-PBS and store it in the humid chamber until needed.

4   Shake the electrophoresed gel for 1 h in 250 ml NP40-PBS and place it on 3–4 thicknesses of moist 3 MM paper in the humid chamber.

5   Overlay the gel with the antibody-paper, remove any trapped bubbles and cover with 3 sheets of dry 3 MM paper. Leave for 2 h at room temperature.

6   Remove gel and paper from the chamber, stain the gel (Section 7.1.1) and dry the blot (room temperature, hair-drier or in an oven at 45°C).

7   Carry out autoradiography of the paper blot (Section 1.5).

Note

Use the immunoglobulin fraction of antisera (Section 3.3), preferably affinity purified (Section 10.3.1). Antibody concentration should be about 0.05–0.1 mg/ml; total volume should be sufficient to completely cover the diazotized paper.

8.5.2   FAT sandwich

This technique is a modification of direct FAT (Section 8.5.1) in which antigens bound to the antibody-coupled blot are detected by application of a second radiolabelled antibody. The advantages over the direct technique are that it is not necessary to radiolabel each antigen preparation, and that it is more specific because each antigen has to be recognized twice by antibody before it will be detected by autoradiography (cf. IRMA, Section 11.3).

Materials and equipment

As for Section 8.5.1 except antigen preparations must not be radio-labelled.
Appropriate ^{125}I-labelled antibody (Section 5.2)
PBS-Hb-NP40 solution (Section 8.4.4)

Procedure

1 Carry out steps 1–5, Section 8.5.1.
2 Remove gel and paper from the chamber and stain the gel (Section 7.1.1).
3 Incubate the paper blot with 30–50 ml ^{125}I-labelled antibody (about 2×10^6 c.p.m.) diluted in PBS-Hb-NP40 for 2–6 h at room temperature (shake gently using the orbital shaker).
4 Wash for 2–6 h (6 changes; 200 ml each) with PBS-Hb-NP40 and then for 15 min with PBS-azide.
5 Dry blot in air or with a hair-drier or in an oven at 45°C.
6 Carry out autoradiography (Section 1.5)

Note

The bound antigen can be detected by an indirect binding method using unlabelled first antibody and radiolabelled second antibody directed against the first provided it does not recognize the immunoglobulin initially insolubilized on the paper (cf. Sections 11.1 and 8.4.3). This procedure removes the requirement to radiolabel each antibody but it is longer (more washing). If the F(ab')$_2$ fraction (Section 3.4.3) of the antibody is covalently coupled to the diazotized paper, then ^{125}I-labelled protein A or G (Section 10.2.2) can be used instead of the second antibody (protein A binds to the Fc part of some IgG molecules). Protein A or G will not detect all antibodies (see Table 10.3).

8.6 MODIFICATIONS

Lectins can be used in place of antibodies in all the techniques described in this chapter (see Table 10.5). The lectin may be radiolabelled (Section 5.2) or can be detected by using a radiolabelled antilectin antibody.

Radiolabelled protein A or G can be used in place of radiolabelled anti-immunoglobulin, but it will not detect all classes of immunoglobulins (see Table 10.3).

Enzyme labelled anti-immunoglobulins can be used in all cases in place of their radiolabelled equivalents (cf. ELISA, Section 11.4).

198

9 Preparative gel techniques

Preparative gel techniques may be classified under two headings:
1 Isolation of precipitated antibody–antigen complexes either for subsequent analysis or for use as immunogens.
2 Isolation of purified proteins.
These two types of preparative technique are discussed below.

9.1 ISOLATION OF PRECIPITATED ANTIBODY–ANTIGEN COMPLEXES

It seems that antibody–antigen complexes can be more immunogenic than antigen alone. Also, more specific antiserum can be obtained by immunizing with this material because contaminants in the original antigen preparation may not be present in the immunoprecipitate.

Immunoprecipitates can be analysed by SDS-polyacrylamide gel electrophoresis (Section 7.3.1) which shows the polypeptide composition and molecular weight of the antigen.

Immunoprecipitates can be obtained easily by excision from agar gels, and double diffusion (Section 6.3.1) is an ideal method for preparation of such material. In general immunoprecipitates should be visible without staining to ensure that sufficient protein is obtained for subsequent procedures. The gels should be washed exhaustively (3–4 days) before cutting out the immunoprecipitate, to remove any unwanted soluble proteins which may be present. Although double diffusion is easily scaled up for preparative purposes, other precipitative techniques can be modified similarly (e.g. Section 6.4).

9.1.1 Preparative double diffusion

Materials and equipment

Agar (Difco — Appendix 3)
Phosphate buffered saline (PBS — Appendix 2)
Petri dish — 9 cm
Boiling water bath
No. 2 cork borer
Scalpel blade
Humid chamber (Section 6.3)
Rotary shaker (Luckham — Appendix 3)

199

Procedure

1 Carry out analytical double diffusion (Section 6.3.1): establish the antigen and antibody concentrations that give a sharp immunoprecipitin line away from both wells.

2 Prepare 1% w/v agar in PBS (Section 6.3.1).

3 Allow to cool to 45°C and then pour 15 ml into a Petri dish. Allow to solidify.

4 Bore 2 wells 1.5 cm apart using the cork borer (Section 6.3.1).

5 Fill one well with antigen and the other with antiserum (concentrations established in step 1) using a Pasteur pipette. Place in the humid chamber and incubate at room temperature (or at 4°C for temperature sensitive antigens) for 24–36 hours until immunoprecipitin lines are visible.

6 Excise the agar containing the immunoprecipitate using a scalpel blade and place in a 250 ml beaker. Add 150 ml PBS and *slowly* agitate using a rotary shaker. Change the PBS after 2 hours, and then at 10-hourly intervals for 2 days.

9.1.2 Immunization with isolated precipitates

Place the portion of agar containing the immunoprecipitate and 0.5 ml PBS in an all-glass homogenizer and macerate completely. Such material is suitable for immunization directly or it can be mixed with adjuvant (Section 2.2). The material should not be injected intravenously.

The antisera produced will contain antibodies against the first antibody as well as the antigen. These can be minimized by using the same species for both immunizations (anti-allotypic or idiotypic activities may still be present). However, use of the same species for both immunizations can result in a poor immune response with some antigens. Affinity chromatography can be used to remove unwanted antibodies or to purify the required activity from the antisera (Section 10.3.1).

9.1.3 Analysis of precipitates by SDS–polyacrylamide gel electrophoresis

Place the agar containing the immunoprecipitate in a test tube, add 0.25 ml SDS sample buffer (Section 7.3.1) and heat at 100°C for 3 min. Carry out electrophoretic analysis in SDS as usual (Section 7.3.1).

The analysis will show bands due to heavy and light chains of the antibody (molecular weights approximately 55 000 and 22 000 for IgG) as well as the antigen. The antigen may be detected specifically by autoradiography (Section 1.5) if it was radiolabelled before precipitation (Section 5.2). This is also useful when only small amounts of antigen are available.

200

9.2 ISOLATION OF PURIFIED PROTEINS

The high resolution obtained by polyacrylamide gel electrophoretic techniques (Chapter 7) can be of great use for the production of purified proteins. The preparative techniques normally employed are simply large-scale versions of the analytical procedures described in Chapter 7. The major difference between the analytical and preparative methods is the means by which proteins are located after electrophoresis. The fixation and staining used in most analytical procedures usually makes elution of proteins from gel very difficult and can also lead to denaturation of the proteins.

Increasing gel thickness is not recommended for scaling up isoelectric focusing (Section 7.5) because this leads to a reduction in resolution mainly due to uneven heating effects. However, replacing polyacrylamide by a layer of granulated gel (e.g. Sephadex) enables isoelectric focusing to be carried out on a preparative scale.

There is also a practical limit to the thickness of polyacrylamide gel for other electrophoretic techniques, and in some cases it may be preferable to carry out electrophoresis in a different supporting anti-convection medium. Originally starch gel was used for this, but other materials are also available (e.g. Pevikon). Using such materials almost always sacrifices resolution for the increased yield of protein.

These techniques are described individually below.

9.2.1 Preparative SDS–polyacrylamide gel electrophoresis

The analytical technique described in Section 7.3.1 can be adapted easily for preparative purposes by increasing gel thickness. For this purpose thicker spacers are used in the gel mould. A 3 mm gel thickness allows considerable sample to be loaded, whilst maintaining most of the resolution of the analytical technique. The use of thicker gels may lead to considerable loss of resolution due to uneven heating effects, and the gel also tends to fall out of the mould.

A 3 mm deep stacking gel is polymerized above the separating gel (without the use of a comb) leaving approximately a 3 cm space above the gel for sample application. The sample is loaded across the whole width of the gel, and up to 4 ml can be applied with little loss of resolution. After electrophoresis, proteins are located by quick surface staining. The portion of gel containing protein is excised and placed in buffer, and the protein which diffuses from the gel is recovered by precipitation.

Materials and equipment

As for analytical SDS-PAGE (Section 7.3.1), except 3 mm thick
  spacers are required and the comb is not used
Light box
Strip razor blade (Dako — Appendix 3)

201

Orbital shaker (Luckham — Appendix 3)
Glass Universal containers
Acetone
Tris base
Triethylamine
10 ml plastic syringes
Windmill or roller agitators

Solutions

As for analytical technique (Section 7.3.1) except:

Staining solution — 0.1% w/v Coomassie brilliant blue R in methanol: water: acetic acid, 50:45:5, by volume

Eluting solution — 0.1 M tris-HCl pH 7.0

Precipitating solution — acetone: triethylamine: acetic acid, 90:5:5, by volume

Procedure

1 Assemble the gel mould using 3 mm thick spacers (Section 7.3.1).

2 Prepare 60 ml separating gel solution and seal the base of the gel mould (Section 7.3.1). Pour the gel solution into the mould leaving a 6.5 cm space at the top. Overlay with water-saturated isobutanol and allow to polymerize.

3 Wash off the isobutanol with water and polymerize a 3 cm deep stacking gel (30 ml) on top of the separating gel. Do not use a comb, but overlay with isobutanol and allow to polymerize.

4 Wash off isobutanol with water and clamp gel to the electrophoresis chamber (Section 7.3.1). Fill upper and lower electrode compartments with electrode buffer, and connect to power pack (lower chamber +ve).

5 Prepare sample for electrophoresis as described in Section 7.3.1. When cool carefully load up to 4 ml of sample into the space above the stacking gel using a 5 ml pipette (see note 1 below). Carry out electrophoresis at 50 V until bromophenol blue reaches the bottom of the gel (about 16 h). Turn off power.

6 Remove gel from mould (Section 7.3.1) and place in stain. Shake on orbital shaker for 1–3 min until stained bands are visible. Rinse gel with water and place on light box. Cut out required bands using the strip blade.

7 Cut gel bands into 0.5 cm long pieces and place in the syringe barrel. Force the gel through the aperture and collect the disrupted gel in a Universal container. Add 3 ml eluting buffer and agitate using a windmill or roller mixture for 48 h at room temperature.

8 Decant off the liquid into a *glass* Universal container, or centrifuge tube (at least 30 ml capacity), taking care to leave all gel particles behind.

9 Cool decanted liquid and precipitating solution on ice for 30 min.

Add 20 ml precipitating solution to each 3 ml sample and leave on ice for 15 min.

10 Centrifuge at 400 *g* for 10 min. Carefully pour off supernatant, invert tubes on tissue paper and allow to drain for 2 min. Store precipitate at $-20°C$ or lower.

Notes

1 The amount of protein which can be loaded depends upon the resolution of the required band from other bands in the sample. An analytical gel should be run first loading various amounts of sample (e.g. 5, 15, 30, 60 μl loaded in 1 cm wide slots). If the required band is separated by at least 1 cm from other bands then up to 100 times the amount of sample that gives a fairly strong band (usually 2–5 μg protein) on the analytical gel can be loaded on the preparative gel.

2 Some SDS may be still attached to the final eluted protein. This can be decreased by repeating the precipitation procedure.

3 Preparative polyacrylamide gel electrophoresis using non-denaturing conditions (Section 7.4) can also be carried out using the scaled up procedure. Use the solutions described in Section 7.4.1 and volumes and procedure described above. It is difficult to scale up disc electrophoresis (Section 7.3.4), because of heating effects. However, apparatus for very large-scale disc electrophoresis is described by Gordon & Louis (1967) and other designs are available commercially (Shandon — Appendix 3).

4 It is possible to electrophoretically elute proteins from polyacrylamide gel slices (rather than relying on diffusion), but this is most troublesome and does not seem particularly advantageous.

9.2.2 Preparative isoelectric focusing

Preparative isoelectric focusing can be carried out conveniently using granulated gel as an anti-convection medium. The gel is prepared as a thick ampholyte-containing slurry which is poured onto a glass plate. After partial drying, the gel is placed in an electrophoresis chamber, sample applied in a line across the whole width of the gel, and focusing carried out. Protein bands are detected by blotting the surface of the gel with hard filter paper and staining this replica with Coomassie blue. Protein bands of interest are then located in the gel by comparison with the blot, and gel containing the required proteins is scraped off the glass plate. Proteins are isolated from the gel suspension by centrifugation.

Materials and equipment

Ampholytes (LKB, Pharmacia — Appendix 3)
Sephadex G-50 or G-75 *superfine*
Glass plate 20 × 20 × 0.4 cm washed in chromic acid (Appendix 2)

0.2 M sulphuric acid
0.4 M ethylene diamine
Coomassie brilliant blue R
Electrophoresis chamber (Shandon — Appendix 3)
High voltage power pack (LKB, Pharmacia, Shandon — Appendix 3)
Cellulose acetate strips
Whatman 3 MM filter paper
Oven at 110°C
10% (w/v) trichloroacetic acid
Methanol
Acetic acid
Water vacuum pump
Orbital shaker (Luckham — Appendix 3)
Ammonium sulphate

Solutions
Stain: as for preparative SDS-PAGE (Section 9.2.1)
Destain: water:methanol:acetic acid, 57:33:10, by volume

Procedure

1   Add 7.5 g Sephadex powder to 97.5 ml water and swirl until the Sephadex is fully dispersed. Add 2.5 ml of 40% (w/v) ampholyte solution and degas using the vacuum line. This solution can be stored for up to 3 weeks at 4°C.

2   Place the glass plate on a level surface and pour 30 ml of gel solution carefully onto the plate surface. Any unevenness may be removed using a glass rod and by raising one side of the plate about 5 cm above the bench and allowing it to fall.

3   Air dry the gel at room temperature for 20 min — 1.5 h until the surface assumes a matt appearance and the edges appear granular and *slightly* cracked. Place in the electrophoresis chamber.

4   Fill the electrode compartments with 0.2 M sulphuric acid (anode) and 0.4 M ethylene diamine (cathode). Set up electrical contact using cellulose acetate strips soaked in electrode solution (see Fig. 6.3).

5   Prepare sample for focusing as described in Section 7.5.2 and apply across the whole width of the plate using a Pasteur pipette. The position of sample application for focusing is usually irrelevant, but see Section 7.5. Up to 1 ml (containing 20 mg protein in each focused band) can usually be accommodated.

6   Carry out focusing at 200 V for 4 hr followed by 600 V for a further 4 h. Alternatively focus overnight at 200 V. Turn off power.

7   Remove gel from the chamber and cover with a piece of filter paper ensuring complete contact between the paper and gel surface. Leave for 2 min, remove paper and dry in the oven (about 10 min).

8   Wash paper quickly in 3 changes of trichloroacetic acid and then stain for 1–2 min. Destain for 5 min on the orbital shaker. Blot dry and locate protein bands in the gel by comparison with the stained paper.

9   Scrape off gel containing the required proteins and resuspend it in 50 ml water. Mix thoroughly and allow to stand at room temperature for 10 min. Centrifuge at 400 g for 5 min.

10 Remove the supernatant and precipitate protein from it by the addition of solid ammonium sulphate to give 95% saturation (0.72 g/ml). Collect precipitated protein by centrifugation for 10 min at 2500 g.

Note

It is also possible to prepare proteins by isoelectric focusing in columns although the authors' preference is for the gel technique described above.

9.2.3   Block electrophoresis

Electrophoresis in media other than polyacrylamide has the advantage of allowing increased protein loading but it usually has the disadvantage of lower resolution.

Originally starch or agarose was used as an anti-convection medium, but considerable electroendosmosis (Section 6.4.1) occurs with such materials. This problem can be avoided by using Pevikon (a copolymer of polyvinyl chloride and polyvinyl acetate).

Materials and equipment

Electrophoresis chamber (Shandon — Appendix 3)
Glass plate of appropriate size for the electrophoresis tank
Power pack (Shandon — Appendix 3)
Agarose, starch or Pevikon (Shandon — Appendix 3)
Whatman 3 MM chromatography paper
Polythene sheet big enough to cover the whole gel
Microscope slide 5 × 7.5 cm
Barbitone buffer pH 8.2 (Appendix 2)
4 paper clips
Sintered glass funnel
Side-arm flask
Water vacuum pump
Phosphate buffered saline (PBS — Appendix 2)

Procedure

1   Assemble gel mould using chromatography paper, glass plate and paper clips as shown in Fig. 9.1.

2   Prepare a thick slurry (about 50% w/v) of starch or Pevikon (see note 1 below) in barbitone buffer (starch requires heating to dissolve) and pour into the gel mould to a depth of 0.5–1 cm. Allow to dry at room temperature. Prepare agarose for preparative gels as described in Section 6.3.1.

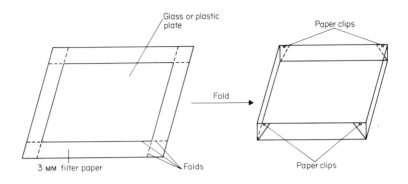

Fig. 9.1 Gel mould for block electrophoresis (Section 9.2.3).

3   When solid, remove the chromatography paper and trim the block to ensure parallel sides.

4   Place gel in electrophoresis chamber, fill electrode compartments with barbitone buffer and set up electrical contact to the gel using 3 thicknesses of 3 MM paper soaked in barbitone buffer.

5 (a)   For starch or Pevikon: cut a trough at a position about one-third of the gel length from the cathodal end across the entire width except for 0.5 cm at each edge by pushing the microscope slide through the gel and removing quickly. *Immediately* fill the trough with sample. Press the gel in the area around the trough with a spatula so that it reforms.

   (b)   For agarose: cut a 0.5 cm wide trough across the entire width of the gel except for 0.5 cm at each edge at a position about one-third of the gel length from the cathodal end using a razor blade. Mix the sample with molten agarose (approximately 45°C), pour into the trough and allow to solidify.

6   Cover the gel with the polythene sheet and carry out electrophoresis at 3 V/cm for 24 h (at 4°C if necessary).

7   Remove block from the electrophoresis chamber and cut into 1.0–1.5 cm wide strips using a razor blade.

8   Elute protein from each strip by washing it twice with 3 ml of PBS either by filtration on a sintered glass funnel or by centrifugation. Filtration only works well for starch and Pevikon; agarose gel must be macerated and centrifuged at 5000 g. Estimate protein in the fractions (Section 1.1.1–1.1.3; barbitone absorbs at 280 nm). Alternatively, see note 2 below.

Notes

1   If Pevikon is used, wash thoroughly with barbitone buffer by filtration before use.

2   The blot overlay method (see Section 9.2.2, steps 7 and 8) can be used as an alternative method for locating protein bands providing that the sample loaded does not contain too many different proteins.

206

10 Affinity chromatography and immunoprecipitation

10.1 INTRODUCTION

Affinity chromatography is a delightfully simple procedure which can provide dramatic purification of biologically active molecules. It involves a specific interaction between an insoluble ligand (A) and a soluble molecule (B) which temporarily renders molecule B insoluble and allows it to be separated from soluble contaminants (C, D, E, etc). The bonds between molecules A and B can then be disrupted to yield soluble pure B as illustrated in Fig. 10.1a. The affinity constant for the interaction should ideally be between 10^4 and 10^8 M^{-1}. Examples of the use of affinity chromatography in various biological systems are given in Table 10.1. Immunoprecipitation is an analytical version of one kind of affinity chromatography involving specific binding of radiolabelled soluble antigen to antibodies which are subsequently insolubilized by a second specific interaction (Fig. 10.1b).

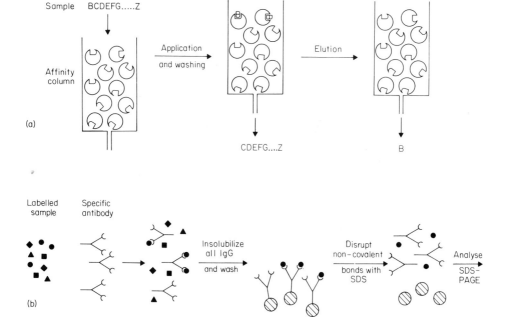

Fig. 10.1 Principles of (a) affinity chromatography to separate molecule B from contaminants C–Z using insolubilized ligand with affinity for B; (b) immunoprecipitation to isolate molecule ● from a radiolabelled mixture using *S. aureus* bacteria to insolubilize IgG.

207

Table 10.1 Examples of specific reversible interactions of use in affinity chromatography

enzyme	substrate
	competitive inhibitor
	co-enzyme
antibody	antigen
	hapten
lectin	glycoprotein
	carbohydrate
mRNA	cDNA
cell surface receptor	hormone

The basis for the purification by affinity chromatography is the specificity and reversibility of the binding of soluble molecule to insoluble ligand. At present, the ultimate in specificity is provided by insolubilized monoclonal antibodies which, for example, have been used to purify a single cell-surface molecule from detergent solubilized membrane in one step (Fig. 10.4; Sunderland *et al.*, 1979). Alternatively, group-specific ligands will bind many different molecules which contain a common structure (for example, it has been calculated that AMP will interact with 31% of all known enzymes!). In between these two extremes are lectins which bind certain carbohydrate structures, Protein A which binds certain immunoglobulins (Table 10.3) and conventional polyclonal antibodies. When using an insoluble ligand which binds several molecules with different affinities, these can sometimes be eluted separately by gradually increasing the dissociating conditions (e.g. Section 10.3.2).

Affinity chromatography has several advantages over alternative separation methods:

1   Simplicity — no sophisticated and expensive chromatographic or electrophoretic apparati are required.

2   Speed — the fractionation is usually rapid, saving time and preserving labile molecules.

3   Yield — can be better than 90% under the right conditions.

4   High purification, by functional selection — can often obtain better than 90% purity from starting material comprising only 1–5% of the required molecule in one step.

5   Applicable even to minor components — the procedure also concentrates the molecule being purified.

There are only two basic technical requirements in affinity chromatography:

1   A suitable insoluble derivative of the ligand (discussed throughout Section 10.2).

2   An effective means of dissociating the complex formed (discussed in Section 10.3).

This chapter will describe the procedures necessary for carrying out an affinity chromatography fractionation. Several specific illustrations are given including antibody–antigen and lectin–sugar interaction, and a group-specific ligand, and these can be modified to cover the majority of applications required. Additional information is given by Lowe (1979) and Dean *et al.* (1985). Immunoprecipitation is described separately in detail (Section 10.4).

10.2 THE INSOLUBLE DERIVATIVE

The method used to insolubilize the ligand is one of the steps crucial to successful affinity chromatography. The following are some of the requirements of the ideal insoluble derivative:

1 Suitable for column chromatography — it should be a loose porous network with a good flow rate.

2 Minimal non-specific adsorption.

3 High capacity — (a) there should be a high concentration of ligand molecules per unit of insoluble support, although too high a substitution may increase non-specific binding, steric hindrance or make subsequent elution difficult; (b) the ligand should be available for interaction with added soluble molecules (i.e. it should retain its native configuration and not be sterically hindered).

4 Permanent insolubility — the ligand should not redissolve to any appreciable extent to contaminate the molecules being separated.

These requirements are most nearly fulfilled by covalently coupling the ligand to agarose beads (e.g. Sepharose, Pharmacia — Appendix 3). Polyacrylamide beads (Bio-Rad — Appendix 3) may be substituted if non-specific binding to agarose is suspected, although these beads have smaller pores and hence sterically hinder some interactions. Most of the ligand on both agarose and polyacrylamide beads is inaccessible to very large multimolecular complexes such as cells, and packed columns of these supports may also trap cells or other particles, effectively producing non-specific binding. Larger agarose beads are claimed to circumvent these problems (Bio-Rad, Pharmacia — Appendix 3). Alternatively proteins may be coupled to erythrocytes or small beads and used to fractionate cells by an affinity, although non-chromatographic, technique (Section 4.3.3).

Macromolecules containing primary amino groups (e.g. proteins, nucleic acids) are most easily coupled to agarose beads by the cyanogen bromide (CNBr) activation method (Section 10.2.1). No comparably simple method exists for coupling to polyacrylamide beads. Smaller ligands should be held out from the beads by spacer arms to decrease steric hindrance and facilitate interaction with added molecules. Various derivates, with and without spacer arms, of both agarose and polyacrylamide beads are commercially available and these are capable of coupling to most ligands through a variety of functional groups (Table 10.2). Full technical details of the coupling conditions are available from the manufacturers.

The insoluble support is usually modified by the coupling proce-

209

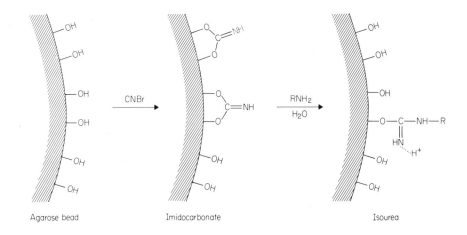

Agarose bead   Imidocarbonate   Isourea

Fig. 10.2 Probable mechanism of cyanogen bromide activation of agarose beads and reaction with primary amino groups of ligand (Section 10.2.1).

dure to a greater extent than merely the addition of ligand. For example, CNBr coupling introduces an isourea group which carries a partial positive charge at neutral pH (Fig. 10.2); blocking of excess reactive groups by some reagents (e.g. glycine) will introduce further charges; spacer arms usually contain alkyl chains and these may interact hydrophobically with some molecules. All of these modifications may lead to 'non-specific' binding (the binding is specific but to portions of the insoluble complex other than the ligand) and should be considered when interpreting the fractionation. In fact, proteins may be fractionated usefully by interaction with insolubilized hydrophobic groups (Amicon, Bio-Rad, Pharmacia — Appendix 3) — a variety of affinity chromatography termed 'hydrophobic chromatography'.

10.2.1 Cyanogen bromide coupling to agarose beads

This method produces an insoluble ligand suitable for most affinity chromatography procedures; it is better to prepare insolubilized antibodies for use in radioimmunoassays (Chapter 11) by other procedures (AH– or CH–Sepharose 4B, Pharmacia; Matrex Pel 102, Amicon — Appendix 3). Cyanogen bromide at high pH reacts with the hydroxyl groups of agarose to form an activated product to which primary amino groups couple rapidly at neutral pH (Cuatrecasas, 1970). The structure of the activated intermediate is still uncertain but the final product probably contains an isourea linkage between agarose and ligand (Fig. 10.2).

Under carefully controlled conditions the activated intermediate is stable enough to be stored and it is available commercially (Table 10.2) which circumvents the problems associated with handling toxic CNBr. However, the procedure described below is simple, almost invariably

Table 10.2 Commercially available supports for insolubilizing ligands for affinity chromatography

Gel derivative	Reactive ligand group	Coupling procedure[a]	Supports	Commercial name[b]
CNBr activated	amino	spontaneous	agarose	CNBr-activated Sepharose 4B or 6MB[1]
amino	carboxyl	carbodiimide	agarose	AH-Sepharose 4B[1] EAH-Sepharose 4B[1] Affi-Gel 102[2]
			polyacrylamide	aminoethyl Bio-Gel P–2 and P–150[2]
carboxyl	amino	carbodiimide	agarose	CH-Sepharose 4B[1] ECH-Sepharose 4B[1] CM Sepharose CL–6B[1] Affi-Gel 202[2] CM Bio-Gel A[2]
hydroxysuccinimide	amino	spontaneous	agarose	Affi-Gel 10 & 15[2] activated CH–Sepharose 4B[1]
epoxy	amino, thiol, hydroxyl	spontaneous	agarose	Epoxy-activated Sepharose 6B[1]
tresyl	amino, thiol	spontaneous	agarose	Tresyl-activated Sepharose 4B[1]
adipic acid hydrazide	aldehyde	spontaneous	agarose	Agarose adipic acid hydrazide[1]
sulphydryl or disulphide	thiol, mercurated base, others	spontaneous or mixed disulphide	agarose	Thiopropyl-Sepharose 6B[1] activated Thiol-Sepharose 4B[1] Affi-Gel 401[2] Agarose thiol coupler[1] AGTHIOL[1]
mercurial	thiol	spontaneous	agarose	Affi-Gel 501[2]

([a]) Spontaneous indicates that the gel derivative reacts directly with the ligand. See manufacturer's literature for details of coupling procedures.
([b]) Manufacturers: ([1]) Pharmacia; ([2]) Bio-Rad; see Appendix 3.

successful, gives a freshly activated product, is considerably cheaper and can be performed safely if an efficient fume cupboard is. also available.

The procedure is described for IgG because this molecule is frequently required insolubilized to make both antigen and antibody columns. Other proteins and macromolecules containing primary ami-

211

no groups (e.g. certain carbohydrates and nucleic acids) can also be insolubilized by this method. Antibodies and lectins should be affinity purified before coupling (Sections 10.3.3 and 10.3.4).

Materials and equipment

Sepharose 4B (Pharmacia — Appendix 3) — 10 ml settled volume
0.1 M sodium citrate pH 6.5 — 2 litres cooled to 4°C
IgG (Section 3.3) — 100 mg in 10 ml of the citrate buffer in a screw-capped 25 ml Universal container at 4°C
Cyanogen bromide
0.5 M sodium carbonate pH 10.5
4 M sodium hydroxide
2 M ethanolamine
Phosphate buffered saline (PBS — Appendix 2)
Rotator for Universal container
Vial or bijou bottle (1–5 ml) *with air-tight seal*
Plastic disposable gloves
Efficient fume cupboard containing:
  pH meter
  Magnetic stirrer and 2 cm magnetic flea
  1 M sodium hydroxide — 250 ml in a 500 ml beaker
  Water pump
  2 litre Büchner (side-arm) flask fitted with 200 ml sintered funnel (no. 3 or 4) or Büchner funnel containing Whatman no. 54 filter paper

Procedure

Warning cyanogen bromide is volatile and extremely toxic if inhaled or absorbed through the skin. All equipment that has contacted CNBr should be soaked in 1 M NaOH in a fume cupboard overnight and the cyanide then washed off.
1 Wash the Sepharose by vacuum filtration with 1 litre water to remove preservative (do not allow to dry out completely) and resuspend in water to a total volume of 18 ml in a 50 ml beaker.
2 Add 2 ml carbonate buffer and the magnetic flea. Place the mixture on the magnetic stirrer in the fume cupboard with the pH electrode in the suspension. Check the functioning of the stirrer and pH meter.
3 Don gloves and *carefully* dispense 1.5 g cyanogen bromide into the vial avoiding large particles. (This is accomplished most safely by placing a balance in the fume cupboard. Alternatively, weigh the empty vial and cap, add CNBr to the vial in the fume cupboard and then carefully seal the vial before removing from the fume cupboard for weighing. The stock bottle of cyanogen bromide and spatula should remain in the fume cupboard.)
4 Stir the Sepharose suspension *gently*, monitor its pH and add the

solid CNBr (drop the spatula and empty vial into 1 M NaOH). Keep the pH 10.5–11.0 by adding drops of 4 M NaOH until all the solid CNBr has dissolved and the rate of decrease of pH slows (10–15 min). If the pH goes above 11.5 discard the Sepharose and start again.

5   Filter the mixture in the sintered glass or Büchner funnel and quickly wash the Sepharose with 2 litres of cold citrate buffer (do not allow it to dry out completely). Carefully dispose of the filtrate (contains CNBr).

6   Quickly add the cake of activated Sepharose to the IgG solution and mix gently on the rotator at 4°C overnight (if a rotator is not available stir the mixture *gently* for 1 h and let stand overnight).

7   Add 1 ml ethanolamine solution and continue to mix gently for 1 h to ensure complete removal of active groups.

8   Allow the Sepharose to sediment under gravity, centrifuge the supernatant at 500 *g* for 5 min and determine its absorbance at 280 nm. Calculate the percentage of IgG not bound to Sepharose (Table 1.1) — assume total volume of supernatant is 11 ml (protein solution + ethanolamine) plus 5 ml (accessible volume of 10 ml Sepharose). The value should be less than 10% and is usually 1–5%.

9   Pack the IgG-Sepharose into a suitable column (disposable syringe barrels fitted with a sintered disc are convenient) and wash with PBS. The column should be stored at 4°C in PBS containing 0.1% sodium azide.

Notes

1   The optimal pH for coupling is much higher than 6.5 (above the pKa of the amino groups). However, at higher pH the coupling is so efficient that each protein molecule is held by many covalent bonds and this leads to deformation of protein structure with consequent loss of activity (Section 10.2, note 3b). The lower pH allows coupling of most of the protein usually without appreciable damage. Buffers other than citrate can be used providing they do not contain amino groups.

2   Sepharose 4B is a suitable support for most applications (see Section 10.2) but Macrobeads (Pharmacia — Appendix 3) should be used for fractionating cells and other particles. Sepharose CL-4B provides greater chemical and mechanical stability and although its crossed-linked structure theoretically reduces its capacity for binding ligand, in practice no decrease in the binding of up to 10 mg protein per ml of gel has been observed.

3   A final concentration of 2–10 mg protein bound to each ml Sepharose is suitable for most applications (Section 10.2, note 3).

4   The protein–Sepharose bonds may break slowly and although the complex can be used for many years, leaching of the protein is sometimes evident and should be monitored. The complex should be washed with the buffer that is to be used to elute the bound molecules before its first use and again after any long periods of disuse. The ligand or the beads may be degraded by proteases or glycosidases

213

present in some crude extracts.

5   Certain proteins (e.g. occasional monoclonal antibodies and some enzymes) lose a significant amount of activity upon coupling. This is presumably caused by an unfortunately highly reactive nucleophilic group in the active site which is quickly derivitized. To overcome this, temporarily block the active site during coupling (only feasible for enzymes with a competitive inhibitor and lectins with the appropriate sugar); decrease the cyanogen bromide concentration (down to 1/5 is still effective) or couple through a different functional group (Table 10.2).

10.2.2   Preparation of *Staphylococcus aureus* adsorbent

Some strains of *Staphylococcus aureus* synthesize Protein A, a group-specific ligand which binds to the Fc region of IgG from many species (Table 10.3). A protein from some strains of group C and group G Streptococci also binds to IgG Fc with some differences in species specificity from Protein A (Table 10.3), notably its improved binding to rat, sheep, cow, horse, goat and worse binding to cat. Protein A is very useful in affinity chromatography (e.g. see Section 10.3.2) and is the usual means of binding antibodies in immunoprecipitation (Section 10.4). It can be isolated from the culture supernatants of strains which secrete it and then insolubilized by coupling to agarose beads (Section 10.2.1); such a preparation is also available commercially (Pharmacia — Appendix 3). However, for immunoprecipitation, it is more expedient to use whole bacteria of a strain which carry large amounts of Protein A on their surface. If facilities are available for the safe culture of these pathogenic organisms, they can be grown and then killed and fixed (Kessler, 1975) as described below to provide a very cheap means of insolubilizing IgG. Such preparations are also available commercially (Pansorbin, Calbiochem; IgGsorb, Enzyme Center — Appendix 3).

Materials and equipment

Staphylococcus aureus, Cowan 1 strain, 10 g packed cells
Phosphate buffered saline (Appendix 2) containing 0.1% sodium azide
    (PBS-azide)
Formaldehyde 37–40% (w/v)
High-speed centrifuge with capped 50 ml tubes
2 litre conical flask
Heated water bath to hold the flask
Sodium hypochlorite solution (Chloros, ICI — Appendix 3)

Procedure

Warning   these organisms are pathogenic and this procedure should only be used if facilities are available for their safe

214

Table 10.3 Bacterial protein binding activities of immunoglobulins. These proteins bind to the Fc portion and so the interaction varies between species, and classes and subclasses within a species. Where the binding is given for a class this represents the composite binding of individual subclasses if they exist. For further information see Richman *et al.* (1982); Reis *et al.* (1986)

Immunoglobulin	Protein A[1]	C and G[2]
human IgG1	+	+
IgG2	+	+
IgG3	−	+
IgG4	+	+
IgM	±	
IgA1	−	
IgA2	±	
IgD	−	
IgE	−	
mouse IgG1	±	+
IgG2a	+	+
IgG2b	+	
IgG3	−	+
IgM	−	
IgA	−	
IgE	−	
rabbit IgG	+	+
rat IgG1	±	±
IgG2a	−	+
IgG2b	−	+
IgG2c	+	+
cat IgG	+	−
chicken IgG	−	−
cow IgG1	−	+
IgG2	+	+
dog IgG	+	+
goat IgG1	−	+
IgG2	±	+
guinea-pig IgG	+	+
hamster IgG	±	±
horse IgGa	+	+
IgGb	+	+
IgGc	−	+
pig IgG	+	+
sheep IgG1	−	+
IgG2	+	+

[1] *Staphylococcus aureus* Protein A — available as pure protein (Pharmacia), insolubilized (Bio-Rad, Pharmacia) and radiolabelled (Amersham) — Appendix 3.

[2] Surface protein of group C and group G *Streptococci* — available radiolabelled (Amersham) and insolubilized (Perstorp) — Appendix 3.

handling. All equipment that has contacted live bacteria should be soaked in Chloros.

1 Resuspend the bacteria in PBS-azide to a total volume of 100 ml using a glass rod to homogenize the mixture. Transfer to centrifuge tubes, cap and centrifuge at 5000 *g* for 10 min at 20°C.

2   Discard the supernatant (into Chloros) and repeat step 1.

3   Resuspend the final bacterial pellet in PBS-azide to a total volume of 100 ml, add 5 ml stock formaldehyde and stir at room temperature for 1.5 h. Heat water bath to 80°C.

4   Centrifuge as in step 1. Discard the supernatant (into Chloros) and resuspend the bacterial pellet in PBS-azide to a total volume of 100 ml in the 2 litre flask.

5   Swirl the flask rapidly in the 80°C water bath for 5 min so that a thin layer of bacterial suspension is heated thoroughly. Cool rapidly in an ice bath with swirling.

6   Wash the bacteria twice by centrifugation (step 1) and resuspension in PBS-azide.

7   The final heat-killed, formalin-fixed bacteria can be kept in 10% (v/v) suspension at 4°C for several months or aliquoted at −70°C for longer periods.

10.3   AFFINITY CHROMATOGRAPHY FRACTIONATION

The second of the two basic requirements of affinity chromatography (Section 10.1) is an effective means of dissociating the complex formed. This has been approached in many different ways. The methods currently used fall into three broad categories depending on the strength of the binding and the nature of the interacting molecules:

1   *True chromatography* — the soluble molecule is bound specifically but can be dissociated and eluted by continued washing with the starting buffer. This procedure is only applicable in a very few situations with low affinity binding.

2   *Specific elution* — the bound molecule is eluted by competitive binding of a second small molecule either to itself or to the insoluble ligand. This procedure is applicable in several cases (Section 10.3.4, 10.3.5 and 10.3.6) and theoretically yields a purer product by leaving non-specifically bound molecules attached to the insoluble derivative. A disadvantage is that the competitive molecule must be removed from the insoluble ligand or the molecule of interest before further experimentation.

3   *Disruptive elution* — the bound molecule is eluted by disrupting the non-covalent bonds with a general dissociating agent (Table 10.4). This procedure has the disadvantage of exposing both the insolubilized ligand and the molecule being fractionated to denaturing conditions; the dissociating agent should be removed quickly. However, it is used frequently because of lack of an alternative.

A variation of methods 2 and 3 employs a gradient of increasing concentration of dissociating agent to elute separately several bound molecules from the insolubilized ligand, thus improving the resolving power of the fractionation (for example, see Section 10.3.2). If the bound molecules cannot be eluted easily from the column and a large amount of hydrophobic binding is suspected (e.g. non-specific binding

216

Table 10.4 Dissociating agents used for eluting antibody–antigen affinity columns. The agents are listed roughly in increasing order of denaturing properties. The last three will denature most proteins to some extent and may cause leaching of the ligand from the insoluble support

high salt
10% (v/v) dioxan
25% (v/v) ethylene glycol
3 M potassium thiocyanate
0.1 M sodium borate pH 10
0.05 M diethylamine pH 11.5
0.1 M glycine HCl pH 2.5
1 M propionic acid
8 M urea
5 M guanidine HCl
1% (w/v) sodium dodecylsulphate

by a spacer arm, Section 10.2, or specific binding within an antigen–antibody complex), the specific eluant or dissociating agent can be made 25% (v/v) in ethylene glycol or 10% (v/v) in dioxan to decrease this interaction.

The specificity of both the binding and elution can be improved by the design of the fractionation protocol. Thus, before use, the insolubilized derivative should be washed with the agents which are to be used subsequently for eluting bound molecules. This minimizes contamination of the eluted molecules by ligand leaching off the support or even by molecules bound to the ligand and not completely eluted during previous fractionations. In addition, crude mixtures (e.g. sera, cell extracts) should first be passed through a control blank column consisting of the insoluble support (e.g. agarose beads) coupled to a ligand structurally similar to, but with different binding properties from, the one used in the actual fractionation. For example, a suitable blank column before a mouse monoclonal antibody-agarose column is normal pooled mouse immunoglubulin-agarose. This procedure will remove molecules from the crude mixture which would stick non-specifically to either the insoluble support or the ligand.

The capacity of an affinity column is difficult to predict accurately (approximate values are given for individual examples in the appropriate Sections). In a novel fractionation, analyse the unretarded pool for overflow of bound molecules or reapply it to the column after regeneration. As a general guide, apply samples and elute at a rate of 4 column volumes/h at room temperature and do not stop the flow throughout the entire procedure. Use a slower flow at lower temperatures for low affinity interactions, or recycle the eluant back through the column using a pump. The column should be washed with 5–10 column volumes of buffer after application of the sample before elution with the dissociating agent.

A sophisticated column is not necessary for affinity chromatography. A perfectly satisfactory one can be made from the barrel of a disposable syringe fitted with a disc cut from a sheet of sintered polythene, Vyon (Porvair — Appendix 3), to support the gel (use a large pore support, 80 μm, for chromatography of cells). Alternatively, small columns are available commercially (Bio-Rad, Wright — Appendix 3).

Most affinity fractionation procedures can also be carried out by batch methods instead of on a column. Such modification is useful for very small-scale separations to prevent excessive dilution of the unbound fraction (e.g. adsorption of small volumes of antisera, Section 10.3.1). Compare analytical immunoprecipitation (Section 10.4).

10.3.1 Immunoadsorption and purification of antibodies

Insolubilized antigens will bind specifically the corresponding antibodies. This interaction can be used either to purify the antibody activity required or to remove unwanted antibody activity from a heterogeneous antiserum (immunoadsorption). A micro-scale version uses the antigen fixed onto nitrocellulose from an immunoblot (Section 8.4.3) to purify the corresponding antibody (see note 4 below). In the example below, antisera against IgM are fractionated into anti-(μ chain) and anti-(light chain) activities because only the latter will bind IgG (see Table 3.2 for immunoglobulin structure).

Materials and equipment

Rabbit antiserum to human IgM — 10 ml
Human pooled IgG (50 mg) coupled to 5 ml Sepharose 4B packed into a column (Section 10.2.1)
20 mM sodium phosphate pH 7.3 containing 0.5 M sodium chloride
0.5 M ammonium hydroxide containing 3 M potassium thiocyanate
Column chromatography equipment (Section 1.2.1)

Procedure

1 Wash the column with 10 ml phosphate buffer, 5 ml thiocyanate solution and 20 ml phosphate buffer.
2 Apply the antiserum at approximately 20 ml/h, monitor the absorbance of the eluant at 280 nm and collect 2 ml fractions.
3 Wash through with phosphate buffer until the absorbance returns to baseline.
4 Elute the column with 10 ml thiocyanate solution followed by 20 ml phosphate buffer.
5 The unretarded pool is antisera made specific for IgM (i.e. μ-chain and possibly J chain; Table 3.2); the pool eluted by thiocyanate consists of pure antibody molecules with anti-(light chain) activity (Fig. 10.3).

218

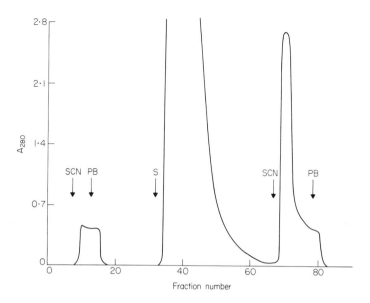

Fig. 10.3 Fractionation of rabbit anti-(human IgM) serum on an affinity column (5 ml) of human IgG coupled to Sepharose CL-4B (Section 10.3.1). Fraction size was 2 ml. The column was pre-eluted with 3 M potassium thiocyanate in 0.5 M ammonium hydroxide (SCN) and washed well with 20 mM sodium phosphate pH 7.3 containing 0.5 M sodium chloride (PB). The antiserum was then applied (S) and washed through with phosphate buffer to give antiserum made specific for IgM (i.e. no anti-(light chain) activity). The column was then eluted with the thiocyanate solution (SCN) to yield pure anti-(light chain) antibodies and then washed back into phosphate buffer. The thiocyanate solution absorbs at 280 nm.

6 Dialyse the thiocyanate eluant against PBS and determine the yield from its absorbance at 280 nm assuming it is mostly IgG (Table 1.1).

Notes

1 The fractions should be analysed for activity by double immuno-diffusion (Section 6.3.1) or radioimmunoassay (Chapter 11) and for protein composition by polyacrylamide gel electrophoresis (Section 7.3.1). The column described is capable of binding antibody from up to 50 ml antiserum; if its capacity is exceeded, anti-(light chain) activity will be detectable in the later fractions of the unretarded peak. Greater than 80% of the pool eluted by thiocyanate should be immunoglobu-lin; this figure can be improved by use of a suitable blank adsorbent (e.g. albumin-agarose) before the specific adsorption (Section 10.3).
2 The alkaline thiocyanate is an efficient disrupter of most antibody–antigen complexes and it does not destroy the antibody's complement fixing ability. Alternative dissociating agents include the milder 0.05 M diethylamine pH 11.5 or 1 M propionic acid which is a more efficient disrupter of the complexes but which partially denatures proteins (it

219

should be neutralized with tris as it elutes from the column). Any aggregated protein can be removed by gel filtration of the eluant on Sephadex G-200 in PBS.

3   Monoclonal antibodies can be purified from culture supernatants or ascitic fluid by this procedure. However, because of their molecular homogeneity, they can be purified simply by isolating the class of immunoglobulin to which they belong (Section 3.3.1, note 3; Section 3.5, note 5; Section 10.3.2) unless the starting material contains substantial amounts of other immunoglobulins (e.g. media containing normal serum or ascitic fluid contaminated with serum).

4   (Courtesy of Phil Robinson). Antibodies can be isolated on a small scale using antigens purified by polyacrylamide gel electrophoresis, usually in SDS, and then immobilized on nitrocellulose. Electrophorese the mixture containing the antigen of interest and transfer to nitrocellulose membrane (Section 8.4.3). Identify the position of the antigen by staining an edge strip of the membrane (Section 8.4.3, note 6) and cut out an *unstained* area of membrane containing the antigen. Block, incubate with antiserum and wash as in Section 8.4.3, steps 7–9. Elute the bound antibody with either 0.1 M glycine HCl pH 2.5, 0.5 M NaCl or 0.05 M diethylamine pH 11.5, 0.5 M NaCl by shaking for 2–5 min. Neutralize immediately and dialyse against PBS. If elution is incomplete, dissociate for longer or use any of the harsher agents in Table 10.4.

10.3.2   Fractionation of IgG into subclasses; isolation of mouse IgG monoclonals

Mouse IgG comprises four major subclasses (designated IgGl, IgG2a, IgG2b and IgG3) which differ in their heavy chain constant region structure. They also differ in the affinity of binding to Protein A (Table 10.3) and they can be separated by affinity chromatography on insolubilized Protein A. This procedure uses the specificity of binding to remove non-IgG contaminants (and IgG3) and then the bound subclasses are eluted separately by different pH buffers (Ey *et al.*, 1978). It is difficult to purify mouse IgG (Section 3.3.1) and this affinity procedure can be used to isolate the majority of IgG directly from serum (or ascitic fluid or culture supernatants in monoclonal antibody techniques). For rat monoclonals see notes 1 and 4 below.

Materials and equipment

All at 4°C (the sodium citrate buffers can be made from the stock
    0.1 M citric acid by addition of NaOH)
Protein A coupled to Sepharose CL-4B (Section 10.2.1 or Pharmacia
    — Appendix 3) — 1 ml containing 2 mg protein
Normal mouse serum — 1 ml
2 M tris base

220

0.1 M sodium phosphate pH 8.0 containing 0.02% sodium azide

0.1 M citric acid

0.1 M sodium citrate pH 6.0

0.1 M sodium citrate pH 4.5

0.1 M sodium citrate pH 3.5

Phosphate buffered saline (PBS — Appendix 2)

Column chromatography equipment (Section 1.2.1) including a 2 ml column (Section 10.3).

Procedure

All at 4°C

1   Pack the swollen gel into the column and wash with 5 ml 0.1 M phosphate buffer, 2 ml citric acid solution and 5 ml 0.1 M phosphate buffer.

2   Bring the pH of the serum to 8.0 by adding tris base. Add 1 ml 0.1 M phosphate buffer, mix and apply to the Protein A column at approximately 5 ml/h. Collect 0.5 ml fractions and monitor the absorbance at 280 nm.

3   Wash with 5 ml 0.1 M phosphate buffer. The unretarded fraction contains non-immunoglobulin components together with IgA, IgM and IgG3.

4   Elute with 5 ml citrate buffer pH 6.0 to obtain IgG1.

5   Place 60 μl 2 M tris in the next 20 empty fraction collector tubes. Elute with 5 ml citrate buffer pH 4.5 to obtain IgG2a.

6   Elute with 5 ml citrate buffer pH 3.5 to obtain IgG2b.

7   Wash the column with 2 ml citric acid solution and then 5 ml 0.1 M phosphate buffer. Dialyse the eluted fractions against PBS.

Notes

1   This procedure can also be used to isolate monoclonal antibodies from culture supernatants or ascitic fluid (alternatively see Section 3.3.1, note 3). In general 1 mg of Protein A is capable of binding 10 mg of IgG (the value varies from batch to batch and between species). As a rough guide and allowing a safety factor of 2, 2 mg protein A on 1 ml Sepharose is capable of adsorbing the IgG from 1 ml serum, 1 ml ascitic fluid or 250 ml culture supernatant (if the media contained only immunoglubulin-free serum). Removal of lipids from ascites fluid improves the separation (Neoh *et al.*, 1986). For rat monoclonals use group C or group G *Streptococci* surface protein (Table 10.3).

2   The procedure also allows the subclass of a particular monoclonal antibody to be determined (compare analytical techniques, and Section 2.3.5).

3   IgM and IgG3 can be obtained in the unretarded pool when partially purified preparations (Section 3.3.1, note 3; Section 3.5, note 5) are applied to Protein A-Sepharose. Alternative affinity chroma-

221

tography procedures involve affinity purified (Section 10.3.1) insolubilized antibodies (Section 10.3.3) against IgM, IgG or light chain. In addition insolubilized protamine sulphate (10 mg) binds pentameric IgM (2 mg) through the Fc_μ region if applied in 1/4 dilution of PBS (or serum) and left in contact for several hours (i.e. low affinity). The IgM is displaced by 0.1 M sodium phosphate pH 7.5 containing 1 M sodium chloride.

4   A similar procedure can be used to fractionate IgG subclasses from other species (Table 10.3). It is advisable to apply a continuous pH gradient (use equal volumes of 0.1 M sodium phosphate pH 8.0 and 0.1 M citric acid in the mixing chambers of a gradient maker — Fig. 1.3) to elute the IgG from uncharacterized species. For convenience, a stepwise elution can then be devised from these initial calibration data. The surface protein of group C or group G *Streptococci* may be better than Protein A for some species (Table 10.3), e.g. rat.

5   Bio-Rad (Appendix 3) sell a set of buffers (MAPS) which is claimed to improve the fractionation, especially the binding of IgG1 to Protein A thus increasing its recovery. Alternatively substitution of a high salt buffer (3 M NaCl, 0.1 M sodium glycine pH 8.9) for the phosphate buffer used to apply the sample in step 2 also increases binding of most IgG1 antibodies (Pharmacia literature).

10.3.3   Insolubilized antibodies

Antibodies form a group of ligands with both the highest degree of selectivity (manifested practically by monoclonal antibodies) and the greatest potential range of specificity (they can be produced against anything in the biological world). They are therefore involved in a large proportion of affinity chromatography applications.

Ideally the antibody should itself be affinity purified (Section 10.3.1) before insolubilization to produce a more effective column with high capacity and low non-specific binding. At the very least the IgG should be isolated from conventional antisera (Section 3.3.1) but only 5–20% of this will have antibody activity. Simple procedures (Section 3.3.1, notes 1 and 3; Section 3.5, note 5; Section 10.3.2) applied to hybridoma supernatants will provide monoclonal antibodies (of various classes) of sufficient purity providing the culture media contained only immunoglobulin-free serum.

The example below involves the fractionation of a simple mixture of molecules to illustrate the technique. It gives a purer product than the alternative separation by ion exchange chromatography (Section 3.4.2). Insolubilized antibodies have been used to purify a single molecule from a complex mixture in one step (Fig. 10.4; Sunderland *et al.*, 1979).

Materials and equipment

Papain digested human IgG (Section 3.4.2, step 1) — 10 mg

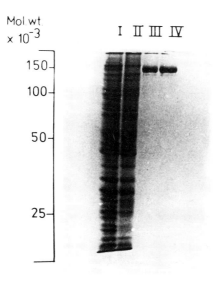

Mol. wt.
× 10⁻³

I II III IV

150
100
50
25

Fig. 10.4 Purification of leucocyte-common antigen from rat thymocyte membrane using a column of monoclonal antibody (MRC OX1) coupled to Sepharose 4B. The fractions were analysed by polyacrylamide gel electrophoresis in SDS and stained for protein. I, thymocyte membrane solubilized in 0.5% sodium deoxycholate; II, membrane extract unretarded by the affinity column and eluted with deoxycholate buffer; III, material bound to the affinity column and eluted with 0.05 M diethylamine pH 11.5 in deoxycholate; IV, eluted material further purified by gel filtration on Sephadex G-200 in deoxycholate. The monoclonal antibody affinity column provided a 100-fold purification with a 50% yield. Reproduced from Sunderland *et al.* (1979) with permission.

Affinity purified rabbit anti-(human light chain) antibody (Section 10.3.1) — 10 mg coupled to 1 ml Sepharose 4B (Section 10.2.1) and packed into a 2 ml column
20 mM sodium phosphate pH 7.3 containing 0.5 M sodium chloride
0.5 M ammonium hydroxide containing 3 M potassium thiocyanate
Column chromatography equipment (Section 1.2.1)

Procedure

1   Wash the antibody column with 2 ml phosphate buffer, 2 ml thiocyanate solution and 5 ml phosphate buffer.
2   Dialyse the digest against 500 ml phosphate buffer and set up the apparatus to collect 0.5 ml fractions and to monitor the absorbance at 280 nm.
3   Apply the digest to the column and elute with phosphate buffer at approximately 4 ml/h until the absorbance returns to baseline.
4   Elute with 2 ml thiocyanate solution followed by 5 ml phosphate buffer.
5   The unretarded pool is pure Fc fragment (and papain); the pool eluted by thiocyanate is mostly Fab with some undigested IgG. Dialyse

223

the latter pool against PBS and purify the Fab by gel filtration on Sephadex G-100 (fine) in PBS.

Notes

1 See Section 10.3.1, note 2.
2 Lower affinity antibodies or lower temperatures may require a longer interaction time. Recycle the eluant in step 3 back through the column using a pump for 16 h.
3 Insolubilized antibodies can also be used in detergents (up to 2% Nonidet P40, 0.5% deoxycholate, 0.05% sodium dodecyl sulphate, Tables 4.3 and 4.4). Complex mixtures (e.g. cell extracts) should be passed through an appropriate blank adsorbent column first (Section 10.3).

10.3.4 Insolubilized lectins

Lectins are a remarkable group of proteins, obtained mostly from plants and lower orders of animals, which interact specifically with certain sugars or groups of sugars (for review see Sharon, 1983). They are somewhere between group-specific ligands and antibodies, having an affinity for many different molecules including carbohydrate, glycoproteins and glycolipids, and also cells which carry these structures. Their binding affinity for macromolecules is generally lower than antibodies and for the free sugar is lower still. This property allows the bound macromolecules to be eluted specifically from insolubilized lectins by an excess of free competing sugar (usually 0.1–0.25 M or 2–5%) which can then be removed by washing with buffer.

There is a large variety of lectins (Table 10.5), most of which can be isolated from cheap starting material and many are commercially available so that one with the required binding specificity can usually be found. Two carbohydrate structures commonly found in glycoproteins and glycolipids are shown in Fig. 10.5. To test for which lectin will interact with the molecule of interest, separate the mixture by polyacrylamide gel electrophoresis and stain the electrophoretogram with various radioiodinated lectins (Chapter 8) or use crossed immunoelectrophoresis (Section 6.4.6). As for antibodies, it is advisable to include an affinity chromatography step in the isolation of lectins to ensure the purification of functionally active molecules. For example, concanavalin A and *Lens culinaris* lectin bind to Sephadex G-50 (medium) and are specifically eluted by 5% glucose. The glucose can either be removed by dialysis or the lectin–glucose complex coupled to agarose beads (the sugar will protect the binding site) and the glucose removed by washing.

Insolubilized lectins have been very useful in the isolation of cell surface glycoproteins (see, for example, Crumpton & Snary, 1977). Like antibodies, most insolubilized lectins retain their binding activity

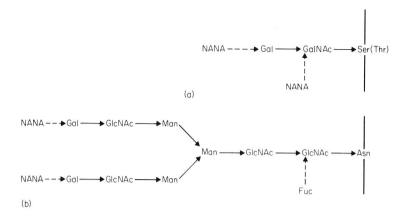

Fig. 10.5 The carbohydrate structures commonly present in glycoproteins. (a) O-glycosydically linked serine or threonine. (b) N-glycosydically linked asparagine.

in low concentrations of non-ionic or mildly ionic detergents (Section 10.3.3, note 3) and the latter (e.g. deoxycholate) have the advantage of decreasing non-specific binding. The example below describes the fractionation of detergent solubilized lymphocytes. The majority of glycoprotein in this preparation is derived from the plasma membrane and the technique provides dramatic purification of these cell surface molecules. The procedure is similar for any other membrane preparation on the insolubilized lectin of your choice although the optimal pH and ionic strength depends on the individual lectin.

Materials and equipment

1 ml *Lens culinaris* lectin-Sepharose 4B (Pharmacia — Appendix 3, or isolate the lectin from common lentils (Howard *et al.*, 1971) and couple to Sepharose, 5 mg/ml, Section 10.2.1)

10^8 lymphocytes (Section 4.2) radioiodinated (100 μCi) using lactoperoxidase (Section 5.2.3) and solubilized in 1 ml 1% Nonidet P40 *without* EGTA (Section 4.4.2)

2 ml column (Section 10.3)

1 M sodium chloride

0.5% (w/v) Nonidet P40 in phosphate buffered saline (Appendix 2)

2% (w/v) α-methyl mannoside in the detergent buffer

Fraction collector

Gamma counter

Protein assay compatible with Nonidet P40 (Sections 1.1.2 and 4.4.1)

Procedure

1   Pack the insolubilized lectin into the column and wash with 2 ml

225

Table 10.5 Properties of some common lectins[a]

Common name	Source	Carbohydrate specificity[b]	Molecular weight ($\times 10^{-3}$)[c]	Glycoprotein	Metal ion requirement[d]	
concanavalin A	*Canavalia ensiformis* (jack bean)	α-D-Man α-D-Glc α-D-GlcNAc	104	No	Mn^{2+}	Ca^{2+}
lentil lectin	*Lens culinaris* (lentil)	α-D-Man α-D-Glc } + Fuc α-D-GlcNAc	42–63	Yes	Mn^{2+}	Ca^{2+}
phytohaemagglutinin (leucoagglutinin)	*Phaseolus vulgaris* (red kidney bean)	GlcNAcβ1→2Man	126	Yes	Mn^{2+}	Ca^{2+}
phytohaemagglutinin (erythroagglutinin)	*Phaseolus vulgaris* (red kidney bean)	β-D-Gal-GlcNAc	126	Yes	Mn^{2+}	Ca^{2+}
wheat germ agglutinin	*Triticum vulgaris* (wheat germ)	GlcNAcβ1→4GlcNAc GlcNAc NeuNAc	36	No	Mn^{2+} Zn^{2+}	Ca^{2+}
soybean agglutinin	*Glycine max* (soybean)	α-D-GalNAc β-D-GalNAc	120	Yes	Mn^{2+}	Ca^{2+}
helix pomatia lectin	*Helix pomatia* (garden snail)	D-GalNAc D-GlcNAc	79			
peanut agglutinin	*Arachis hypogaea* (peanut)	β-D-Gal	110	No		
ricin$_{60}$	*Ricinus communis* (castor bean)	GalNAc β-D-Gal	60	Yes		
ricin$_{120}$	*Ricinus communis* (castor bean)	β-D-Gal α-D-Gal	120	Yes		

Species	Carbohydrate specificity	M	Requirement	Mn	Ca
Bandieraea simplicifolia	α-D-Gal β-D-GalNAc	114	Yes	Mn^{2+}	Ca^{2+}
Dolichos biflorus (horse gram)	α-D-GalNAc	111	Yes		
Pisum sativum (garden pea)	α-D-Man α-D-Glc } + Fuc	50	Yes	Mn^{2+}	Ca^{2+}
Sophora japonica	β-D-GalNAc β-D-Gal α-D-Gal	133			
Ulex europaeus (common gorse)	α-D-Fuc GlcNAcβ1→4GlcNAc	31–65	Yes		
Phytolacca americana (pokeweed) pokeweed mitogen		$(22)_n$ and 19–31	Yes		
Lotus tetragonolobus	L-Fuc	58–120			
Wistaria floribunda	D-GalNAc	67–136			
Limulus polyphemus (horseshoe crab)	NeuNAc	335			
Phaseolus limensis (lima bean)	αGalNAc	130–270			
Vicia villosa	GalNAcα1→3Gal				

(a) Most of these lectins are available from BDH, Vector, Pharmacia or Sigma (Appendix 3).
(b) Where more than one carbohydrate group is given, these are listed in decreasing order of affinity. Lectins often have a higher affinity for methyl glucosides and oligosaccharides than the simple sugars shown.
(c) Lectins are virtually all composed of several sub-units.
(d) Blanks do not necessarily mean that there is no requirement.

227

1 M NaCl, 2 ml α-methyl mannoside solution and 10 ml Nonidet P40 solution.

2 Apply the detergent solubilized cells to the lectin column and elute with 5 ml Nonidet P40 solution at approximately 2 ml/h at 4°C. Collect 1 ml fractions.

3 Elute with 4 ml α-methyl mannoside solution followed by 10 ml Nonidet P40 solution, at 4°C.

4 Take 100 μl aliquots of each fraction for assay of protein and count the radioactivity present in the remainder both before and after precipitation with ethanol (Section 7.1.5). The profile obtained is shown in Fig. 10.6 and pools analysed by polyacrylamide gel electrophoresis in Fig. 10.7.

Notes

1 UV absorbance (Section 1.1.1) can be used for protein detection if deoxycholate is used instead of Nonidet P40 (Section 4.4.1). The ^{125}I serves as a marker for cell surface molecules (Section 5.2.3).

2 *Lens culinaris* lectin (and many other lectins; Table 10.5) require Ca^{2+} and Mn^{2+} for activity but their affinity for these ions is high and the chromatography buffer need not contain divalent cations. However, chelators like EDTA and EGTA will destroy the lectins' activity.

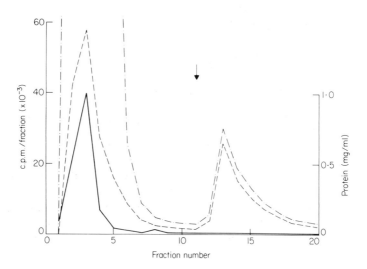

Fig. 10.6 Fractionation of lactoperoxidase radioiodinated lymphocytes solubilized in 1% Nonidet P40 on a column of lentil lectin coupled to Sepharose 4B (Section 10.3.4). The extract was applied and washed with detergent solution and the column eluted with competitive sugar (2% α-methyl mannoside) at the arrow. ——— protein detected by supernatant of Lowry assay (Section 1.1.2); —·—·— total c.p.m. fractions; — — — ethanol precipitable c.p.m. (i.e. protein-bound) in fractions. Greater than 95% of protein is not bound by the lectin column. Approximately 50% of iodinated (cell surface) proteins are bound by the column and specifically eluted with sugar (i.e. glycosylated). None of the ethanol soluble c.p.m. (i.e. free ^{125}I) are bound by the column. The labelled polypeptides of the two fractions are compared in Fig. 10.7.

228

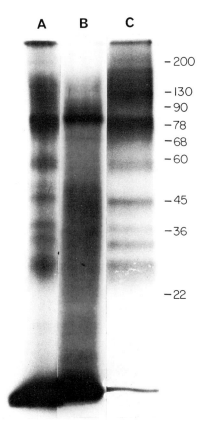

Fig. 10.7 Autoradiography of polyacrylamide gel electrophoresis in SDS (tris-bicine system, 7.5%; Section 7.3.1, method ii) of fractions from Fig. 10.6. A, unfractionated lymphocytes; B, unretarded pool (fractions 2–6); C, retarded and specifically eluted pool (fractions 12–16). The positions of marker proteins of known molecular weight ($\times$ 10^{-3}) are indicated on the right. The major labelled polypeptide chain in the lymphocytes (80 000 molecular weight, track A) is not retarded by the lectin column (track B) but most of the remaining surface-labelled molecules are bound (track C).

3   Several commercial batches of insolubilized lectins have been observed to release free lectin slowly into solution. The high salt wash (step 1) reduces but does not totally alleviate this problem.

4   As a rough guide, 1 mg of lectin will bind up to 1 mg of glycoprotein, but it is advisable to test the column's capacity by reapplying the unretarded fraction (Section 10.3).

5   If bound molecules are not completely eluted by competiton with sugar, the following agents may be tried together with the sugar: 1 M KCl, 25% (v/v) ethylene glycol, 10% (v/v) dioxan, 0.05 M diethylamine pH 11.5, 1 mM EDTA, 6 M urea, 1% (w/v) sodium dodecyl sulphate. The last three will denature the lectin and possibly induce leaching from the insoluble support.

6   Chromatography of detergent solubilized plasma membrane on insolubilized lectin followed by specific insolubilized antibody can yield very pure cell surface molecules (Crumpton & Snary, 1977).

229

10.3.5 Insolubilized boronic acid (courtesy of Dr. G. Williams)

Phenylboronic acid is a group-specific ligand that binds various sugars containing appropriately oriented hydroxyls to the borate ion. Hydrophobic interactions with the phenyl ring are also evident. Bound molecules can be displaced by competition with free sugar (cf. lectins, Section 10.3.4) and 10% dioxan will disrupt the hydrophobic interactions.

   Phenylboronic acid can be purchased coupled to cellulose, polyacrylamide or agarose (Uniscience, Bio-Rad, Amicon — Appendix 3) and used to fractionate nucleotides, ribonucleic acids, glycoproteins and other sugar-containing molecules, The example below describes the fractionation of detergent solubilized erythrocyte membrane because this is easily obtained; the procedure can be applied to most molecules with minor modifications.

Materials and equipment

0.5% (w/v) sodium deoxycholate in 10 mM morpholine-HCl pH 9.0
Erythrocyte membrane (200 μg) solubilized in the deoxycholate buffer
   (Section 4.4.3) and radioiodinated (100 μCi) using Chloramine T
   (Section 5.2.1)
2 ml chromatography column (Section 10.3)
Phenylboronic acid agarose (Amicon — Appendix 3) — 1 ml
0.1 M sorbitol in the deoxycholate buffer
10% (v/v) dioxan in the sorbitol-deoxycholate buffer
Column chromatography equipment (Section 1.2.1) including fraction
   collector
Gamma counter

Procedure

1   Pack the phenylboronic agarose into the column and wash with 2 ml sorbitol-deoxycholate buffer, 2 ml dioxan solution and 5 ml deoxycholate buffer.
2   Apply the solubilized membrane and elute with 5 ml deoxycholate buffer at a flow rate of 1 ml/h at 4°C. Collect 1 ml fractions.
3   Elute with 5 ml sorbitol solution followed by 5 ml dioxan solution, at 4°C, and wash the column back into the deoxycholate buffer (at least 10 ml) for re-use.
4   Take 10–100 μl aliquots from each fraction, precipitate the protein with ethanol (Section 7.1.5) and measure its radioactivity.

Notes

1   The ^{125}I serves as a simple label for small amounts of protein (the capacity of phenylboronic-agarose is lower than that of lectin-agarose in the deoxycholate buffer). If larger preparations are carried out the

protein can be detected by UV absorbance or other assay (Sections 1.1.1–1.1.3).

2 In the example given, proteins are bound through hydroxyls and by hydrophobic forces. The hydrophobic interactions can be decreased by including 10% dioxan in the buffers throughout the fractionation. Tris interferes with binding of hydroxyls. Deoxycholate is better than non-ionic detergents at decreasing other non-specific interactions.

10.3.6   Affinity chromatography of cells

Cells can be fractionated by several physical methods that use the specific interaction between determinants on the cell surface and added ligand. For example, B lymphocytes (and some other cells) bind to nylon fibre and human T lymphocytes to sheep erythrocytes (Sections 4.3.1 and 4.3.2). The binding is more specific if lectins or antibodies are used. Such ligands can be insolubilized (using large agarose beads to avoid trapping cells; Section 10.2) and used to fractionate cells by affinity chromatography.

Unfortunately the interaction between a multi-determinant cell and antibody insolubilized on a solid support is of such high avidity (Section 6.1.1) that it is difficult to dissociate the complex without damaging the cell. However, insolubilized antibodies can be used to remove unwanted cell populations. The least damaging approach to dissociating bound cells is by competitive binding. Thus, B lymphocytes can be specifically bound by insolubilizing antibodies against IgG because of their surface light chain. They can subsequently be recovered from the column by elution with a suitable culture medium containing 20 mg/ml IgG (or neat serum). Unfortunately this method is not generally applicable because of the lack of appropriate competing soluble antigen.

The technique can be modified for use with most antibodies by using insolubilized Protein A or appropriate second antibody (Pharmacia, Bio-Rad — Appendix 3) to adsorb cells which have previously been coated with specific antibody (cf. flow microfluorimetry, Section 12.2.2). The bound cells can be eluted from the column by competition with 20 mg/ml IgG or neat serum from appropriate species (Ghetie et al., 1978). There may be non-specific binding caused by Fc receptors on the surface of some cells. The antibodies coating the cells are removed by culturing for 6 h.

Alternatively, cells can be bound specifically by antibody or $F(ab')_2$ fragments coupled to erythrocytes (Section 4.3.3). The bound cells are separated by centrifugation as rosettes and the erythrocytes lysed (Section 4.2.4). This procedure leaves $F(ab')_2$ molecules and fragments of erythrocyte membrane attached to the cells.

Insolubilized lectins are somewhat better than insolubilized antibodies for cellular fractionation, in that bound cells can be dissociated by competition with the appropriate sugar. However, the removal is

231

usually not complete (presumably because of the high avidity associated with the multivalency of the cells) and consequently cell recovery is low. This drawback and the expense of (usually rare) lectin means that the procedure is only practical for small scale isolations. Lectins coupled to Macrobeads are commercially available (Pharmacia — Appendix 3). *Helix pomatia* lectin binds to neuraminidase treated T cells but not B lymphocytes (except a small subpopulation) and wheatgerm agglutinin binds with varying affinities to different populations of T lymphocytes.

Thus affinity chromatography of cells is more problematical than that of soluble molecules. In addition, cells can be altered drastically by binding to and elution from a solid matrix and the final isolated preparation may be significantly different (both structurally and functionally) from the corresponding population *in vivo*. The use of a flow microfluorimeter (Section 12.2.2) to fractionate cells on the basis of a bound fluorescent antibody is vastly superior to affinity chromatography, although it is very slow for large numbers of cells. Unfortunately, the expense and consequent scarcity of these machines means that the techniques described in this Section are the best that are available to many researchers.

Another solid support that has been refined recently is magnetic beads (which can subsequently be separated by a magnet) and this is probably now one of the better ways of separating cell populations on a large scale. Again negative selection by removal of unwanted cells is preferable (although an excess of the beads is required to ensure complete depletion) but positive selection has recently been reported to have no obvious drawbacks if the surface molecule bound by the beads is not involved in activation of the cells (Lea *et al.*, 1986). The beads ('Dynabeads' from Dynal — Appendix 3) are uniform, magnetic polystyrene particles, 4.5 μm diameter, coated with a hydrophilic polymer to decrease porosity and allow ligand binding. They are available already coated with a second antibody against mouse IgG. Alternatively, antibodies (or other ligands) can be non-covalently absorbed onto uncoated beads or (better) covalently bound after activation with a sulphonyl chloride (cf. Table 10.2) (Nustad *et al.*, 1984). The coated beads are mixed with cells and binding monitored by rosette formation under a microscope (cf. erythrocyte rosetting, Sections 4.3.2 and 4.3.3); the bound cells can then be isolated by cobalt samarium magnets and detached from the beads if desired by overnight incubation. For further details see Lea *et al.* (1986) and the manufacturer's literature (Dynal — Appendix 3).

The separation of lymphocytes into T and B cells by insolubilized *Helix pomatia* lectin (Schrempf-Decker *et al.*, 1980) is described below as an example of affinity chromatography of cells.

Materials and equipment

Human peripheral blood lymphocytes (Section 4.2) — 10^7

232

Helix pomatia lectin-Sepharose 6MB (Pharmacia — Appendix 3) —
  1 ml
Balanced salts solution containing 0.02% sodium azide (BSS —
  Appendix 2)
BSS containing 2% (v/v) heat inactivated human AB serum (Section
  4.1)
BSS containing AB serum and 2% (w/v) N-acetyl glucosamine
RPMI medium (Table 4.1) containing 30% (v/v) heat inactivated fetal
  calf serum (Section 4.1)
Neuraminidase, protease free (Behringwerke — Appendix 3)
2–10 ml chromatography column fitted with large mesh (80 μm) nylon
  support (Pharmacia — Appendix 3)
Heated water bath
Polystyrene screw-capped tubes 16 mm $\times$ 100 mm (Sterilin —
  Appendix 3)

Procedure

1   Pack the lectin-Sepharose into the column and wash with 10 ml
BSS, 1 ml N-acetyl glucosamine solution, 10 ml BSS and 5 ml BSS
containing serum.
2   Suspend the lymphocytes in 10 ml BSS in a 16 mm $\times$ 100 mm
tube and centrifuge at 250 g for 5 min. Discard the supernatant and
resuspend the pellet in 1 ml BSS.
3   Add 7 i.u. neuraminidase and incubate at 37°C for 45 min.
4   Wash the cells twice by suspension in 10 ml BSS containing serum
and centrifuge at 250 g for 5 min.
5   Determine the cell number and viability (Section 4.1.1) and resuspend to 10^7/ml in BSS containing serum.
6   Apply 100 μl (10^6) cells to the lectin-Sepharose column, allow to
enter the gel and stop the flow and incubate for 15 min at room
temperature.
7   Place 5 ml RPMI medium containing serum into two 16 mm $\times$
100 mm tubes. Elute the unbound B cells from the column with 5 ml
BSS containing serum, at 0.5 ml/min, and collect the eluant in one
medium-containing tube.
8   Wash the column with a further 5 ml BSS containing serum and
discard the eluant. Then elute the bound T cells with 5 ml N-acetyl
glucosamine solution at 0.5 ml/min and collect the eluant in the
second medium-containing tube.
9   Incubate the 2 fractions at 37°C for 30 min to allow the cells to
recover and wash the column with 20 ml BSS.

Note

Beware of cells binding to 'inert' parts of the column, e.g. the gel
support (cf. nylon fibre, Section 4.3.1).

10.4 IMMUNOPRECIPITATION

This procedure is a means of identifying small amounts of a protein in a complex mixture by its interaction with antibody (Fig. 10.1b). The antigen is isolated from a radiolabelled mixture by specific precipitation and analysed by polyacrylamide gel electrophoresis (Section 7.3.1) followed by autoradiography (Section 1.5). This allows detection of the antigen, characterization of its molecular weight (especially useful in biosynthetic studies) and identification of other proteins closely associated with it. One of its main uses is characterization of the molecular species recognized by a novel antibody (including monoclonal ones). In this respect it provides an alternative approach to applying the antibody to electrophoretically separated mixtures (Chapter 8) and to gel electrophoresis of a precipitin line in agar (Section 9.1.3). In addition, the method of radiolabelling the initial mixture may be varied (Chapter 5) and information obtained on the structure and orientation of the antigen.

The procedure is usually applied to cell extracts and consequently it is carried out in the presence of detergents (Section 4.4). The most common means of precipitating the antibody involves binding it to *Staphylococcus aureus* bacteria or Protein A-Sepharose (Section 10.4.1). Unfortunately not all classes or subclasses of immunoglobulin bind tightly to Protein A (Table 10.3) and for those that do not a second antibody must be added to induce precipitation (Section 10.4.2). Non-specific binding is decreased by 'pre-clearing' the labelled extract with non-immune IgG, immune complexes or, more simply, *S. aureus* bacteria (compare the pre-adsorption in affinity chromatography, Section 10.3). A control precipitation with pre-immune sera should always be carried out.

10.4.1 Immunoprecipitation using *Staphyloccus aureus*

The example below is a general illustration of the technique and the information that can be gained from it. The cell type and method of radiolabelling can be varied and the procedure is applicable to all antibodies which bind Protein A with high affinity (Table 10.3).

Materials and equipment

Human peripheral blood lymphocytes (3×10^7, Section 4.2.1), enriched for B cells (Section 4.3.2), radioiodinated (300 μCi ^{125}I) using lactoperoxidase (Section 5.2.3) and solubilized in 1 ml 0.5% Nonidet P40 (Section 4.4.2)

Fixed and heat killed *S. aureus* bacteria, Cowan I strain, or Protein A-Sepharose (Pharmacia — Appendix 3), 10% (v/v) suspension (Section 10.2.2)

Rabbit anti-(human μ chain) serum (Dako, Miles — Appendix 3)

Rabbit anti-(human β_2-microglobulin) serum (Dako, Miles — Appendix 3)

Normal rabbit serum

10% (w/v) bovine serum albumin

0.5% (w/v) Nonidet P40 in 10 mM tris-HCl pH 7.3 containing 0.5 M NaCl

0.05% sodium dodecyl sulphate in the Nonidet P40 buffer

10 mM tris-HCl pH 7.3

Conical capped polypropylene centrifuge tubes 10.5 mm × 39 mm (Alpha, Beckman, Eppendorf — Appendix 3)

Rotator for gentle continuous mixing of above tubes

Bench centrifuge for above tubes (Beckman, Eppendorf — Appendix 3)

or

High speed centrifuge with adaptors for above tubes

Procedure

Warning take care when handling a large number of tubes containing radioactivity (Section 5.1.1).

1   Wash 300 μl of the 10% suspension of bacteria or Sepharose twice in 1 ml of Nonidet P40 solution by centrifugation (2 min bench model in cold room or 5 min 5000 g 4°C high speed model) and resuspend the final pellet to 300 μl in the same solution. Add 10 μl of albumin solution and store on ice.

2   Add 100 μl of the washed bacterial or Sepharose suspension to the lymphocyte extract in a polypropylene tube and mix gently on the rotator for 30 min at 4°C.

3   Centrifuge (4 min bench model; 5 min 10 000 g high speed model).

4   Transfer 300 μl of the supernatant to each of 3 polypropylene tubes and add 650 μl of the Nonidet P40 solution and 10 μl of albumin solution to each tube. Discard the pellet (radio-active waste).

5   Add 2 μl of the three rabbit sera to separate samples. Mix and incubate at room temperature for 30 min.

6   Add 50 μl of washed bacterial or Sepharose suspension (step 1) to each of the 3 samples and mix on the rotator for 1 hr at 4°C.

7   Centrifuge as in step 1. Discard the supernatants (radioactive waste) and resuspend each pellet in 1 ml of the Nonidet P40 solution by vortexing.

8   Centrifuge as in step 1. Discard the supernatants and resuspend each pellet in 1 ml of the dodecyl sulphate solution by vortexing.

9   Centrifuge as in step 1. Discard the supernatants and resuspend each pellet in 1 ml of 10 mM tris buffer.

10   Centrifuge as in step 1 and discard the supernatants. The pellets can be stored at −20°C until analysed.

11   Analyse the precipitates by 10% polyacrylamide gel elec-

trophoresis in sodium dodecyl sulphate (Laemmli buffer; Section 7.3.1, method i) followed by autoradiography (Section 1.5). Resuspend each pellet in 50 μl sample buffer containing reducing agent (Section 7.3.1), boil for 1 min and then apply the supernatants to the gel.

Interpretation of results

Figs. 10.8 and 7.2 show the results obtained using various antisera and peripheral blood lymphocytes from a patient with chronic lymphocytic leukaemia (greater than 80% B cells).

1   The background in the normal serum track is low.

2   Anti-(β_2-microglobulin) serum precipitated a polypeptide of molecular weight 43 000 in addition to β_2-microglobulin (molecular weight 12 000, ran off gel). This is the heavy chain of the HLA-A, –B and –C antigens which is non-covalently associated with β_2-microglobulin.

3   Anti HLA-DR serum precipitated 2 polypeptide chains (molecular weights 28 000 and 34 000) which are non-covalently associated to form this antigen and a 46 000 doublet contaminant also precipitated by anti-(μ chain) serum.

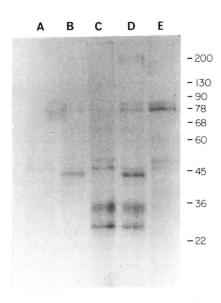

Fig. 10.8 Autoradiography of polyacrylamide gel electrophoresis in SDS (Laemmli system, 10%, Section 7.3.1) of specific immunoprecipitates of lactoperoxidase radioiodinated lymphocytes (Section 10.4.1). A, normal rabbit serum; B, anti-(β_2-microglobulin) serum; C, anti-(HLA-DR) serum; D, anti-(whole lymphocyte) serum; E, anti-(μ chain) serum. The position of marker proteins of known molecular weight ($\times$ 10^{-3}) are indicated on the right. The radioactive profile of these tracks as determined by cutting and counting the gel is presented in Fig. 7.2.

4 Anti-(whole lymphocyte) serum precipitated many bands but the major activity was against HLA-A, –B, –C and –DR and immunoglobulin (μ chain).

5 Anti-(μ chain) serum precipitated light chain (molecular weight 22 000; faint) in addition to μ chain doublet (?) (molecular weight 80 000). These chains are covalently linked to form monomeric IgM in the lymphocyte plasma membrane.

6 All of the polypeptides detected are labelled by lactoperoxidase catalysed radioiodination of whole lymphocytes and hence are probably exposed on the cell surface (Section 5.2.3).

Notes

1 The pre-adsorption of the cell extract (step 2) is important for reducing non-specific precipitation. However, this will remove the molecule of interest if it unfortunately has an affinity for Protein A.

2 In any radiolabelled preparation 10^5–10^6 trichloroacetic acid insoluble c.p.m. (Section 5.1.2) should be present in each immunoprecipitate tube (step 4).

3 In general, 1 μl of packed *S. aureus* cells is capable of binding 10–20 μg of IgG. Therefore up to 5 μl of serum can be used in step 5.

4 The efficiency of the *S. aureus* immunoadsorbent can be monitored by staining the polyacrylamide electrophoretogram for protein (Section 7.1.1). Strong bands of molecular weights 55 000 and 22 000 should be detected from the reduced IgG.

10.4.2 Immunoprecipitation using antibodies which do not bind Protein A

Some antibodies, including many monoclonals, do not bind well to Protein A (Table 10.3) and these can be precipitated by a second antibody directed against the first. Because each monoclonal is, by definition, different, there is no universally applicable procedure, but two methods are described below and at least one of them should work in most cases. The first is the simpler and uses an excess of second antibody of a kind that binds to Protein A; this was used to obtain Fig. 10.9. The second is somewhat more complicated and uses the correct amount of second antibody to cross-link and form a lattice with the first to induce precipitation (Section 6.1). Ideally the optimal amount of second antibody should be determined by a preliminary experiment (see note 1) but the details given work in most cases.

Method i Second antibody and Protein A

Materials and equipment

As for Section 10.4.1 but substitute monoclonal antibodies for rabbit

237

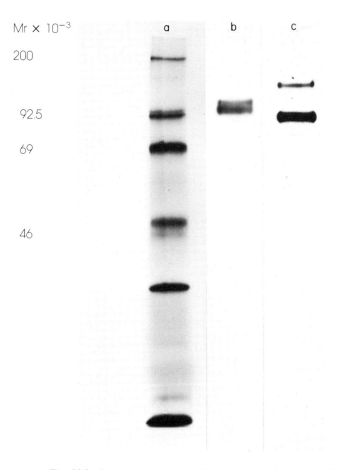

Fig. 10.9 Immunoprecipitation of human platelet glycoprotein II$_b$–III$_a$ complex using a monoclonal antibody (Bird *et al.*, 1986). The immunoprecipitate was analysed by SDS-polyacrylamide gel electrophoresis (Section 7.3.1, method i) and fluorography (Section 1.5.2). (a) Molecular weight markers, (b) immunoprecipitate analysed reduced, (c) immunoprecipitate analysed unreduced (courtesy of Chris Bird).

antisera and an irrelevant monoclonal antibody for normal rabbit serum.

Rabbit anti-(mouse immunoglubulin) or anti-(rat immunoglobulin), depending on species and class of monoclonals (Dako, Miles, Nordic — Appendix 3)

PBS

Procedure

1 Centrifuge 1 ml of the 10% suspension of bacteria or Protein A-Sepharose (2 min bench model in cold room or, for bacteria, 5 min 5000 g at 4°C high speed model). Discard the supernatant, resuspend the pellet in 1 ml PBS and add 100 μl of rabbit antiserum. Mix on rotator for 1 h at 4°C.

2   Centrifuge as in step 1 and wash the pellet twice with PBS. Resuspend the final pellet in 1 ml PBS, add 10 µl albumin solution and keep on ice. The preparation can be stored for long periods at 4°C if azide is added to 0.1%.

3   Add about 20 µg of irrelevant monoclonal antibody (2 µl of ascites or 200 µl of culture supernatant) to the lymphocyte extract in a polypropylene tube and incubate for 30 min at 4°C.

4   Add 100 µl of the antibody-Protein A suspension (step 2) to the extract and continue the incubation on the rotator for a further 30 min.

5   Centrifuge as in step 1 for Sepharose but 5 min in bench model or 5 min at 10 000 g in high speed model for bacteria.

6   Transfer the supernatant to a fresh tube, add a second 100 µl of antibody-Protein A (step 2) and incubate and centrifuge as in steps 4 and 5.

7   Transfer 300 µl of the supernatant to each of 3 polypropylene tubes and add 5 µl of albumin solution to each tube. Discard the pellet (radioactive waste).

8   Add about 10 µg of the three monoclonals (1 µl of ascites fluid or 100 µl of culture supernatant) to separate samples. Mix and incubate on ice for 1 h.

9   Add 50 µl of antibody-Protein A (step 2) to each of the three samples and mix on the rotator for 2 h at 4°C.

10   Centrifuge and wash and analyse the pellets as in Section 10.4.1, steps 7–11.

Method ii   Second antibody precipitation
(Courtesy of Edith Sim)

Materials and equipment

As for Section 10.4.1 but substitute:
   mouse monoclonal antibodies for rabbit antisera;
   irrelevant mouse monoclonal antibody for normal rabbit serum;
   rabbit anti-(mouse immunoglubulin) as appropriate for the monoclonals (Dako, Miles, Nordic — Appendix 3) for Protein A bacteria or Sepharose;
   0.1% Nonidet P40 in 10 mM tris-HCl, 0.15 M NaCl, 0.1% bovine serum albumin pH 7.3 for the Nonidet P40 buffer;
   tris buffered saline (TBS — Appendix 2) for the tris buffer
Normal mouse IgG (Sections 3.3.1 and 10.3.2) or (not so good) normal mouse serum (as a 'carrier' to help precipitation of the very small amount of specific monoclonal antibody)

Procedure

1   Add 10 µg of normal mouse IgG (or 10 µl of serum diluted 1:10) and 40 µl (see note 1) of anti-(mouse IgG) to the lymphocyte extract in a polypropylene tube. Mix and incubate for 2 h on ice.

239

2 Centrifuge at 4°C for 10 min at 10 000 *g*.

3 Transfer 200 μl of the supernatant to each of 3 polypropylene tubes. Discard the pellet (radioactive waste).

4 Add the three monoclonal antibodies (100 μl of hybridoma supernatant or 1 μl of ascites fluid) to separate samples, mix and incubate for 4 h on ice.

5 Add 5 μg of normal mouse IgG (or 5 μl of serum diluted 1:10) and 20 μl (see note 1) of anti-(mouse IgG) to each tube. Mix and incubate at 4°C overnight.

6 Centrifuge at 10 000 *g* for 5 min at 4°C. Discard the supernatants (radioactive waste) and resuspend each pellet on ice in 1 ml of cold Nonidet P40 buffer by vortexing.

7 Repeat step 6.

8 Centrifuge as in step 6, discard the supernatants and resuspend the pellets on ice in 1 ml of cold TBS.

9 Centrifuge as in step 6 and discard the supernatants. The pellets can be stored at −20°C until analysed according to Section 10.4.1, step 11.

Notes

1 Although the amount of second antibody given above usually works, it may not be optimal leading to either some loss of first antibody (and associated radiolabelled antigen) or wastage of second antibody. The correct amount can be determined by a preliminary test which will tell you how much to use in any subsequent precipitation so long as the same batch of normal mouse IgG and anti-(mouse IgG) is used. Radioiodinate some normal mouse IgG (Section 5.2.1) and dilute into the Nonidet P40 buffer containing 0.1 mg/ml of normal mouse IgG (or 10 μl of serum per ml) to a radioactive concentration of about 2 million c.p.m. per ml. Dispense 50 μl (containing 5 μg of normal IgG and 100 000 c.p.m.) into each of 8 polypropylene tubes together with 100 μl of the Nonidet P40 buffer and cool on ice. Add 0, 1, 2, 5, 10, 20, 50 or 100 μl of the anti-(mouse IgG) contained in 100 μl of TBS to separate tubes and incubate at 4°C overnight. Centrifuge and wash as in steps 6–9 above and determine the radioactivity of the pellets in a gamma counter (Section 1.4). Identify the least amount of second antibody that will precipitate all of the radiolabelled IgG (i.e. the TCA-precipitable counts added, Section 5.1.2) and use this in subsequent immunoprecipitations (step 5, and twice as much in step 1).

2 For rat monoclonals, substitute rabbit anti-(rat immunoglobulin) and normal rat IgG or serum in appropriate steps.

11 Immunoassays

Immunoassays use the specific interaction of antibody with antigen to provide quantitative information about antigen (or antibody) concentration in unknown samples. The most common techniques use a radioactively labelled antigen or antibody and are thus known as radioimmunoassays (originally this term was reserved for techniques which involved competition for antibody binding between radiolabelled and unlabelled antigens, Section 11.2). Alternative labels such as enzymes (ELISA, Section 11.4) or fluorochromes (fluorescence immunoassay) have been used in place of radioisotopes. More recently chemiluminescence technology has been used in an attempt to increase sensitivity.

Immunoassays can be very sensitive and specific and therefore are commonly used for a great variety of measurements both in research and analytical laboratories. Several refinements of the basic technology have been developed, and some of these are discussed after a description of the more commonly used procedures.

11.1 SOLID-PHASE RADIOBINDING IMMUNOASSAYS

These are the simplest form of immunoassay, and are especially useful for testing the sera from immunized animals for antibody response and for screening hybridomas for secretion of specific antibody (Chapter 2).

Antiserum or hybridoma supernatant is incubated with antigen which has been immobilized either by covalent attachment to agarose or polyacrylamide beads (Section 10.2) or by non-covalent 'sticking' to plastic beads or more commonly to the wells of microtitre plates. After exhaustive washing, bound antibody is detected by incubation with radiolabelled anti-immunoglobulin. Ideally this second antibody should be affinity purified to ensure that most labelled proteins are active (cf. immunocytochemistry, Section 12.1). At the very least the IgG fraction should be isolated from the antiserum for labelling (Section 3.3.1).

This assay protocol can be used for detection of antibodies against surface components of intact cells. The $F(ab')_2$ fragment of the second antibody should be isolated (Section 3.4.3) before radiolabelling to decrease non-specific binding to Fc-receptors on cells.

Modifications to this technique are normally necessary if accurate quantitation of antigen is required. The amount of antigen that sticks to plastic is usually not simply related to its concentration and plates differ in their ability to bind proteins. It is usually best to use the two-site modification of the immunoradiometric assay (Section 11.3) to quantitate antigen.

Solid-phase radiobinding assays for use with soluble or cell surface antigens are shown diagrammatically in Fig. 11.1a and 11.1b respectively and described separately in Sections 11.1.1 and 11.1.2.

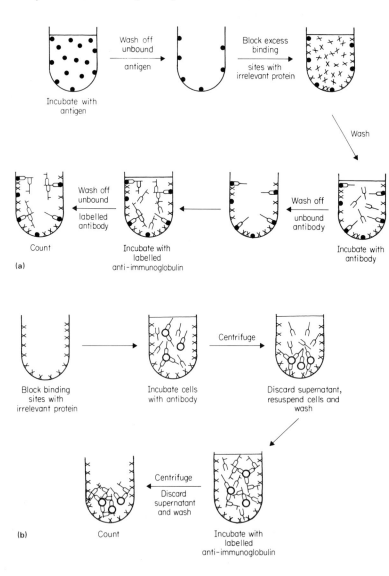

Fig. 11.1 Diagrammatic representation of solid-phase radiobinding assays; (a) for antibodies directed against soluble antigens (Section 11.1.1); (b) for antibodies directed against cell surface antigens (Section 11.1.2).

11.1.1 Antibodies directed against soluble antigens

The procedure described below is carried out in microtitre plates and is ideal for screening hybridoma supernatants, for detecting antigen in unknown samples and for testing for cross-reactivity in antibody preparations. After coating the wells with antigen or immunoglubulin it is essential to 'block' the remaining protein binding sites with an irrelevant protein (e.g. haemoglobin) to avoid non-specific binding of subsequent reagents to the well walls. The amount of protein needed to coat the wells varies but 1–5 μg in 50 μl is usually sufficient for each well. Only a small proportion of this protein actually adheres to the plastic and so the same solution can be used for at least 5 coatings. For highly aggregated proteins it is advisable to use much higher amounts for coating (up to 75 μg of protein/well).

Materials and equipment

Flexible microtitre plates 96 well (Dynatech — Appendix 3)

Antigen (100 μg/ml in phosphate buffered saline-azide — Appendix 2)

Phosphate buffered saline containing 0.02% sodium azide and 2% w/v haemoglobin (PBS-Hb)

Antiserum or hybridoma supernatant

Negative control: pre-immune serum or irrelevant hybridoma supernatant

Anti-immunoglobulin directed against first antibody (see above), ^{125}I-labelled (100 μCi/5 μg protein; Section 5.2.1)

Gamma counter

Hot nichrome wire plate cutter (optional)

Procedure

1   Pipette 50 μl of antigen solution into each well of the microtitre plate and incubate at room temperature overnight. Such plates can be stored at 4°C for several weeks.

2   Remove antigen solution from wells using a Pasteur pipette (cover the pipette tip with a small piece of soft plastic tubing to prevent scratching the antigen coated wells). Store the aspirated solution at 4°C — it can be used for at least 4 subsequent coatings.

3   Wash the plate by filling wells with PBS-Hb and rapidly discarding the well contents (invert plate over sink and tap briskly). Repeat this twice more, then fill wells with PBS-Hb and incubate at room temperature for 30 min–1 h. Wash 3 more times with PBS-Hb.

4   Pipette 45 μl of immune serum, control serum, or hybridoma supernatant into each well (see note 1). Incubate for 1–16 h at room temperature (see note 2).

5   Wash with PBS-Hb 4 times as described in step 3.

6   Dilute the ^{125}I-labelled anti-immunoglobulin in PBS-Hb to give

$2\text{--}3 \times 10^6$ c.p.m./ml. Add 45 μl to each well and incubate for 30 min – 1 h at room temperature.

7   Wash with PBS-Hb as in step 3.

8   Cut out individual wells using scissors or a hot nichrome wire plate cutter, and determine the radioactivity bound by counting in the gamma counter.

Notes

1   All assays should be carried out in duplicate or triplicate. Hybridoma supernatants should be asssayed neat. Immune serum or ascitic fluid (Section 2.3.3) should be diluted and titred. For this, order of magnitude dilutions should be made in PBS-Hb (10^{-1}, 10^{-2}, 10^{-3}, 10^{-4} is normally sufficient). It is essential to include a negative control and it is also advisable to include a known positive.

2   Suitable time of incubation with antibody depends upon the antibody concentration and avidity (Section 6.1.1). High titre antisera will give good binding after 1 h but weaker antisera and hybridoma supernatants will give better results if longer incubation periods are used.

3   Some antigens do not stick to plastic. In these cases the antigen can either be coupled covalently to beads (Section 10.2.1) or coupled using glutaraldehyde (0.05% v/v for 10 min followed by 3 washes with PBS) to polylysine coated plates (5 μg/well overnight incubation). Alternatively, if antibody to the antigen is available the assay described in Section 11.3 can be used.

4   Although the assay is only semi-quantitative, an approximate measure of the concentration of antibody can be obtained by reference to standard antisera. The assay can be made more quantitative by competing for the binding of ^{125}I-labelled standard antibody with added standard and unknown unlabelled antibodies (see Section 11.2).

5   Some antibodies bind non-specifically in this type of assay. It is always best to confirm immunoreactivity with another immunochemical technique such as immunoblotting (Section 8.4), immunohistochemistry (Chapter 12) or immunoprecipitation (Section 10.4).

6   The amount of antigen absorbed onto the wells can be monitored using the techniques described in Section 1.1.2, note 3, or Section 1.1.3.

7   Antigens solubilized in detergents (Section 4.4 *et seq.*) do not usually bind as well to the plates. Non-ionic detergents can be removed by absorption to beads during the coating (Drexler *et al.*, 1986).

11.1.2   Antibodies directed against cell surface antigens

The procedure described in Section 11.1.1 can be easily adapted to permit detection of antibodies directed against surface antigens of cells in suspension (e.g. lymphocytes, erythrocytes, etc.). The technique is slightly more involved because the cells are pelleted by centrifugation after each incubation and wash. Care is required during washing as cells can easily be lost when emptying the plate. Cell surface antigens can be measured by a competitive binding modification of this assay (Williams, 1977) and together with immunofluorescence microscopy (Section 12.2.4) and flow microfluorimetry analysis (Section 12.2.2) this method represents the most recent approach to the study of cell surface structure.

Materials and equipment

As for Section 11.1.1 substituting cells in suspension ($2 \times 10^5 - 5 \times 10^5$/well; see note 1) for soluble antigen
Centrifuge with a rotor suitable for microtitre plates (Dynatech — Appendix 3)
BMEE medium (Table 4.1) containing 0.1% sodium azide and 0.1% albumin or 5% serum

Procedure

1　Incubate plate with 150 μl/well of Hb-PBS at room temperature for 1 h to block binding sites on the plastic. Discard PBS-Hb by inverting plate over sink and tapping briskly.
2　Suspend the cells in protein-containing medium to a concentration of $4-20 \times 10^6$/ml). Pipette 50 μl of antibody into each well (see note 1, Section 11.1.1) and add 50 μl of cell suspension. Mix and incubate at room temperature for 2 h.
3　Centrifuge plate for 7.5 min at 400 *g*.
4　Invert the plate over a sink and discard the supernatants by a single rapid downward movement that is stopped suddenly. Do not shake or repeat the movement or cells will be lost.
5　Wash by pipetting 150 μl protein-containing medium into each well (ensure that cells are resuspended by this process) and centrifuging and discarding supernatants as described in steps 3 and 4. Repeat twice.
6　Dilute the ^{125}I-labelled antibody in PBS-Hb to $2-4 \times 10^6$ c.p.m./ml and resuspend each final cell pellet in 50 μl of this. Incubate at room temperature for 1 h.
7　Centrifuge and wash as in step 5. Cut out individual wells (care is required so as not to lose cells) and count in the gamma counter.

Notes

1　A microtitre plate shaker (Dynatech — Appendix 3) will ensure cell resuspension during washing and before incubation.
2　Glutaraldehyde fixed cells (Section 4.1.2) can be used to provide a long term supply of reproducible target cells. However, non-specific binding and hence background is increased. Also some antigenic determinants are destroyed by the fixation procedure.
3　See note 4, Section 11.1.1.

4   The final cell washing can be performed using a cell harvester (Dynatech, Ilacon — Appendix 3). This will avoid the problem of radioactivity adsorbed directly onto the cell walls.

11.2   COMPETITIVE BINDING RADIOIMMUNOASSAYS

Competitive binding, or inhibition radioimmunoassay (regarded by some people as the 'real' radioimmunoassay technique) combines high sensitivity and specificity with economic use of reagents and good reproducibility.

In the classical method, a fixed amount of radiolabelled antigen competes for a limited amount of specific antibody with unlabelled antigen. A standard curve is constructed using known amounts of unlabelled antigen and, by reference to this, antigen concentration in unknown samples can be determined. This technique is shown diagrammatically in Fig. 11.2

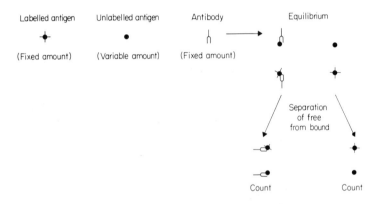

Fig. 11.2   Diagrammatic representation of competitive binding (inhibition) radioimmunoassay (Section 11.2).

Radioimmunoassays have been developed for virtually every type of biological molecule and their overall strategy is similar. Individual techniques vary mainly in the way in which free antigen is separated from antibody-bound antigen and in whether the reaction is carried out in liquid phase or with antibody coupled to a solid support (solid phase radioimmunoassay).

In this section the technical considerations for setting up a radioimmunoassay are given, followed by some specific examples.

11.2.1   Setting up a competitive radioimmunoassay

Antisera. The specificity and sensitivity of any radioimmunoassay is largely determined by the antibody used. Antibodies of high avidity (Section 6.1.1) are necessary for good sensitivity and reproducibility.

246

largely determined by the antibody used. Antibodies of high avidity (Section 6.1.1) are necessary for good sensitivity and reproducibility. However, to produce these several boosting immunizations (Section 2.2.1) are usually required and this may be undesirable or impossible with scarce antigens. In addition, high avidity may be achieved only at the expense of specificity. It is advisable to use more than one animal for the production of antiserum and to test the potency and if possible the specificity of the serum after each booster injection. When a good titre antiserum of acceptable specificity is obtained the animal should be exsanguinated and the serum frozen in small aliquots. The very small amount of antiserum needed for radioimmunoassay allows one batch of antiserum to last for a long period. If antiserum is obtained commercially it should be screened in a similar way. Monoclonal antibodies (Section 2.3) are exquisitely specific but low avidity can cause problems in radioimmunoassays.

For assays using radiolabelled antibodies, it is necessary to affinity purify them (Section 10.3.1). The F(ab')$_2$ fragment is preferable for assays involving cells to decrease non-specific binding by Fc receptors.

Radiolabelled target antigen. It is essential to minimize structural changes to the antigen during radiolabelling, as these changes can lead to diminished recognition of the labelled antigen by the antibody and can cause reduced specificity and sensitivity. ^{125}I is usually the radioisotope of choice because it is easily conjugated to many antigens and can be measured simply (Sections 5.2 and 1.4). However, the bulky iodine atom can cause antibody recognition problems especially for haptens (e.g. steroids), and the radiolabelling reagents may cause structural damage to some proteins and peptides (the milder procedures of Sections 5.2.2 and 5.2.3 will decrease this). Alternative isotopes are ^{14}C and ^{3}H, and a range of radiolabelled compounds are available commercially. These isotopes are more time consuming and expensive to measure than ^{125}I (see Section 1.4).

Separation of free from bound antigen. The use of solid-phase techniques involving antibody bound to microtitre plates, plastic tubes, beads (most recently magnetic; Amersham — Appendix 3) or some other solid support (a new generation of monosized polymer particles, easily coupled to antibodies, is now available: Dynospheres from Dyno Particles — Appendix 3) simplifies the separation of free and bound antigen (see solid-phase radiobinding assays in Section 11.1). Matrix pad technology provides a solid support with built-in washing facility by means of an absorbent pad; this is used in a commercial kit for a rapid ELISA (Section 11.4) pregnancy test based on a two-site IRMA (Section 11.3; Monoclonal Antibodies Inc. — Appendix 3). For liquid phase techniques several separation techniques can be used (Table 11.1)

247

Table 11.1 Some methods for separation of free from antibody-bound antigen in liquid-phase radioimmunoassays

Separation technique	Type of molecule
adsorption of free antigen on dextran coated charcoal	peptides and other small molecules e.g. steroids
binding of bound antigen to ion-exchange resins	proteins and peptides
precipitation of bound antigen with ammonium sulphate, sodium sulphate or polyethylene glycol (PEG)	proteins
precipitation of bound antigen using precipitating anti-immunoglobulin	all molecules

Preliminary binding assay. It is necessary to establish the correct antiserum dilution for use in the competitive assay by carrying out a preliminary binding assay. For this a fixed amount of radiolabelled antigen is incubated with various dilutions of antibody (for most antisera use serial dilutions 1/100 to about 1/500 000; a suitable incubation period is normally 1–2 h but weak antisera may require longer). Free antigen is then separated from antibody bound antigen and the radioactivity in the bound fraction counted. A plot of c.p.m. bound against log antiserum dilution is constructed and used to determine the dilution of antiserum that binds 50–80% of the maximum bound (e.g. see Fig. 11.4). This dilution should be used in the competitive assay to ensure that the antibody is in limiting concentration.

Construction of a standard curve. A standard curve enables the antigen concentration in unknown samples to be calculated. It is constructed by incubating known concentrations of unlabelled antigen with fixed concentrations of labelled antigen and antibody (limiting — see above). The radioactivity bound to antibody is plotted on a linear scale against antigen concentration on a log scale. It is advisable to use only the linear part of the standard curve for determining antigen concentration in unkown samples. It may be more accurate to plot log [c.p.m. bound/(maximum c.p.m. bound − c.p.m. bound)] against log antigen concentration.

Other considerations. A carrier protein (normally haemoglobin or bovine serum albumin) is used at all stages of the radioimmunoassay because of the very low concentrations of antigen and antibody present. This prevents non-specific binding and stabilizes the antibody. Thorough mixing of reagents is very important at every stage. Antisera should be

248

centrifuged (10 000 *g*; 10 min) before use to remove sticky aggregates and complexes. It is essential to include positive and negative controls in all assays.

Accurate pipetting is also vital for the success of all immunoassays. For repetitive pipetting of small volumes of a single solution a Hamilton syringe fitted with a repeat dispenser is recommended. For separate pipetting of individual solutions any accurate pipette is suitable. Check the accuracy of the pipettes occasionally by weighing the liquid they deliver during multiple dispensing (use the buffer used in the assay).

Many commercially produced kits are available for the estimation of a variety of biological compounds by radioimmunoassay (Amersham, Uniscience — Appendix 3).

For further information on radioimmunoassay see Chard (1986) and Teale (1978). The application of the technique to hormone assay is thoroughly presented in Jaffe & Behrman (1974).

11.2.2   Farr-type assay

The antigen in a sample is measured by its inhibition of the binding between an antiserum and the appropriate radiolabelled antigen. The amount of bound antigen is determined by precipitation of all whole immunoglobulin molecules (including antibodies) under conditions in which the free radiolabelled antigen remains soluble (Fig. 11.3). The precipitation is induced by polyethylene glycol 600 (PEG); this gives better reproducibility than the ammonium sulphate originally used in Farr assays. The precipitates are collected conveniently by filtration on a cell harvester allowing the assay of a large number of samples but centrifugation can be used if preferred.

The assay can be used to measure any antigen provided that it (or a fragment of it carrying antigenic determinants) is soluble under the conditions used to precipitate the antibodies. By way of example the assay applied to albumin is described below. This illustrates the proce-

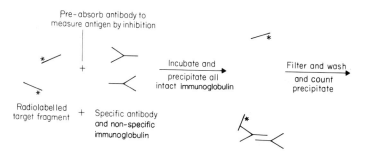

Fig. 11.3   Principle of Farr-type assay (Section 11.2.2). The assay can be used to measure a wide variety of antigens and, as an illustration, Table 11.2 lists the reagents used to apply it to individual immunoglobulins.

249

dure and the principle and it would be suitable as a class practical or demonstration. By changing the radiolabelled antigen (or antigen fragment) and antiserum a wide variety of substances can be assayed; the application to measure immunoglubulin classes is detailed in Table 11.2 and illustrative results presented in Fig. 11.5.

As for all inhibition assays, a binding assay is carried out first to determine the conditions under which antibody is limiting.

Table 11.2   Reagents for immunoglobulins assays

Immunoglobulin measured	^{125}I-labelled target fragment[a]	Antiserum specificity	Inhibitor for standard curve
IgM	Fc_μ	anti-μ chain	IgM
IgG	Fab_γ or Fc_γ	anti-γ chain[b]	IgG
IgA	Fab_α	anti-α chain[b]	IgA
IgD	Fc_δ	anti-δ chain	IgD
Igλ[f]	λ chain[c]	anti-λ chain[e]	myeloma Igλ or λ chain[d]
Igκ[f]	Fab_γ	anti-κ chain[e]	myeloma Igκ or κ chain[d]

[a] See Chapter 3 for preparation of fragments.
[b] Not all anti-H chain sera react with Fab fragments.
[c] The λ assay does not work well with Fab_γ as target because of the low proportion of λ chain in normal pooled IgG (see Table 3.1).
[d] When using free L chain as standard inhibitor, multiply the weight by 3 to obtain the amount of immunoglobulin this represents.
[e] Some anti-L chain sera preferentially recognize free L chain as opposed to L chain in immunoglobulin molecules. These antisera should be avoided.
[f] Igλ, Igκ — any class of immunoglobulins containing λ or κ light chain respectively.

Titration of antiserum

Materials and equipment

Human albumin, radioiodinated (Section 5.2.1; 500 μCi ^{125}I/10 μg protein)
Anti-(human albumin) serum (Dako, Miles — Appendix 3)
0.1% w/v haemoglobin in phosphate buffered saline (PBS) containing 0.02% sodium azide (Appendix 2)
10% w/v chicken serum in PBS
28% w/v PEG 6000 in PBS
15% w/v PEG 6000 in PBS, containing 0.1% w/v Tween 20 detergent
Flat-bottomed 96-well microtitre plates, non-sterile, not coated for tissue culture
Sealing film for microtitre plates (Dynatech, Falcon — Appendix 3)
Cell harvester (Dynatech, Ilacon — Appendix 3)

250

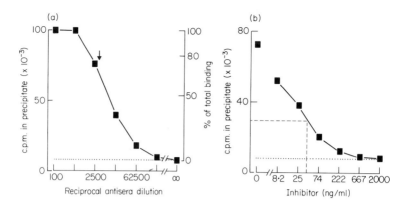

Fig. 11.4 Farr-type assay for soluble albumin (Fig. 11.3; Section 11.2.2). (a) Preliminary binding assay to determine conditions in which antibody is limiting, using a constant amount of ^{125}I-labelled albumin and varying the amount of anti-albumin serum. The antibody dilution indicated by the arrow (1/3000; falling between 50–80% total binding) was then used for the competitive binding assay in (b) in which various concentrations of standard albumin competed with radiolabelled albumin for the limited amount of antibody. In both assays the background c.p.m. precipitated in the absence of antibody is indicated by a dotted line. From the standard curve in (b) the amount of albumin in an unknown solution can be determined — e.g. 30 000 c.p.m. in the precipitate indicates a concentration of 40 ng/ml in the sample (dashed line).

Whatman GF/B paper for cell harvester
Microtitre plate shaker (Dynatech — Appendix 3)
Microtitre plate centrifuge carriers (Dynatech — Appendix 3)
Microfiltration apparatus (Millipore, Sartorius — Appendix 3)
Gamma counter

Procedure

1   Prepare a 1/100 dilution of anti-albumin serum in haemoglobin containing buffer and then 200 μl of 1:5 serial dilutions of this (i.e. 50 μl + 200 μl) in the same buffer down to 1/312 500 (total 6 dilutions).

2   Add 50 μl of each antiserum dilution in triplicate to separate wells of the microtitre plate and 50 μl of haemoglobin-containing buffer to a further three wells.

3   Dilute the ^{125}I-labelled albumin in 10% v/v chicken serum to approximately 1 μCi/ml and filter through GF/B paper in the microfiltration apparatus.

4   Add 100 μl of radiolabelled albumin to each well (approximately 0.1 μCi and 1–2 ng of protein). Cover with a plate sealer, mix thoroughly but carefully on the shaker and incubate at room temperature for 4 h.

251

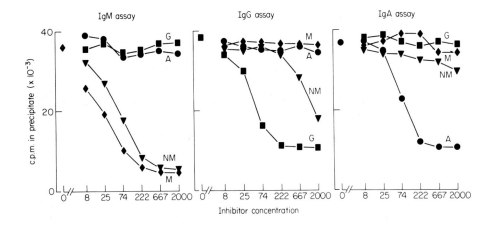

Fig. 11.5 Use of competitive binding radioimmunoassays to compare the purity of human immunoglobulin preparations. The assays are described in Table 11.2 and Section 11.2.2. The immunoglobulin preparations used as inhibitors were pooled IgG (G, ■, Section 3.3.1); pooled secretory IgA (A, ●, Section 3.7.2); myeloma IgM$_k$ (M, ◆, Section 3.5); pooled normal IgM (NM, ▼, Section 3.5). Preparations M, G and A contained less than 1% of contaminant immunoglobulins. Preparation NM showed lower inhibition per unit weight than pure IgM in the IgM assay, indicating lower purity. From the other assays NM contained approximately 5% IgG and 1% IgA.

5 Carefully remove the plate sealer and add 150 μl of 28% PEG to each well.

6 Replace plate sealer ensuring that each well is sealed and mix thoroughly by inverting the plate 4 times followed by 1 min on the shaker. Incubate at room temperature for at least 1 h.

7 Centrifuge the microtitre plate at 250 g for 1 min to remove the liquid adhering to the plate sealer.

8 Collect the precipitates by filtration through GF/B paper on the cell harvester and wash each well and precipitate with 1 ml of 15% PEG solution.

9 Determine the radioactivity of each precipitate and plot this on a linear scale against reciprocal of dilution of antiserum on a log scale (Fig. 11.4a).

10 The antiserum should bind greater than 80% of the trichloro-acetic acid-insoluble radioactivity (Section 5.1.2) in the antigen down to a dilution of 1/500. If it does not it is of low titre and better results will be obtained with a different batch.

11 From the graph determine the dilution of antiserum necessary to bind 50–80% of the maximum activity which can be bound (Fig. 11.4a). This is the antiserum dilution used for the inhibition assay.

252

Inhibition assay

Materials and equipment

As for **titration of antiserum** but substitute 20% v/v for 10% v/v chicken serum

Human albumin — 1 mg/ml solution accurately measured from absorbance at 280 nm (Table 1.1)

Human IgG — 1 mg/ml measured similarly

Procedure

1   Prepare an accurate 1/500 dilution of albumin and IgG standard solutions in haemoglobin-containing buffer and then 200 μl of accurate 1:3 serial dilutions (i.e. 100 μl + 200 μl) in the same buffer (total 6 dilutions, 2 μg/ml — 8.2 ng/ml). Also prepare an accurate 1/25 000 dilution of albumin (40 ng/ml) as a test 'unknown' solution.

2   Place 50 μl of each albumin and IgG dilution in triplicate into separate wells of the microtitre plate and 50 μl of haemoglobin-containing buffer into a further 6 wells.

3   Prepare 2.5 ml of anti-albumin serum diluted in haemoglobin containing buffer to the concentration determined in the binding assay above.

4   Add 50 μl of haemoglobin-containing buffer to 3 of the wells containing no inhibitor and 50 μl of diluted antiserum to the remaining wells. Cover with a plate sealer, mix thoroughly but carefully on the shaker for 1 min and incubate at room temperature overnight (16 h).

5   Dilute the ^{125}I-labelled albumin in 20% chicken serum to approximately 2 μCi/ml (twice the concentration used in the binding assay above) and filter through GF/B paper in the microfiltration apparatus.

6   Carefully remove the plate sealer and add 50 μl of radiolabelled albumin to each well (approximately 0.1 μCi and 1–2 ng of protein). Replace the plate sealer, mix thoroughly on the shaker and incubate for 4 h at room temperature.

7   Carry out steps 5–7 of the **titration of antiserum** and plot radioactivity in the precipitate on a linear scale against reciprocal of the dilution of inhibitor on a log scale (Fig. 11.4b). Indicate also the radioactivity for no inhibitor and for no antibody (background). IgG should give no inhibition even at the highest concentration, indicating the specificity of the assay.

8   The activity in the precipitate is inversely related to the amount of albumin in the inhibitor solution. From the standard curve the concentration of albumin in an unknown solution can be accurately determined if diluted appropriately to fall within the measurable range (8–100 ng/ml in Fig. 11.4b). Determine the concentration of albumin in the test 'unknown' solution (step 1).

Notes

1   The procedure can be modified to measure the concentration of

any molecule provided that it, or a fragment of it carrying antigenic determinants, is soluble in 15% w/v PEG 6000 and so can be used as the radiolabelled target antigen.

2   The assay can be performed in the presence of non-ionic detergents (Section 4.4.1) so that antigen in cell extracts can be measured.

3   The chicken serum provides the carrier immunoglobulin which facilitates the precipitation of the minute quantities of antibody. GF/B paper is more efficient than other grades for the collection of precipitates.

4   As in all assays, it is very important to mix the reagents thoroughly. The plate shaker does this most efficiently but an ordinary vortex mixer can be used with care.

5   The assay can be performed in polystyrene tubes (10.5 mm × 63.5 mm), using 1.5 ml of 15% PEG 6000 to precipitate the immunoglobulin, with a consequent improvement in reproducibility but a decrease in convenience for a large number of samples. A cell harvester equipped with the appropriate suction head and tube rack is required. Alternatively remove and wash the precipitate by centrifugation.

11.3   IMMUNORADIOMETRIC ASSAY (IRMA)

A modification of radioimmunoassay known as immunoradiometric assay (IRMA) is often used where purification of antigen for radiolabelling is difficult or if radiolabelling appreciably alters the immunological properties of the antigen. In this technique labelled antibody reacts with a limited concentration of unlabelled antigen (Fig. 11.6). The procedure usually employs a solid-phase method for

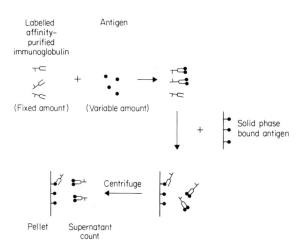

Fig. 11.6   Diagrammatic representation of immunoradiometric assay (IRMA — Section 11.3).

254

separation of free from bound fractions, e.g. antigen coupled to agarose or polyacrylamide beads (Section 10.2). Although IRMAs were developed originally in an attempt to improve sensitivity, their practical advantages are that no labelling of antigen is required and the methodology is usually very simple and fast. However, more washing than in conventional radioimmunoassays is required and so some lower affinity antibodies may not be suitable. The procedure requires specific affinity purified immunoglobulins (Section 10.3.1)' and solid-phase bound antigen (Section 10.2).

A two-site modification of IRMA carried out using plastic microtitre plates as the solid phase support (cf. Section 11.1) is now often used to measure an antigen and this technique is particularly applicable for use with monoclonal antibodies. Unless the antigen is multivalent (see, for example, Fig. 11.8), it requires two monoclonal antibodies which recognize different determinants on the antigen or the combined use of a polyclonal antiserum and a monoclonal antibody. Microtitre plate wells are coated with one antibody (or antibodies from a polyclonal antiserum) and this is then used to trap antigen from the test solution. Bound antigen is then detected by reaction with the second radiolabelled antibody (Fig. 11.7). The amount of label bound is proportional to the concentration of the antigen in the test solution. An ELISA (Section 11.4) version of this provides a simple, sensitive and rapid (3–20 min) pregnancy test (Monoclonal Antibodies Inc., Unipath — Appendix 3). With care, considerable accuracy can be achieved, but it is essential to ensure that the assay is valid for the antigen concentration range being measured. For this, the amount of antibody bound to the wells must be in large excess over antigen. The

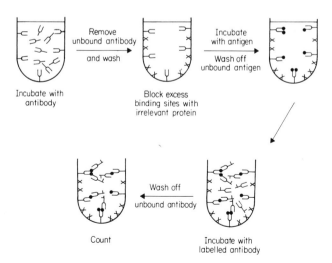

Fig. 11.7 Diagrammatic representation of a two-site immunoradiometric assay (IRMA) for estimation of antigens.

standard curve of c.p.m. bound versus log antigen concentration should be linear (individual plates may vary in ability to bind antibody). Typical results are shown in Fig. 11.8.

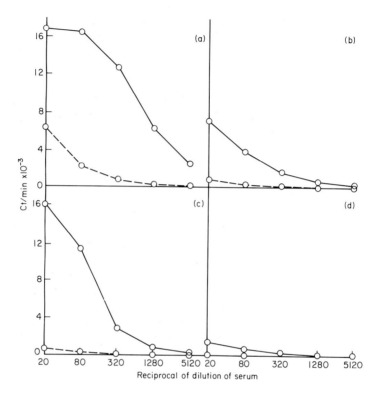

Fig. 11.8 Immunoradiometric assay (IRMA) for human IgE using the method described in Section 11.3. Plots a–d represent assays carried out using combinations of different monoclonal antibodies. The solid line shows the curve obtained using pooled serum from allergic individuals; the broken line is the curve obtained using sera from normal individuals (for full details see Alterman *et al.*, 1987). Note that different monoclonal antibodies can behave very differently in such assays, and it is necessary to carefully evaluate all combinations before selecting the best system.

Materials and equipment

As for Section 11.1.1
Affinity purified (Section 10.3.1) antibody against the antigen — unlabelled *and* ^{125}I-labelled (Section 5.2.1)

Procedure

1 Dilute the *unlabelled* antibody in PBS to 2–20 μg/ml and add 50 μl to each well of a microtitre plate. Incubate at 4°C overnight. overnight.
2 Aspirate immunoglobulin solution and wash and block plate as described in Section 11.1.1, steps 2 and 3.

256

3   Dilute standard antigen and unknown solution in PBS–Hb and pipette 45 μl of each dilution in duplicate into separate antibody-coated wells. Incubate at room temperature (or 4°C) for 4–16 h (see note 2, Section 11.1.1).

4   Wash 4 times with PBS–Hb as described in Section 11.1.1, step 3.

5   Dilute the ^{125}I-labelled immunoglobulin in PBS–Hb to give 2–4 × 10^6 c.p.m./ml. Add 45 μl to each well and incubate at room temperature for 1–2 h.

6   Wash as in step 4.

7   Cut out individual wells with scissors or a hot nichrome wire plate cutter and determine the radioactivity bound by counting in the gamma counter.

Notes

1   Quantification can be achieved by reference to a standard curve of c.p.m. bound versus log antigen concentration over its linear range.

2   This assay is very specific because the antigen must be recognized twice by antibody to be detected (once for binding and again by radiolabelled immunoglobulin). However, problems can arise if the binding of antigen to the immobilized immunoglobulin inhibits binding of the labelled antibody. This should not occur if a high-titre antiserum is used as a source of immunoglobulin and if the antigen has several determinants. It is advisable to use different antisera preferably produced in different species for binding and labelling. The combination of antibody isolated from a conventional antiserum with monoclonal antibody is particularly suitable.

11.4   ENZYME-LINKED IMMUNOSORBENT ASSAYS (ELISA)

Recently efforts have been made to develop immunoassay systems that use non-radioactive labels. Many alternatives have been tried (e.g. fluorescent labels, light emitting systems) and the most successful of these is ELISA which replaces the radioisotope with an enzyme. Originally ELISA was introduced in an attempt to increase sensitivity, but as this is largely dependent on the avidity of the antibody the attempt was not successful. The technique does have several advantages. No precautions against radioactivity are needed and the enzyme conjugates are more stable than radioiodinated proteins (Section 5.2). One drawback of ELISA is that a spectrophotometer suitable for measuring small volumes of sample is required. For large numbers of samples it is worth buying an automatic machine designed for ELISA (Dynatech, Flow, Wellcome — Appendix 3). They can be interfaced with computers to aid analysis of results. Even without such machines an idea of the reaction can be obtained by eye, making them suitable for use in the field (e.g. screening for circulating antibodies to detect infection in third-world countries) or by non-technical person-nel (e.g. over-the-counter pregnancy test kits). Considerable effort is being made by commercial companies to develop and optimize 'dip-stick' and other simplified modifications of appropriate assays.

Several enzymes can be conjugated to antigens and antibodies, and if robust enzymes are used the conjugates are stable for long periods. In practice enzymes are selected which show simple kinetics, and can be assayed by a simple procedure (normally spectrophotometric). Cheapness, availability and stability of substrate are also important considerations. For these reasons the most commonly used enzymes are alkaline phosphatase, β-D-galactosidase and horseradish perox-idase.

Both binding and competitive binding assays can be used in proce-dures analogous to radioimmunoassay (Sections 11.1 and 11.2; there are also ELISA versions of the two-site IRMA to detect and measure antigen, Section 11.3). A simple binding ELISA using alkaline phos-phatase conjugated anti-immunoglobulin for detection of specific anti-bodies is described below (cf. radioimmunoassay, Section 11.1).

11.4.1   Preparation of alkaline phosphatase conjugated antibody

Most commercial preparations of enzyme-conjugated antibodies are reliable and are usually better than can be made in the ordinary laboratory (see also reagents for immunohistochemistry — Section 12.3.1). However, the procedure below usually produces a workable conjugate if you do not wish to purchase or if the one required is not commercially available.

Materials and equipment

Affinity purified antibody (Section 10.3.1) — 2 mg/ml
1 pellet alkaline phosphatase (Sigma — Appendix 3)
Phosphate buffered saline (PBS — Appendix 2)
0.05 M tris-HCl pH 8.0
Glutaraldehyde (25% v/v)

Procedure

1   Add 0.85 ml antibody to the enzyme pellet. Dialyse against PBS at 4°C overnight (this removes the ammonium sulphate present in the enzyme pellet).
2   Make up volume to 1 ml with PBS and add 8 μl of glutaraldehyde. Incubate at room temperature for 2 h.
3   Dialyse at 4°C overnight against PBS (2 changes of 500 ml) and then for 24 h against tris buffer (3 changes of 500 ml each). Store the conjugate at 4°C.

11.4.2 ELISA for antibody

The procedure described below works for most antigens; it can be applied to albumin as an illustration for a class practical or demonstration. A similar assay can be used routinely to screen for antibodies against rubella to assess whether an individual has already been exposed, and hence is immune, to these organisms. The assays for antibodies against HIV (AIDS virus) used in blood transfusion centres to screen for donations likely to contain the AIDS virus, are also similar although other assays using competitive binding based on the two-site IRMA (Section 11.3) have recently been developed.

Materials and equipment

0.05 M sodium carbonate pH 9.6 containing 0.02% sodium azide
Antigen (1–20 μg/ml in carbonate buffer)
Phosphate buffered saline (PBS — Appendix 2) containing 0.05% Tween 20 and 0.02% sodium azide
Microelisa plates (Dynatech, Nunc, Sterilin — Appendix 3)
Antiserum against antigen
Alkaline phosphatase conjugated anti-immunoglobulin (Section 11.4.1) specific for species of first antibody
p-nitrophenyl phosphate, disodium hexahydrate (Sigma — Appendix 3) — 1 mg/ml in carbonate buffer containing 0.5 mM magnesium chloride
1 M sodium hydroxide
Spectrophotometer with microcuvette for 250 μl, or microelisa reader (Dynatech, Flow, Wellcome — Appendix 3)

Procedure

1   Pipette 200 μl antigen solution into each well of the microelisa plate and incubate overnight at 4°C (this coats the wells with antigen).
2   If the antigen is not precious then remove the solution by inverting over a sink. Otherwise remove with a Pasteur pipette (cover the tip with a small piece of soft plastic tubing to prevent scratching the antigen-coated wells); the aspirated solution can be stored at 4°C and used for at least 4 subsequent coatings.
3   Wash the wells three times by filling with PBS-Tween (a 5–20 litre aspirator makes this convenient) and emptying (invert plate over a sink and tap briskly). Avoid getting air bubbles in the wells which interfere with the washing.
4   Rinse with water, allow to dry inverted and store covered at room temperature.
5   Prepare doubling dilutions of first antibody in PBS-Tween from 1/100 to about 1/51 200 (10 dilutions) and add 200 μl of each dilution in duplicate to separate wells. Cover and incubate at room temperature for 2 h.

6   Invert plate over a sink and tap to remove antibody dilutions. Wash three times as in step 3. Place inverted on a paper towel for 1 min to remove excess liquid.

7   Prepare 1/1000 dilution of alkaline phosphatase conjugated anti-immunoglobulin in PBS-Tween and add 200 μl of this to each well. Cover and incubate at room temperature for 2 h.

8   Invert plate over sink and tap to remove conjugate. Wash three times as in step 3. Place inverted on a paper towel for 1 min to remove excess liquid.

9   Add 200 μl p-nitrophenyl phosphate solution to each well and incubate at room temperature for 20–30 min.

10   Add 50 μl sodium hydroxide to each well, mix and read the absorbance of each well at 405 nm in the spectrophotometer or microelisa reader.

Notes

1   This procedure will work for most antigens but the concentration may need to be increased (see Section 11.1.1). Microelisa plates are designed to give high reproducible binding with most proteins. Other types of plate can be used in some cases and these are usually cheaper. If problems with antigen binding are encountered, try another type of plate.

2   See Section 11.1.1, notes 1–5.

3   The absorbance of the samples should be measured as soon as possible. If it is read immediately then the sodium hydroxide step can be omitted. For large numbers of samples some type of automatic spectrophotometer is essential.

4   The optimum dilution of the conjugate should be determined by experiment, but 1/1000 works for most conjugates.

5   Incubation times with antibody can be decreased to 30–40 min (with some loss of binding) if speed is important — e.g. class practical. Incubation at 37°C will speed the reactions.

6   The amount of antigen absorbed onto the wells can be monitored using the detergent-insensitive BCA protein reagent (Section 11.1.2, note 3) after step 3.

7   Antigens solubilized in detergents (Section 4.4 *et seq.*) do not usually bind as well to the plates. Non-ionic detergents can be removed by absorption to beads during the coating (Drexler *et al.*, 1986).

12 Immunocytochemistry and immunohistochemistry

12.1 INTRODUCTION

This chapter discusses ways of directly visualizing the cellular distribution of a molecule using labelled antibodies or other ligands. The label can be fluorescent for fluorescence microscopy (Section 12.2), enzymic (Section 12.3), radioactive for autoradiography (Section 12.4) or electron dense for electron microscopy (Section 12.5). The target structures can be whole cells (for examination of surface molecules), cells fixed onto slides or sections through solid tissue. Immunohistochemical examination of an antibody or antiserum on sections from a wide range of tissue types enables the tissue distribution of the antigen to be determined.

In most cases an 'indirect' binding or 'sandwich' technique is preferred (cf. radioimmunoassay, Section 11.1). This involves addition of unlabelled antibody to the target structure and detection of bound molecules by a labelled second antibody directed against the first. The indirect procedure removes the complication of labelling many different antibodies (e.g. when screening hybridoma supernatants for monoclonal antibodies) by using just a few labelled second antibodies. It is also more sensitive than 'direct' binding because of the signal amplification provided by several labelled second antibodies attaching to each first antibody. A simple control should be included to determine the background direct binding between the labelled second antibody and the target structure (e.g. pre-immune serum if the first antibody is conventional serum or another hybridoma antibody with irrelevant specificity if it is monoclonal). A useful modification of the indirect binding procedure employs the specific high affinity interaction (affinity constant, 10^{15} M^{-1}) between biotin (a low molecular weight vitamin) and avidin (an egg-white protein). The first antibody or other ligand is conjugated to biotin and then detected by interaction with labelled avidin (see example in Plate 1). Several labelled avidin/biotinyl antibody and lectin systems are commercially available (Sera-Lab, Vector — Appendix 3).

Direct binding is used for convenience during complicated manipulations if it is sensitive enough. It should also be used for measuring the number of binding sites of a ligand (Section 12.4).

Ideally the labelled antibody should be affinity purified (Section 10.3.1) or monoclonal (Section 2.3) to ensure that most labelled molecules are active and so reduce the background non-functional label (cf. radioimmunoassay, Chapter 11). Many commercial conjugates are made from IgG preparations, not affinity purified antibodies.

A reagent for recognizing all classes and subclasses of immunoglobulin is best raised against Fab (Section 3.4.2) so that a greater proportion of antibodies recognize the light chain (common to all classes). The use of pepsin-digested antibody fragment, F(ab')$_2$ (Section 3.4.3), prevents antibody binding to Fc receptors on cell surfaces. All antisera and antibody preparations should be centrifuged (10 000 g, 5 min or Beckman Microfuge, 2 min) before use to remove aggregates and complexes which can bind artefactually to cells.

For a comprehensive discussion of immunocytochemical techniques see Sternberger (1986).

12.2   IMMUNOFLUORESCENCE TECHNIQUES

These involve the use of fluorochrome labelled antibody to determine the distribution of antigen in fixed or unfixed microscopical preparations. The fluorochromes most commonly used are fluorescein (yellow-green) and tetramethylrhodamine (red), both of which can be readily conjugated to immunoglobulin (Section 12.2.3).

12.2.1   Fluorescence microscopes

Most large microscope manufacturers produce microscopes equipped with fluorescence optics (e.g. Leitz, Zeiss — Appendix 3). These are of two basic types: transmitted light and incident light (epifluorescence), which differ in the manner by which the specimen is illuminated with excitatory radiation. Transmitted light microscopes rely on illumination of the specimen from below, in a manner analogous to conventional visible light microscopes. Incident light microscopes illuminate the specimen by passage of excitatory light down through the objective lens onto the upper surface of the specimen. Figure 12.1 shows these processes diagrammatically.

Incident light microscopes are preferable for most immunofluorescence techniques, and most modern microscopes are of this type. Background fluorescence is usually lower and this arrangement also has some optical advantages. Transmitted light microscopes are unsuitable for examination of cells labelled in suspension (e.g. for cell surface investigations) or if the less sensitive direct labelling technique is used.

Selection of the correct lamp, filters and beam splitters is important for good results (Fig. 12.1). Normally a high pressure mercury lamp is used to provide excitatory light because, although ultra-violet wavelengths are not required for fluorescein or rhodamine, most non-UV light sources lack suffcent energy in the required ranges to give good fluorescence. A range of filters suitable for selecting correct excitatory radiation for fluorescein (λ_{max} = 495 nm) or tetramethylrhodamine (λ_{max} = 515 nm) are available commercially as are appropriate barrier filters and beam splitters.

262

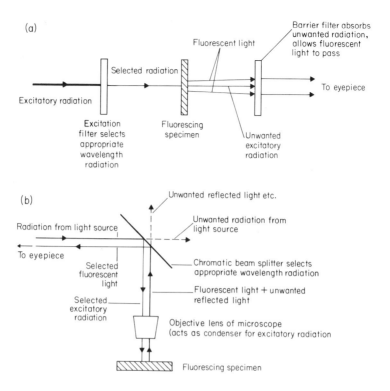

Fig. 12.1 Diagram of the methods of specimen illumination used in fluorescence microscopy. (a) Transmitted light fluorescence. (b) Incident light fluorescence (epi-fluorescence). See Section 12.2.1 for explanation.

12.2.2 Flow microfluorimetry

The flow microfluorimeter analyses and can separate cells on the basis of their fluorescence and light scattering properties. This is achieved by introducing cells in suspension into a liquid jet and causing them to pass one at a time through the beam of a laser. Each cell is characterized by its ability to scatter light (usually related to cell size, but can be modified to show other properties) and by its fluorescence emission when excited by the laser. A detailed description and discussion of the flow microfluorimeter is beyond the scope of this book, but a simplified diagram of the essential parts is shown in Fig. 12.2.

The flow microfluorimeter will quantitate the fluorescence of labelled cells (it is very difficult to obtain the quantitative data from immunofluorescence microscopy). Once the machine is set up, results can be obtained quickly and the technique is much less laborious than alternative approaches (e.g. autoradiography, Section 12.4).

Data from the flow microfluorimeter can be displayed in two ways:
1 as a dot-plot which records for each cell the intensity of fluorescence as abscissa and light scatter as ordinate;

263

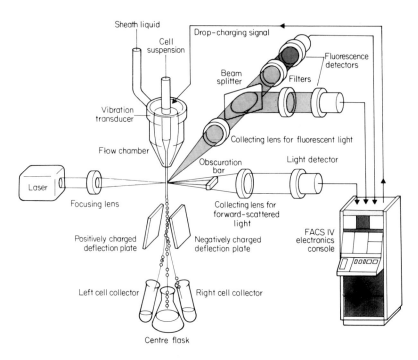

Sheath liquid
Cell suspension
Drop-charging signal
Fluorescence detectors
Beam splitter
Filters
Vibration transducer
Collecting lens for fluorescent light
Flow chamber
Obscuration bar
Light detector
Laser
Focusing lens
Collecting lens for forward-scattered light
Positively charged deflection plate
Negatively charged deflection plate
FACS IV electronics console
Left cell collector
Right cell collector
Centre flask

Fig. 12.2 The flow microfluorimeter (FACS IV) system (Section 12.2.2). Reproduced from Becton Dickinson manual with permission.

2 as a profile histogram with fluorescence intensity or light scatter as the ordinate and number of cells as abscissa.

Examples of these displays are shown in Figs. 12.3 and 12.4. More recent models of the flow microfluorimeter are capable of 3-dimensional 'isometric' display of 3 parameters (usually number of cells, light scatter and the fluorescence intensity).

The flow microfluorimeter is able to sort cells according to parameters set by the operator. Hence, a required cell population can be isolated from a mixture and this can be accomplished aseptically for subsequent cell culture.

This procedure is usually much more reliable and reproducible than specific cell isolation by affinity chromatography (Section 10.3.6). The drawbacks of the flow microfluorimeter are its cost and the specialized knowledge required for operation and maintenance of the instrument.

12.2.3 Conjugation of fluorochromes to immunoglobulins

Any fluorochrome capable of covalent attachment to immunoglobulin can be used for immunofluorescence microscopy. Fluorescein or tetramethylrhodamine isothiocyanate are normally preferred because they react readily with immunoglobulin (no coupling reagents required), produce stable conjugates and give bright distinctive fluoresc-

264

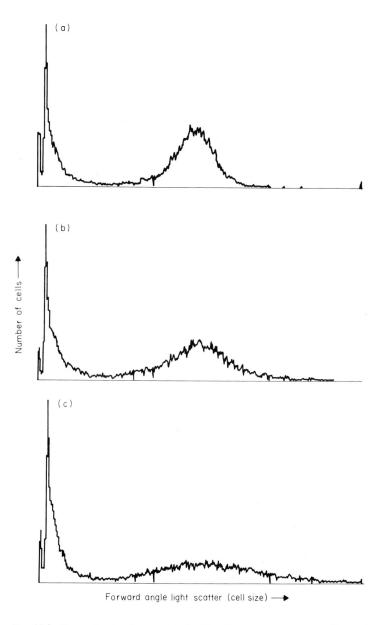

Forward angle light scatter (cell size) ⟶

Fig. 12.3 Flow microfluorimetry analysis of lymphocytes separated according to their size on Percoll gradients (courtesy of Susan King and John Murphy). B lymphocytes (4 × 10^7) from a human tonsil (Section 4.3.2) were suspended in 2 ml 72% Percoll (Pharmacia — Appendix 3) and layered under a step gradient composed of 62.5%, 57.5% and 40% Percoll (2 ml of each). The gradients were centrifuged for 10 min at 800 *g*. Cells at the interfaces were removed and analysed by forward angle light scatter using an EPICS V flow cytometer (Coulter Electronics — Appendix 3). (a) 62.5/72% interface — no large, activated cells; (b) 57.5/62.5% interface — some larger cells; (c) 40/57.5% interface — many large, activated cells. The Percoll suspension from the manufacturers is diluted 9+1 with 9% (w/v) NaCl to give isotonic medium. This stock is called 100% and further diluted with 0.9% (w/v) NaCl to give the concentrations used.

265

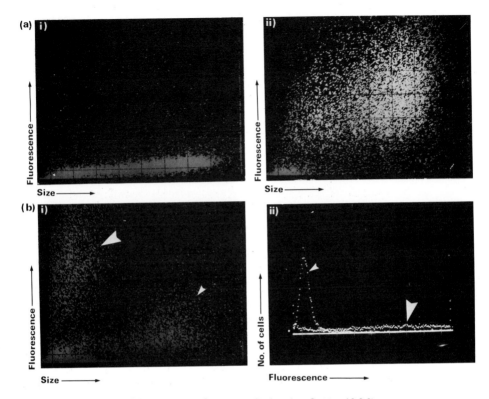

Fig. 12.4 Flow microfluorimeter displays (see Section 12.2.2).
(a) Dot plots of erythrocytes labelled with rabbit anti-β-globin chain followed by fluorescein labelled anti-rabbit IgG, (i) from a fetus with β-thalassaemia (negative for β-globin), (ii) from a normal fetus (positive for β-globin).
(b) Analysis of a mixture of adult erythrocytes (large arrows) and fetal erythrocytes (small arrows) labelled as in (a). The two cell populations are analysed on the basis of both size (adult erythrocytes are smaller than fetal erythrocytes) and fluorescence intensity (adult cells are more intensely labelled with anti-β-globin than fetal cells). (i) Dot plot; (ii) a profile histogram. Courtesy of Dr S. Thorpe.

ence. More recently Texas red and phycoerythrin have been used as fluorochromes for immunohistochemistry and flow microfluorimetry. Their individual fluorescences are easily distinguishable with appropriate filters, making them ideal for use in double-labelling techniques.

For single-labelling techniques, selection of fluorochrome is a matter of personal choice; some people prefer the harsher fluorescein whereas the softer rhodamine is reported to be less susceptible to quenching.

Many fluorochrome-conjugated antibodies are available commercially, especially species-specific anti-immunoglobulin (Miles, Nordic — Appendix 3), and there is little to be gained in conjugating an antibody in the laboratory if it can be purchased. However, for novel antibodies, the conjugation technique is described below. It is essential to prepare the immunoglobulin fraction from an antiserum before

266

conjugation (see Chapter 3) and it is better to use affinity purified antibody (Section 10.3.1). Conjugation can be problematical with some antibodies.

Materials and equipment

Immunoglobulin
Fluorescein or tetramethylrhodamine isothiocyanate (Sigma — Appendix 3)
Phosphate buffered saline (PBS — Appendix 2)
0.25 M sodium carbonate pH 9.0 containing 0.1 M sodium chloride
Sephadex G-25 column equilibrated with PBS (Section 1.2.1) 3 cm × 15 cm (fluorescein) or 3 cm × 30 cm (tetramethylrhodamine)
UV spectrophotometer

Procedure

1 Dissolve or dialyse the immunoglobulin in the carbonate buffer to give a protein concentration of 10–20 mg/ml. The final volume should be less than 8 ml for the Sephadex columns described.
2 Add 0.05 mg of fluorochrome isothiocyanate per mg of protein and mix at 4°C overnight.
3 Apply the mixture to the Sephadex column and elute with PBS. Two coloured fractions will be visible. Collect the first one (conjugate) and discard the second (unbound fluorochrome).

Notes

1 The fluorescein/protein ratio can be found by measuring the absorbance of the conjugate at 280 and 495 nm:

$$\text{molar ratio} = \frac{2.87 \times A_{495}}{A_{280} - 0.35 \times A_{495}}$$

This should be 2–4 for most purposes.
2 The relative impurity of most tetramethylrhodamine isothiocyanate preparations makes it difficult to calculate the conjugation ratio for this fluorochrome. More than 0.05 mg/mg of protein may be required for sufficient substitution.
3 The conjugates should be titrated to find the dilution most suitable for use (i.e. high specific fluorescence with low background) and then appropriately diluted aliquots stored at −20°C or lower. Include 1 mg/ml albumin or haemoglobin in the diluent for antibody concentrations less than 0.1 mg/ml.

12.2.4 Labelling of whole cells in suspension

Cell surface components can be visualized by the addition of ligands to whole cells in suspension. Large ligands, such as antibodies, cannot penetrate the plasma membrane of viable cells to interact with internal components. In certain cells, notably lymphocytes, the cross-linkage by antibodies or other ligands causes the surface molecules to aggregate into 'patches' which then accumulate as a 'cap' over one pole of the cell and are eventually endocytosed or shed (Taylor *et al.*, 1971). The movement of these molecules is easily followed by a fluorescent label. Such observations can provide valuable information on the interaction between molecules. In one such procedure, molecule A is induced to cap by a fluorescein-labelled anti-A antibody and molecule B is observed later by the addition of rhodamine-labelled anti-B antibody under non-capping conditions (see below). If there is a strong inter-action between A and B, then B will also be capped along with A (this is termed 'co-capping'); conversely, if there is no such interaction, B will remain dispersed around the cell periphery. For example, capping of β_2-microglobulin causes the co-capping of the major transplanta-tion antigens (HLA-A, –B and –C in man; H–2K, D and L in mouse), thus proving the strong interaction between these polypeptide chains in the whole HLA or H–2 molecule (cf. Section 10.4.1).

However, investigation of the binding of antibodies to cells (as opposed to the consequences of such binding) should be carried out under non-capping conditions to prevent rearrangement or even loss of surface molecules. Sodium azide at 0–4°C deprives the cell of the energy necessary for capping. When looking specifically for cell sur-face molecules, the viability of the initial preparation of cells should be high (Section 4.1.1).

Although the example below involves antibodies, the procedure can be applied to any ligand affinity system (e.g. lectins, hormones, drugs) providing the ligand can be labelled fluorescently (Section 12.2.3). A flow microfluorimeter can be used to fractionate fluor-escently labelled cells or to measure the number of labelled molecules they have bound (Section 12.2.2).

Materials and equipment

Human peripheral lymphocytes (2×10^7) cultured overnight in RPMI 1640 containing 10% fetal calf serum (Section 4.2)
Rabbit anti-(human immunoglobulin, all classes) serum (Miles, Nor-dic, Seward — Appendix 3)
Rabbit anti-(human β_2-microglobulin) serum (Dako, Miles — Appen-dix 3)
Pre-immune, or normal rabbit serum
Fluorescein conjugated anti-(rabbit immunoglobulin) (Miles, Nordic — Appendix 3)
BMEE (Table 4.1) containing 0.1% albumin and 0.1% sodium azide
Mounting fluid (Appendix 2)
Polystyrene round-bottomed tubes 10.5 mm × 63.5 mm (Luckham — Appendix 3)

268

Pre-cleaned microscope slides and coverslips
Nail varnish
Incident light fluorescence microscope, preferably with phase contrast
(Section 12.2.1)

Procedure

1 Suspend the lymphocytes in 10 ml BMEE and centrifuge at 250 *g* for 5 min. Discard the supernatant and repeat the suspension and centrifugation.

2 Resuspend the final cell pellet in 1 ml BMEE and dispense 50 μl into each of 18 numbered polystyrene tubes. Place the BMEE on ice to cool.

3 Prepare 150 μl of 1/5, 1/15 and 1/50 dilutions of each rabbit serum in BMEE and add 50 μl of each dilution of each serum in duplicate to separate tubes containing the cells. Mix carefully and incubate at room temperature for 30 min.

4 Add 1 ml of cold BMEE to each tube, mix and centrifuge at 250 *g* for 5 min at 4°C. Aspirate the supernatants and repeat the suspension and centrifugation.

5 Aspirate the supernatants and resuspend the final cell pellet in the residual supernatant.

6 Prepare 500 μl of 1/10 and 1/25 dilution of fluorescent antibody and add 50 μl of the 1/10 dilution to one sample of each rabbit serum dilution (step 3) and 50 μl of the 1/25 dilution to the duplicate. Mix gently and incubate at room temperature for 30 min.

7 Wash the cells 3 times as in step 4 and resuspend the final cell pellet in the residual supernatant.

8 Add about 10 μl of mounting fluid to each tube, mix and transfer about half to a labelled microscope slide (there is room for 2 samples on each 26 mm $\times$ 76 mm slide). Place a coverslip over each sample and seal around the edge with nail varnish.

9 View with a fluorescence microscope using oil or water immersion lenses, objective magnification $\times 20 - \times 100$. First locate the cells under phase or transmitted light and then switch to UV illumination to observe the fluorescein label. Figure 12.5 shows examples of fluorescently labelled lymphocytes.

Pick dilutions of antisera that have given bright fluorescent cell staining when compared with the same dilution of control normal serum. Select a field of view under normal light containing a good spread of cells and record the total number of cells in the visible area. Switch to UV illumination and record the number of cells *in the same area* that are peripherally stained with fluorescence. Record separately cells which are brightly stained all over — these are dead. Select a second field of view and continue until at least 200 cells have been recorded.

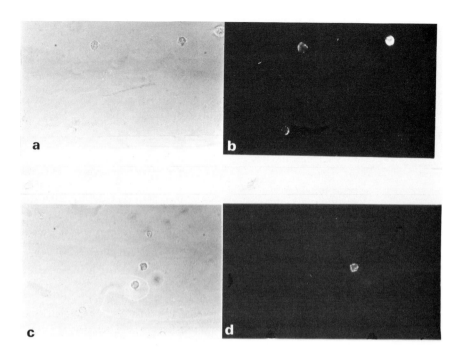

Fig. 12.5 Indirect fluorescence microscopy of surface labelled cells (Section 12.2.4). a and b, human peripheral blood lymphocytes reacted with rabbit anti-β_2-microglobulin followed by fluorescein-labelled anti-rabbit IgG, the same field viewed for (a) transmitted light or (b) fluorescence showing 3 cells labelled to various degrees (the amount of antibody bound can be quantitated by flow microfluorimetry analysis, Section 12.2.2). c and d, the same lymphocyte preparation reacted with rabbit anti-human immunoglobulin followed by fluorescein labelled anti-rabbit IgG, the same field viewed for (c) transmitted light or (d) fluorescence, showing only 1 labelled cell (B lymphocyte) out of 6. Compare peroxidase (Fig. 12.9) and autoradiography (Fig. 12.10).

For each antiserum:

$$\text{percentage positively stained} = \frac{\text{number peripherally stained}}{\text{total cells} - \text{dead cells}} \times 100$$

This value should be greater than 95% for β_2-microglobulin (present on all lymphocytes) and 5–15% for immunoglobulin (present on B cells only).

Notes

1 To observe capping, incubate with the first antisera at 37°C for 15–30 min without azide (step 3). Subsequent procedures should be at 0–4°C in the presence of azide to prevent endocytosis or shedding of caps. Not all surface molecules cap well; immunoglobulin is one of the best. For a review of capping, see Schreiner & Unanue (1976).

2 Once the dilution of each antiserum giving good staining has been established, the titration can be omitted in subsequent tests. If high

270

staining is seen in the control, adsorb the fluorochrome conjugate on whole lymphocytes (10^8 cells/ml conjugate, 30 min, 0–4°C).

3   The incubation times should be extended for low affinity antibodies. Incubation at 37°C may increase sensitivity without increasing the background. Beware of capping occurring during long incubations — carry out at 0–4°C if necessary.

4   The lymphocytes are cultured in immunoglobulin-free medium (Section 4.1) before staining to decrease extrinsic cytophilic immunoglobulin.

5   The two antigens can be detected on the same sample using different fluorochromes for the two antibodies (e.g. fluorescein anti-rabbit/rabbit anti-β_2-microglobulin and rhodamine anti-mouse/mouse anti-immunoglobulin). Ensure that none of the antibodies cross-react and adsorb if necessary. In this experiment you will find that all of the immunoglobulin positive cells (i.e. B cells) also carry surface β_2-microglobulin.

6   For screening hybridomas (Section 2.3) use neat culture supernatant but dilute ascites fluid as for serum (step 3) or even more. For large numbers of samples the procedure can be carried out in U-shaped microtitre plates as described for the similar radioimmunoassay (Section 11.1.2) and the cells then dried and methanol or acetone fixed (Section 12.2.5 and 12.4) on 10-sample slides (Hendley — Appendix 3)

7   For better comparative work, a large number of target cells can be fixed with glutaraldehyde (Section 4.1.2) and stored until used. However, this increases non-specific binding; 1% albumin partially reduces this.

8   Internal antigens can be detected on cells in suspension if they are fixed and then permeabilized to allow antibody molecules to enter (cf. Section 12.2.5). The following procedure works for erythrocytes; different organic solvents may be better for other cells.

Wash 2–10 μl packed erythrocytes 3 times by suspension in 10 ml PBS and centrifugation (500 *g*, 4 min). Resuspend in 10 ml 3.7% w/v formaldehyde in PBS and incubate at room temperature for 30 min. Wash twice in PBS as above.

Treat the packed cells sequentially, at −20°C, with 50% (v/v) acetone for 2 min, acetone for 5 min and 50% (v/v) acetone for 2 min — centrifuge at 1000 *g* for 4 min and discard the supernatant between each treatment.

Wash twice more in PBS and label with antibodies in suspension as described above.

12.2.5   Labelling of fixed cells and tissue sections

Intracellular components can be visualized by addition of antibodies to cells fixed onto a microscope slide. The fixation procedure dissolves and removes some of the lipid so that all of the cellular protein (both

271

surface and intracellular) and nucleic acids are accessible to added antibodies. The fixed, dried cell approximates to a two-dimensional projection of the molecules and organelles of the living whole cell. A fixed cell cannot be capped.

The slides of fixed cells can be produced in large numbers (steps 1–4 below) and stored desiccated at −20°C to provide standard target structures for regular screening. The procedure is more convenient than that for whole cells (Section 12.2.4) for screening a lot of samples, especially if a multi-sample slide is used, and hence it is ideal for the routine assay of hybridoma supernatants. However, it usually gives a lower staining of surface components.

Because of the scarcity of well-defined antisera against internal cellular components, no specific example has been included in the procedure below. However, it will work well with antibodies against cytoskeletal elements (e.g. actin, myosin, tubulin, intermediate fila-

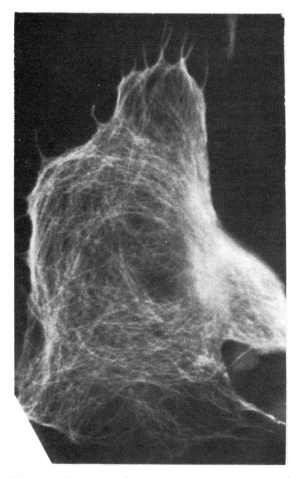

Fig. 12.6 Visualization of microtubules in a fixed human fibroblast by immuno-fluorescence microscopy (Section 12.2.5). The cells were treated with rabbit anti-tubulin followed by fluorescein labelled anti-rabbit IgG.

ment proteins; Fig. 12.6) or nuclear antigens (e.g. Epstein-Barr viral nuclear antigen) or internal organelles or even cytoplasmic proteins (Fig. 12.7). Alternatively, other specific binding systems can be used — e.g. lectin–glycoprotein and heavy meromyosin–actin. This procedure can be used to stain tissue sections (either cryostat or paraffin embedded) but rigorous controls must be included to reveal artefactual staining. High non-specific background fluorescence can also be a problem.

Materials and equipment

Cells under study
Antiserum against internal components
Appropriate control for antiserum (i.e. pre-immune serum or different monoclonal antibody)
Fluorescently labelled antibody specific for the immunoglobulin of the first antibody (Nordic, Miles — Appendix 3)
Phosphate buffered saline (PBS — Appendix 2)
5% (w/v) bovine serum albumin in PBS

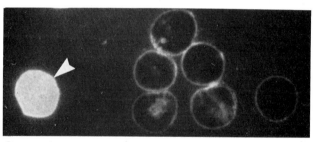

a

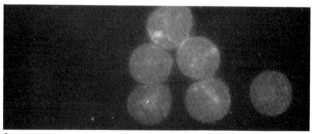

b

Fig. 12.7 Micrograph of a fixed blood smear from a fetus afflicted with β-thalassaemia viewed for (a) fluorescein or (b) rhodamine fluorescence. The smear was treated with rabbit anti-β-globin chain and guinea-pig anti-γ-globin chain followed by fluorescein-labelled anti-rabbit IgG and rhodamine-labelled anti-guinea-pig IgG. The fluorescein-labelled (arrowed) cell (a) contains only β-globin chains and is derived from the mother. The other cells (b), which are labelled with rhodamine contain only γ-globin chains and are derived from the fetus. Courtesy of Dr S. Thorpe.

273

Fixative — acetone cooled to −20°C (not in freezer unless spark-proof)

Mounting fluid (Appendix 2)

Pre-cleaned microscope slides, 26 mm × 76 mm, and cover slips

Diamond marker

Humid chamber

Incident light fluorescence microscope, preferably with phase contrast (Section 12.2.1)

Nail varnish

Procedure

1   Wash the target cells twice by centrifugation and resuspension in PBS. Suspend the final cell pellet in albumin solution to 5×10^7 cells/ml (the protein solution cushions the cells against damage during smearing).

2   Prepare cell smears:

(a) Place 10 μl of cell suspension about 2 cm from the end of a microscope slide.

(b) Touch the drop with the edge of a second slide held at 30–45° to the first so that it spreads across the width of the slide.

(c) Smear the cells along the length of the slide with one smooth quick movement. Do not press the slides together too hard.

(d) Check with a microscope for an even spread of cells (i.e. high density without touching) and adjust the cell concentration used if necessary.

3   With the conditions established in step 2, smear all the cells onto slides and allow to dry tilted slightly downwards in the direction of smearing.

4   Label the slides at the uncoated end with the diamond marker and engrave a 1 cm diameter circle on the centre as the test area. Dip the slides in acetone at −20°C for 30 sec and allow to dry.

5   Dilute the specific antiserum and control in PBS (for example, as in Section 12.2.4, step 3) and apply 100 μl of each to the scribed test areas of different slides. Incubate in a humid chamber for 30 min at room temperature.

6   Wash the slides by soaking in 3 changes of PBS each for 5 min and remove excess liquid with a tissue around the *edge* of the slide (do not touch the central test area or allow it to dry out).

7   Dilute the fluorescently labelled antibody in PBS as in Section 12.2.4, step 6, and apply 100 μl to the scribed test area of each slide. Incubate in a humid chamber for 30 min at room temperature.

8   Wash the slides as in step 6. Place about 10 μl of mounting fluid on top of the test area. Cover with a cover slip and seal around the edge with nail varnish.

9   View on a fluorescence microscope as in Section 12.2.4, step 9. Fixed cells are not visible easily under transmitted light and so it is

274

difficult to detect and count non-fluorescent cells without phase contrast.

Notes

1   As an alternative to steps 2 and 3, cells can be spread on a slide easily, reproducibly and with little damage by the use of a cyto-centrifuge.

2   Double labelling with two fluorochromes can be carried out as in Section 12.2.4, note 5. In addition, whole cells can be surface labelled (or even capped) with one fluorochrome-antibody, and then fixed on a slide and their internal components visualized by a second fluorochrome-antibody. Either fluorescent method can be combined with autoradiography (Section 12.4), although the silver grains produced by the isotope may quench the fluorescence somewhat.

3   The procedure is also applicable to thin sections cut through solid tissue and mounted and fixed on a slide. If artefactual staining and/or high background fluorescence is a problem try enzyme-labelled second antibody (Section 12.3).

4   See notes 2–5, Section 12.2.4.

5   The method is useful for the rapid screening of samples during hybridoma production — see the beginning of this Section and note 6, Section 12.2.4.

12.3   ENZYME LABEL TECHNIQUES

These techniques use antibody conjugated to an enzyme (usually peroxidase or alkaline phosphatase) to detect antigen. The enzyme label is localized by reaction with an invisible substrate that produces a visible, insoluble product. This can be detected by conventional light microscopy or electron microscopy.

The principal advantages of enzyme over fluorescent labels are that a less sophisticated microscope can be used (no necessity for fluor-escence optics), greater sensitivity can be achieved and identification of labelled cells may be easier, especially in sections of tissue showing complex morphology.

A disadvantage is that many cells possess endogenous enzyme activity (particularly peroxidase). High backgrounds and false positives can be a problem and so careful controls are necessary. In general, alkaline phosphatase is less susceptible than peroxidase to these arte-facts.

Both direct and indirect procedures can be used (Section 12.1) and also further sophistications such as the peroxidase–anti-peroxidase technique or biotin–avidin system. Although conjugation of antibodies to enzymes can be carried out in the ordinary laboratory it is fairly difficult to produce good reagents for immunocytochemistry and immunohistochemistry. It is recommended that the indirect technique

275

be used and conjugated second antibodies purchased (Dako, Sigma — Appendix 3). However, if necessary, the conjugation methods for peroxidase (Section 12.3.1) and alkaline phosphatase (Section 11.4.1) work for some purposes.

12.3.1 Conjugation of peroxidase to immunoglobulins

Peroxidase is normally obtained from horseradish root because this plant produces a stable, highly active enzyme which is easily purified in good yield. Conjugation is achieved using glutaraldehyde to cross-link immunoglobulin to enzyme. There are many other conjugation methods; most are more complex but may give a better reagent.

Materials and equipment

Horseradish peroxidase (Sigma — Appendix 3)
Immunoglobulin or antibody (see Section 12.1)
0.1 M sodium phosphate pH 7.0
Glutaraldehyde — 0.02% in the phosphate buffer, freshly prepared
Phosphate buffered saline (PBS — Appendix 2)
Sephadex G-25 column (1 cm × 30 cm) equilibrated with PBS (Section 1.2.1)

Procedure

1 Dialyse or dissolve the immunoglobulin in the phosphate buffer. Adjust the final protein concentration to 2 mg/ml.
2 Dissolve 5 mg of peroxidase in 0.5 ml of phosphate buffer and add this to 0.5 ml of immunoglobulin solution (1 mg protein) and 1 ml of glutaraldehyde solution. Mix at room temperature for 1 h.
3 Apply the mixture to the Sephadex column and elute with PBS. Monitor the absorbance at 280 nm. The peroxidase–immunoglobulin conjugate (and any free proteins) are eluted in the exclusion volume.
4 Aliquot the complex and store at −20°C or lower.

12.3.2 Labelling using peroxidase conjugated antibodies

Peroxidase conjugated antibodies are extremely sensitive reagents for immunohistochemical or immunocytochemical investigations. They are detected by the reaction of the enzyme with hydrogen peroxide and 3,3′-diaminobenzidine which produces a brown insoluble product (see Plate 1). The procedure described below is for staining tissue sections, but it can be adapted easily for use with cells.

Materials and equipment

Humid box suitable for incubations
Tissue sections (see note 1)

276

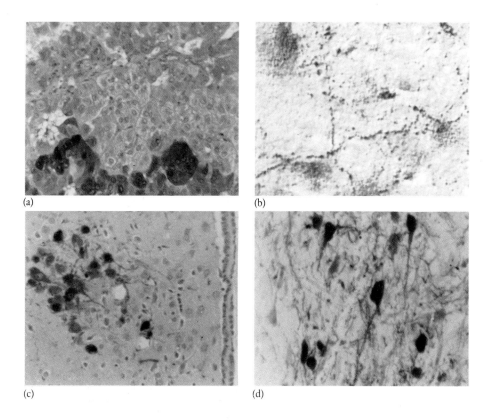

(a)

(b)

(c)

(d)

Plate 1 Immunohistochemistry using peroxidase and 3,3′–diaminobenzidine.

(a) 7 µm section of hamster adrenal fixed in bouins and paraffin embedded then incubated with anti-oxytocin antibody which was subsequently detected with biotinylated anti-immunoglobulin followed by strepavidin – peroxidase complex. The section was counter-stained with haematoxylin (blue). Pale brown is the cortex. The medulla consists of nor-adrenergic cells (unstained) and adrenergic cells (dark brown). Magnification × 180.

(b) 20 µm section of human locus coeruleus fixed at post-mortem in bouins and then incubated with anti-vasopressin which was subsequently detected using the PAP technique. The section was visualized using Nomarski optics which give the 3-dimensional effect. The specific staining shows fibres; the brown clumps are caused by natural pigmentation of the cells. Magnification × 810.

(c) 7µm section of rat hypothalamus fixed in bouins and paraffin embedded then incubated with anti-oxytocin which was subsequently detected using the PAP technique. The section was counter-stained with haematoxylin. Some, but not all, of the neurons in the paraventricular nucleus are stained (both cell bodies and fibres). The unstained line of cells is the ependyma of the third ventricle. Magnification × 85.

(d) 20 µm section of human hypothalamus fixed at post-mortem in bouins and then incubated with anti-vasopressin which was subsequently detected using the PAP technique. Compare with (c) where a similar distribution of stain is seen but the thinner section has given sharper definition. These immuno-stained thicker sections are useful for subsequent ultra-thin sectioning for electron microscopy. Magnification × 100.

Courtesy of Jan Hawthorn.

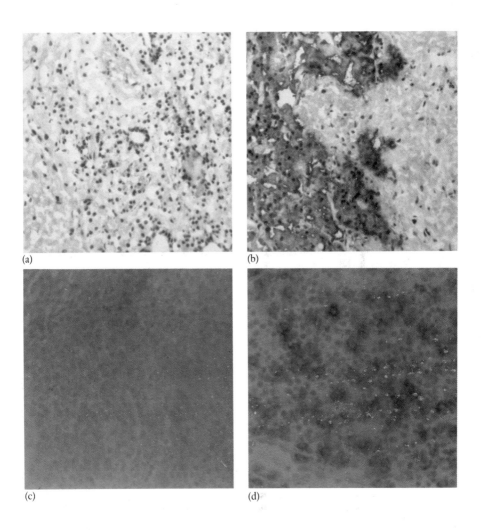

(a)   (b)

(c)   (d)

Plate 2 Immunohistochemistry using alkaline phosphatase conjugated antibodies.

(a) and (b) cryostat sections of pituitary gland processed with (a) irrelevant monoclonal antibody (negative control) and (b) monoclonal antibody specific for the neuropeptide β-lipotropin. Immunoreactivity was detected using alkaline phosphatase conjugated anti-mouse immunoglobulin and visualized using naphthol AS-BI phosphate/fast red substrate. The intense red immuno-staining is confined to the anterior/intermediate lobe, the posterior lobe (which contains no antigen) being negative. The sections are counter-stained with haematoxylin (nucleii stain blue). Courtesy of Lynne Trickett.

(c) and (d) cryostat sections of human tonsil processed with (c) irrelevant monoclonal antibody (negative control) and (d) monoclonal antibody specific for the CD8 (T8) suppressor/cytotoxic T lymphocyte antigen. Immunoreactivity was detected using alkaline phosphatase conjugated anti-mouse immunoglobulin and visualized using naphthol-AS phosphate/fast blue substrate. The CD8 antigen positive lymphocytes are stained blue, the red staining is due to the neutral red counter-stain. Courtesy of Varsha Patel.

Phosphate buffered saline (PBS; Appendix 2)
Antiserum or antibody against tissue antigen(s)
Appropriate control for antibody (i.e. pre-immune serum or different
  monoclonal antibody)
Peroxidase conjugated anti-immunoglobulin antibody, specific for the
  species of the first antibody (Dako, Miles, Sigma — Appendix 3)
Hydrogen peroxide, '100 vols', 30% (v/v)
0.2 M tris-HCl pH 7.6
3,3'-diaminobenzidine (Sigma — Appendix 3)
Dishes, slide holders and equipment for routine histology
Haematoxylin (Appendix 2)
Acetone
Xylene
Ethanol
DPX mountant (Raymond Lamb — Appendix 3)

Procedure

Steps 2–7 should be carried out in the humid box.
1 Fix sections for 10 min in acetone. Wash 3 times in PBS, 5–10 min
each (see note 3).
2 Incubate with diluted antibody or antiserum for 30–60 min at room
temperature (see note 2)
3 Wash 3 times in PBS, 5–10 min each.
4 Incubate with diluted peroxidase conjugated anti-immunoglobulin
for 30 min at room temperature (see note 2).
5 Wash as in step 3.
6 Prepare substrate solution: dissolve 5 mg 3,3'-diaminobenzidine in
10 ml tris-HCl buffer and just before use add 0.1 ml 1% (v/v) hydrogen peroxide solution.
7 Incubate section with substrate solution for 10 min at room
temperature and then wash once with PBS for 5–10 min.
8 Counter-stain with haematoxylin for 10 min (see note 4) and wash
under running *tap* water (see note 4).
9 Dehydrate sections by incubating for 2–3 min in 70% (v/v) ethanol
and then twice in absolute ethanol.
10 Clear by washing 3 times with xylene and mount in DPX. View
using transmitted light optics.

Notes

1 Cryostat sections 5–10 μm thick are usually best for immunohistochemistry but paraffin embedded sections can be used. However,
processing for embedding can lead to loss of some antigens or antigenic determinants. Cutting sections, particularly cryostat, is technically difficult and it is best to learn the procedures from an experienced worker. Tissue sections can be air dried, wrapped in foil and
stored desiccated at −70°C for some months, but some antigenic

determinants may be lost if fresh sections are not used. Tissue blocks should be stored in liquid nitrogen. A groove cut round each section with a diamond marker prevents reagents from running off the slide.

2 Each antibody and batch of conjugate should be titrated to determine the optimal working dilution. Most antisera or ascites fluid are used at $1/100 - 1/5000$; hybridoma supernatant at $1/10 - 1/100$; peroxidase conjugates at $1/50 - 1/200$. Addition of 0.02% Triton X100 helps penetration of the antibody into the tissue in some cases.

3 Endogenous peroxidase activity can be problematical. It is possible to inhibit this by pre-incubating sections with methanol/hydrogen peroxide before processing with antibody (step 2 onwards). For this, add 0.2 ml hydrogen peroxide ('100 vols') to 11.8 ml methanol and incubate sections with this solution for 10 min. The inhibitor solution must be freshly prepared.

4 Counter-staining with haematoxylin is not essential, but it allows the tissue morphology to be seen (haematoxylin stains nuclei). It is possible to use phase-contrast or Nomarski optics instead. If haematoxylin is used it is essential to carry out the final wash with tap-water (not distilled) as this is used to cause blueing of the counter stain.

12.3.3 Peroxidase–anti-peroxidase (PAP) labelling

In this technique the label consists of a complex formed between peroxidase and anti-peroxidase antibodies. The procedure is shown

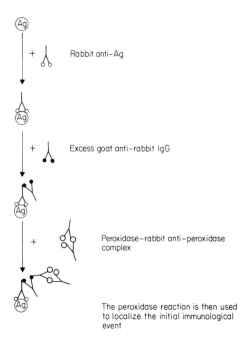

Rabbit anti-Ag

Excess goat anti-rabbit IgG

Peroxidase–rabbit anti-peroxidase complex

The peroxidase reaction is then used to localize the initial immunological event

Fig. 12.8 Diagrammatical representation of the peroxidase–anti-peroxidase (PAP) technique (Section 12.3.3).

schematically in Fig. 12.8. The advantages of the technique are its sensitivity due to several stage amplification and that no potentially destructive chemical coupling of peroxidase to immunoglobulin is required. However, the procedure is longer than the conventional technique and non-specific binding of the PAP complex to certain cells can cause high backgrounds and false positives.

Procedures are given below for labelling cells in suspension or tissue sections.

(a) PAP labelling of cells in suspension

Materials and equipment

Human peripheral lymphocyes (7×10^6) cultured overnight in RPMI 1640 10% fetal calf serum (Section 4.2)

Rabbit anti-(human immunoglobulin, all classes) serum (Miles, Nordic, Seward — Appendix 3)

Rabbit anti-(human β_2-microglobulin) serum (Dako, Miles — Appendix 3)

Normal rabbit serum

Goat anti-(rabbit immunoglobulin) serum (Miles, Nordic, Seward — Appendix 3)

Peroxidase–anti-peroxidase produced in rabbit (Dako, Miles — Appendix 3)

Normal goat serum

BMEE (Table 4.1) containing 0.1% albumin and 0.1% sodium azide

Phosphate buffered saline (PBS — Appendix 2)

50 mM tris-HCl pH 7.3

Acetone

3,3′-diaminobenzidine tetrahydrochloride (Polysciences, Sigma — Appendix 3)

Hydrogen peroxide, '100 vols', 30% (v/v)

Prewashed microscope slides and coverslips

DPX mountant (Raymond Lamb — Appendix 3)

Humid chamber

Coplin jar

Polystyrene round-bottomed tubes 10.5 × 63.5 mm (Luckham — Appendix 3)

Microscope

Nail varnish

Procedure

1   Suspend the lymphocytes in 350 μl of BMEE and pipette 50 μl (10^6 cells) into each of 6 tubes.

2   Prepare 1/5 and 1/50 dilutions of each rabbit serum (including control) and add 5 μl of each to separate cell aliquots. Incubate at room temperature for 30 min.

279

3   Centrifuge and wash the cells 3 times (Section 12.2.4, steps 4 and 5).

4   Smear each sample onto a separate slide and fix in acetone (Section 12.2.5, steps 2–4).

5   Wash slides in 50 ml PBS containing 1% normal goat serum. Dry edges of slides (Section 12.2.5, step 6) and place in humid chamber.

6   Apply 100 μl of a 1/10 dilution of goat anti-(rabbit immunoglobulin) to the test area of each smear. Incubate at room temperature for 30 min.

7   Wash slides twice in PBS containing 1% normal goat serum (50 ml, 5 min each).

8   Dry edges of slides and apply 100 μl of a 1/50 dilution of PAP to each slide. Incubate at room temperature for 30 min in a humid chamber.

9   Wash slides as in step 7 and then once in tris buffer.

10   React with 3,3′-diaminobenzidine, wash, mount and view, as described in Section 12.3.2.

Fig. 12.9 shows examples of PAP labelled lymphocytes.

(b)   PAP labelling of tissue sections

Materials and equipment

Fixed or cryostat cut sections on microscope slides
70% v/v ethanol
Methanol
Hydrogen peroxide, '100 vols', 30% (v/v)
Goat anti-(rabbit immunoglobulin) serum
Rabbit antiserum reacting with tissue antigens
Normal rabbit serum
Normal goat serum
Peroxidase–anti-peroxidase raised in rabbits (Dako, Miles — Appendix 3)
Phosphate buffered saline (PBS — Appendix 2)
50 mM tris-HCl pH 7.3
3,3′-diaminobenzidine tetrahydrochloride (Polysciences, Sigma — Appendix 3)
Cover slips
DPX mountant (Raymond Lamb — Appendix 3)
Microscope
Humid chamber
Coplin jar

Procedure

1   Incubate the sections in 70% v/v ethanol for 10 min, in methanol containing 1% (v/v) hydrogen peroxide for 10 min, and again in 70% v/v ethanol for 10 min and dry (this inactivates any endogenous peroxidase).

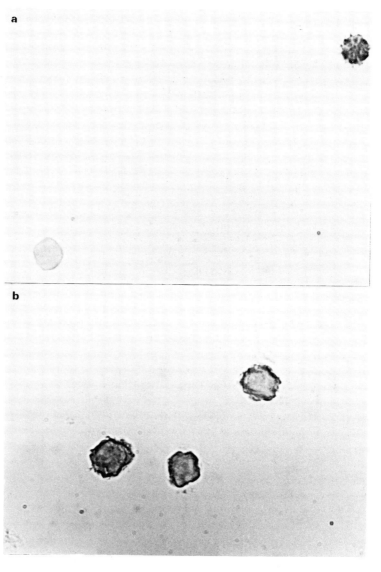

Fig. 12.9 PAP labelling of surface antigens on human peripheral blood lymphocytes (Section 12.3.3). The cells were reacted with (a) rabbit anti-human immunoglobulin or (b) rabbit anti-β_2-microglobulin and the bound antibody detected by the peroxidase–anti-peroxidase procedure. (a) A brown positive (B lymphocyte) and a negative cell; (b) 3 positive cells viewed by transmitted light. Compare fluorescence (Fig. 12.5) and auto-radiography (Fig. 12.10).

2 Incubate for 15 min with PBS, dry edges of slides and place in humid chamber.

3 Prepare dilutions of each rabbit serum (try 1/100 – 1/2000) and incubate separate tissue sections with 100 μl of each dilution at 4°C overnight.

4   Allow slides to warm to room temperature and then wash in 2 changes of 50 ml PBS containing 1% normal goat serum (10 min each).

5   Dry edges of slides and place in humid chamber. Incubate with PBS containing 3% normal goat serum for 15 min, and then with a 1/10 dilution of goat anti-(rabbit immunoglobulin) for 30 min at room temperature (100 μl/slide).

6   Wash in 3 changes of 50 ml PBS containing 1% normal goat serum (10 min each).

7   Dry edges of slides and place in humid chamber. Incubate with PBS containing 3% normal goat serum for 15 min, and then with 1/50 dilution of PAP for 30 min at room temperature (100 μl/slide).

8   Wash slides as in step 6 and then once in tris buffer.

9   React with 3,3'-diaminobenzidine as for Section 12.3.2, steps 6 and 7.

10   Wash with 3 changes of tris buffer (50 ml, 5 min each). Dry and dehydrate the sections and mount and view with transmitted light or Nomarski optics.

Notes

1   All dilutions of antibodies should be made in PBS containing 1% normal goat serum.

2   It is *essential* to carry out control experiments using pre-immune sera.

3   Background staining can sometimes be reduced by including 0.1% Triton X-100 in all washes of fixed cells and sections.

12.3.4   Labelling with alkaline phosphatase conjugated antibodies

Alkaline phosphatase conjugated antibodies can be used to produce intense immunohistochemical staining with low non-specific backgrounds. The enzyme conjugate is detected using a naphthol phosphate derivative as substrate and the substituted naphthol compound produced is visualized by forming a diazonium salt with fast red or fast blue to give a coloured product (see Plate 2). Levamisole is included in the substrate to inactivate the endogenous phosphatase activities of tissues.

Materials and equipment

Humid box suitable for incubations
Tissue sections (see Section 12.3.2, note 1)
Tris buffered saline (TBS — Appendix 2, no azide)
Antiserum or antibody against tissue antigen(s)
Appropriate control for antibody (i.e. pre-immune serum or a different monoclonal antibody)
Alkaline phosphatase conjugated anti-immunoglobulin, specific for

282

the species of first antibody (Sigma — Appendix 3)
Naphthol AS-BI phosphate, sodium salt (Sigma — Appendix 3)
Fast red TR salt (Sigma — Appendix 3; see note 2)
Dimethylformamide
Levamisole (Sigma — Appendix 3)
Veronal acetate buffer (Appendix 2)
Filter paper and funnel
Glycerol jelly (Appendix 2 or BDH — Appendix 3)
Haematoxylin (Appendix 2)
Dishes, slide holders and equipment for routine histology

Procedure

Steps 2–7 should be carried out in the humid box.
1   Fix slides for 10 min in acetone. Wash 3 times in TBS, 5–10 min each.
2   Incubate with diluted antibody for 30–60 min at room temperature (see note 1).
3   Wash 3 times with TBS, 5–10 min each.
4   Incubate with diluted alkaline phosphatase conjugated anti-immunoglobulin for 30 min at room temperature (see note 1).
5   Wash as in step 3.
6   Prepare substrate solution: dissolve 2.5 mg naphthol phosphate in 0.1 ml dimethylformamide and 5 mg fast red in 10 ml veronal acetate buffer. Mix the two solutions and dissolve 2.5 mg levamisole in the mixture. This must be freshly prepared and filtered just before use.
7   Incubate sections with substrate solution for 15 min and then wash once with TBS.
8   Counter-stain with haematoxylin for 10 min and wash for 10 min in running *tap* water (see Section 12.3.2, note 4).
9   Mount in glycerol jelly (do not dehydrate slides as the chromagen is soluble in alcohol — melt solid jelly by warming in boiling water bath). View using transmitted light optics.

Notes

1   Dilutions of first antibody are given in Section 12.3.2, note 2. Working dilution of Sigma alkaline phosphatase conjugates is usually 1/10.
2   Fast red TR salt produces an intense red immunostaining (see Plate 2) which contrasts well with the blue haematoxylin counter-stain. If blue immunostaining is desired, substitute naphthol AS phosphate and fast blue TR salt and use methyl green or (better) neutral red as a counter-stain. Choice of colour depends upon individual preference and any subsequent photographic procedures. Red colour blindness is fairly common in males and these individuals cannot see fast red immunostaining or neutral red counter-stain.

283

12.4 AUTORADIOGRAPHY OF CELLS

Autoradiography can be more sensitive than fluorescence microscopy and it gives some quantitative information on the distribution of molecules, although the flow microfluorimeter (Section 12.2.2) is considerably more convenient when studying whole cells. Autoradiography is a useful complement to the radioimmunoassay involving whole cells (Section 11.1.2) — the assay gives mean quantity of antisera bound by the cells and autoradiography reveals any differences in binding between subpopulations.

A light microscope without phase or UV facilities is adequate, although quantitation is laborious without a photometer system. Like enzyme labelling (Section 12.3), autoradiography has the advantage that the same labelling procedure can be used for both light and electron microscopy, thus giving more information.

The example below is given for comparison with fluorescence and PAP microscopy of whole cells (Sections 12.2.4 and 12.3.3) and with the radioimmunoassay for surface components (Section 11.1.2). It involves indirect binding, but direct techniques also work well because of the sensitivity of the detection system. Any interaction between whole cells and a radiolabelled ligand (e.g. lectins, hormones, drugs) can be visualized in this way. Fixed cells or tissue sections can also be labelled by an analogous procedure (cf. Section 12.2.5).

The labelled cells are smeared and fixed onto glass slides and then coated with an emulsion of radiosensitive material in a warm molten gel which sets as it cools. The radiosensitive film is therefore in direct contact with the molecules of the cells and this accounts for the high resolution which can be obtained. The emulsion is sensitive to all charged particles and so it will detect most radioactive isotopes, usually by their β radiation. For further information on autoradiography see Rogers (1979) and Review 20 from Amersham (Appendix 3).

Cell labelling

Materials and equipment

Human peripheral lymphocytes (1.5×10^7) cultured overnight in RPMI 1640 containing 10% fetal calf serum (Section 4.2)

Rabbit anti-(human β_2-microglobulin) serum (Dako, Miles — Appendix 3)

Rabbit anti-(human immunoglobulin, all classes) serum (Miles, Nordic, Seward — Appendix 3)

Normal rabbit serum

BMEE (Table 4.1) containing 0.1% bovine serum albumin and 0.1% sodium azide

Goat anti-(rabbit IgG), F(ab')$_2$ fragment (Section 3.4.3) of affinity purified antibody (Section 10.3.1), 15 μg radioiodinated with

100 μCi ^{125}I (Section 5.2.1) and then diluted into 1.5 ml of BMEE-albumin

5% (w/v) bovine serum albumin in phosphate buffered saline (Appendix 2) containing 0.1% sodium azide

Polystyrene tubes, round-bottomed 10.5 mm $\times$ 63.5 mm (Luckham — Appendix 3)

Prewashed microscope slides

Diamond marker

Fixative — methanol: acetic acid: water, 89:1:10 by volume

Procedure

1   Suspend the lymphocytes in 10 ml of BMEE-albumin and centrifuge at 300 g for 5 min. Discard the supernatant and repeat the suspension and centrifugation.

2   Resuspend the final cell pellet in 300 μl of BMEE-albumin and dispense 100 μl into each of 3 polystyrene tubes on ice. Also place the medium to cool on ice.

3   Add 2 μl of each rabbit serum to separate tubes. Mix gently and incubate on ice for 1 h.

4   Add 1 ml of BMEE-albumin to each tube, mix and centrifuge at 300 g for 5 min at 4°C. Discard the supernatant and repeat the re-suspension and centrifugation.

5   Discard the supernatant, resuspend the pellet in the residual supernatant and add 100 μl of ^{125}I-labelled F(ab′)$_2$ anti-(rabbit IgG) (i.e. 1 μg protein, approximately 5 μCi ^{125}I). Mix gently and incubate on ice for 1 h.

6   Wash the cells once as in step 4 (radioactive waste).

7   Resuspend the cell pellets in 1 ml of BMEE-albumin and layer each sample onto 1 ml of 5% albumin in a 10.5 mm $\times$ 63.5 mm tube. Centrifuge at 500 g for 10 min at 4°C and discard the supernatants.

8   Repeat step 7.

9   Add 50 μl albumin to each final pellet. Mix gently to resuspend the cells.

10   Smear the cells from each sample onto 5 microscope slides (Section 12.2.5, steps 2 and 3) and allow to dry.

11   Label the slides with a diamond marker and immerse in the fixative for 1 min at room temperature. Allow to dry.

12   Wash under running tap water for 5 min, then rinse with distilled water and allow to dry.

Notes

1   Notes 3, 4 and 7 of Section 12.2.4 also apply to this Section.

2   The azide and low temperature incubation prevent capping and subsequent loss of antigens during the binding.

Autoradiography

Materials and equipment

Nuclear emulsion K5 (Ilford — Appendix 3)
Fine grain developer (e.g. Kodak D19) and fixer
Darkroom containing heated water bath
Coplin jar
Glass stirring rod
Rack to hold slides vertically
Light-tight container to hold rack and slides, containing silica gel (e.g. large blackened biscuit tin inside black plastic bags)
Enclosed plastic slide boxes and black plastic bags to hold them
Light microscope (1000 × total magnification)
May-Grünwald stain (BDH — Appendix 3)
Citrate/phosphate buffer (10 mM citric acid, 25 mM Na_2HPO_4), pH 7.0.

Procedure

Carry out steps 2–5 in a darkroom under safelight illumination (e.g. Ilford F904) at least 1 m away and not directly illuminating the work.
1   Place 40 ml of water in a 50 ml measuring cylinder and heavily mark the 50 ml line (so as to be visible under safelight). Warm the measuring cylinder and contents and the empty Coplin jar to 50°C in the water bath and prepare the remaining equipment.
2   Under safelight illumination only, add K5 emulsion to the heated water to the 50 ml mark (i.e. a 1/5 dilution). Melt the emulsion by stirring and transfer the mixture to the Coplin jar. Remove from water bath.
3   Holding the labelled end, dip each slide separately into the emulsion, allow excess to drain back (about 5 sec) and place vertically in the rack. Keep each group of slides physically separate from now on so that they can be distinguished in darkness.
4   Place the rack and coated slides over silica gel in the light-tight container and leave to dry overnight in total darkness.
5   Transfer the slides to enclosed boxes and place inside 3 layers of black plastic bags. Secure with tape or rubber bands.
6   Expose at 4°C away from radioisotopes.
7   After 4–5 days, develop and fix 1 slide from each group and examine under the microscope.
8   Continue to develop 1 slide from each group every 2–4 days until the positive samples (β_2-microglobulin and immunoglobulin) are clearly labelled (i.e. have many grains over cells with a clear background in between) and the normal serum sample still has less than 10 grains/cell.
9   Immerse the slides in citrate/phosphate buffer for 5 min. Stain with May-Grünwald stain diluted 1/2 in citrate/phosphate for 15 min and wash away excess stain.

286

Examination of slides

Figure 12.10 shows autoradiographs of lymphocytes labelled according to this procedure.

1 Select a set of slides (1 from each group) which have well spread cells, clear background and low labelling by control serum.

2 Using 1000× magnification, count the number of grains/cell of at

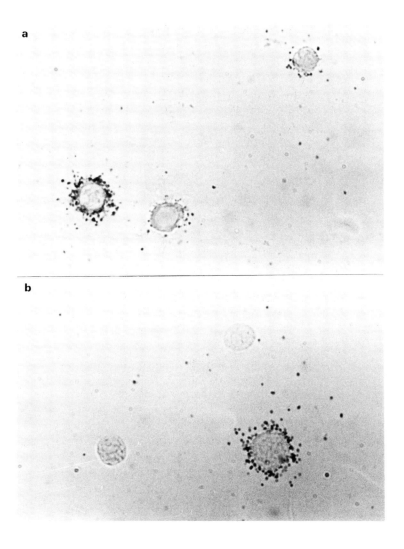

Fig. 12.10 Autoradiography of radiolabelled cells (Section 12.4). Human peripheral blood lymphocytes were reacted with (a) rabbit anti-β_2-microglobulin or (b) rabbit anti-human immunoglobulin and the bound antibody detected by ^{125}I-labelled F(ab')$_2$ fragment of anti-rabbit IgG. Autoradiographs viewed under transmitted light: (a) 3 positive cells labelled to various degrees (the number of grains gives a measure of the amount of antibody bound); (b) 1 labelled (B lymphocyte) and 2 unlabelled cells. Compare fluorescence (Fig. 12.5) and peroxidase (Fig. 12.9).

287

least 200 cells on each slide (the cells are stained light blue giving a good background for viewing the grains). For ^{125}I, the silver grain hit by the emission can be up to 5–10 μm from the site of disintegration. Hence any grains within that distance (i.e. approximately 1 lymphocyte diameter) of a cell are counted as coming from that cell. The corresponding values for ^{14}C and ^{3}H are 1–2 and 0.5 μm respectively. The data can be recorded as a frequency distribution of cells with increments of 5–10 grains/cell (e.g. Fig. 12.11).

3 Alternatively, simply record the percentage of total cells that are positively labelled (i.e. those with significantly more grains/cell than

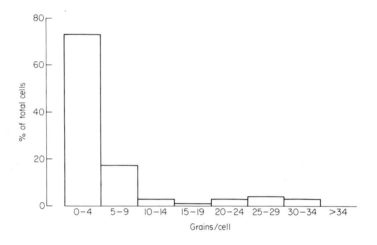

Fig. 12.11 Presentation of quantitative autoradiographic data. Human peripheral blood lymphocytes were reacted with radiolabelled antibodies as described in Fig. 12.10 and Section 12.4 and the number of silver grains on each of 200 cells counted. The histogram plots the data for anti-immunoglobulin serum; for the normal rabbit serum control 95% of cells had 0–4 grains and 5% had 5–9 grains. Hence the histogram shows 11% (or 14%) positive cells (B lymphocytes) containing more than 14 (or 9) grains/cell. For anti-β_2-microglobulin serum 95% of cells had 10–49 grains (positive).

the control serum). This simple method gives as much information as immunofluorescence or immunoperoxidase microscopy (cf. Figs. 12.5, 12.9 and 12.10).

4 For direct binding, the number of antibody molecules per cell (and hence a measure of antigen molecules per cell) can be calculated from the number of grains per cell. However, for whole cells in suspension, the distribution of antigen density throughout the cell population is most easily studied by measuring the amount of fluorescent antibody bound using a flow microfluorimeter (Section 12.2.2).

5 The grain density is more conveniently measured by a photometer detecting reflection of incident light by the silver grains. For details of this and further information on autoradiography in general see Rogers (1979).

12.5 ELECTRON MICROSCOPY

The arrangement of molecules at the subcellular level, below the resolution of the light microscope, can be studied by electron microscopy. For immunocytochemistry, electron microscopy is usually carried out on thin sections cut through solid tissue or packed whole cells (cf. Section 12.2.5). The added antibody or other ligand is labelled either by an electron dense molecule (e.g. ferritin, gold or latex spheres) or by a molecule which yields an electron dense product (e.g. peroxidase, Section 12.3; radioisotopes produce silver grains in an overlying emulsion, Section 12.4). Hence the position of the added ligand can be detected on the micrograph. The peroxidase and radioactive labels have the advantage that they are also visible by light microscopy and so results from both analyses can be correlated. As described for the techniques of light microscopy (Sections 12.2, 12.3 and 12.4), the labelled ligand can be added either to intact whole cells (or sealed membrane vesicles), to react with external structures only, which are then sectioned and fixed, or added to the sections cut though solid tissue or cells to react with all of the cells' components.

A full description of electron microscopic techniques is beyond the scope of this book. However, the principles and concepts of the immunochemical labelling procedures are similar to those used in samples prepared for light microscopy. The reader is referred to the trained personnel who prepare the sample and operate the microscope for further advice.

Appendices

1 ABBREVIATIONS

ABM	aminobenzyloxymethyl
BSA	bovine serum albumin
DBM	diazobenzyloxymethyl
DMSO	dimethyl sulphoxide
ELISA	enzyme linked immunosorbent assay
FCA	Freund's complete adjuvant
FCS	fetal calf serum
FIA	Freund's incomplete adjuvant
IRMA	immunoradiometric assay
PAGE	polyacrylamide gel electrophoresis
PAP	peroxidase–anti-peroxidase
PEG	polyethylene glycol (usually 6000 molecular weight)
POPOP	1,4-bis-2-(5-phenyloxazolyl) benzene
PPO	2,5-diphenyloxazole
SDS	sodium dodecyl sulphate
TPCK	L-1-tosylamide-2-phenylethylchloromethyl ketone

2   BUFFERS

Balanced salts solution (BSS)

NaCl	8.00 g/l	0.14 M
KCl	0.40 g/l	5.4 mM
MgSO$_4$ 7H$_2$O	0.20 g/l	0.8 mM
CaCl$_2$ 2H$_2$O	0.15 g/l	1.0 mM
KH$_2$PO$_4$	0.06 g/l	0.4 mM
Na$_2$HPO$_4$	0.20 g/l	1.4 mM

Sodium azide (0.02–0.1%) may be added.

Barbitone buffer

Dissolve 4.4 g 5′5-diethylbarbituric acid (Barbital) in 150 ml of water at 95°C. Make up to 900 ml with cold water.
Add 12 g 5′5-diethylbarbituric acid, sodium salt and adjust to pH 8.2 with sodium hydroxide. Make up to 1 litre with water.

Chromic acid (for cleaning glassware)

Dissolve 100 g chromium trioxide in 400 ml water.
Slowly add to 2 litres 50% sulphuric acid.

Glycerol jelly (for histology)

This can also be purchased (BDH — Appendix 3).
Mix together 15 g gelatin, 100 ml water and 100 ml glycerol. Dissolve by heating in a boiling water bath and store at 4°C. Melt in a boiling water bath just before use.

Haematoxylin (Meyer's) (for histology)

Haematoxylin	1 g
Sodium iodate	0.2 g
Potassium alum	50 g
Citric acid	1 g
Chloral hydrate	50 g

Allow haematoxylin, alum and sodium iodate to dissolve in 1 litre water (overnight). Add citric acid and chloral hydrate and boil (use anti-bumping granules) for 5 min. When cool the solution is ready for use. It can be re-used and lasts for many months.

Mounting fluid (specifically for fluorescence microscopy)

Glycine	0.42 g
Sodium hydroxide	0.021 g
Sodium chloride	0.51 g
Sodium azide	0.03 g

Dissolve and make up to 30 ml in water. Add 70 ml glycerol.

Phosphate buffered saline (PBS)

NaCl	8.00 g/l	0.14 M
KCl	0.20 g/l	2.7 mM
KH_2PO_4	0.20 g/l	1.5 mM
Na_2HPO_4	1.15 g/l	8.1 mM

Sodium azide (0.02%–0.1%) may be added.

Tris buffered saline (TBS)

10 mM tris-HCl pH 7.3 containing 0.15 M sodium chloride. Sodium azide (0.02%–0.1%) may be added.

Veronal acetate buffer (for immunohistochemistry)

Dissolve 1.47 g sodium barbitone and 0.97 g sodium acetate (trihydrate) in 200 ml water, add 2.5 ml 0.1 M HCl and make up to 250 ml.

3 MANUFACTURERS AND SUPPLIERS

Aldrich Chemical Co. Ltd., The Old Brickyard, New Road, Gillingham, Dorset SP8 4JL, UK.

Alpha Laboratories Ltd., 40 Parham Drive, Eastleigh, Hants SO5 4NU, UK.

Amersham International Ltd., Lincoln Place, Greenend, Aylesbury, Bucks HP20 2TP, UK.

Amicon Ltd., Upper Mill, Stonehouse, Glos, GL10 2BJ, UK; Amicon Corporation, 21 Hartwell Avenue, Lexington, Mass. 02173, USA.

Autodata, 80 Walsworth Road, Hitchin, Herts SG4 9SX, UK.

BDH Chemicals Ltd., Chadwell Heath, Dagenham, Essex RM8 1RZ, UK.

Beckman Instruments Ltd., Sands Industrial Estate, High Wycombe, Bucks HP12 4JL, UK; 2500 Harbor Blvd, Fullerton, CA, USA.

Becton Dickinson Ltd., Between Towns Road, Cowley, Oxford OX4 3LY, UK; Becton, Dickinson and Co., Oxnard, California 93030 and (FACS) Sunnyvale, California 94086, USA.

Behringwerke AG, Marburg-Lahn, W. Germany.

Bio-Rad Laboratories Ltd., Caxton Way, Watford, Herts WD1 8RP, UK; 2200 Wright Avenue, Richmond, California 94804, USA.

Boehringer Mannheim GmbH: Boehringer Corporation (London) Ltd, Bell Lane, Lewes, Sussex BN7 1LG, UK.

Calbiochem-Behring Corp., La Jolla, CA 92037, USA; UK suppliers: CP Laboratories Ltd., PO Box 22, Bishop's Stortford, Herts CM22 7RQ, UK.

Costar, 205 Broadway, Cambridge, MA 02139, USA; UK distributor: LH Engineering, Bells Hill, Stoke Poges, Bucks SL2 4EG, UK.

Coulter Electronics Ltd., Northwell Drive, Luton, Beds, UK; Coulter Electronics Inc., 590 W 20th Street, Hialeah, FL 33010, USA.

Cuthbert-Andrews Ltd., Bushey Village, Watford WD2 1BE, UK.

Dako Ltd., 22 The Arcade, The Octagen, High Wycombe, Bucks HP11 2HT, UK; DakoPatts a/s, Productionvej 42, PO Box 1359, DK 2600, Glostrup, Denmark; Dako Corporation, 22 North Milpas Street, Santa Barbara, CA 93103, USA.

Denley Instruments Ltd., Nolts Lane, Billinghurst, Sussex RH14 9EX, UK.

Difco, Central Avenue, West Molesey, Surrey KT8 0SE, UK.

Dynal AS, PO Box 158, N-0212, Oslo 2, Norway.

Dynatech Laboratories Ltd., Daux Road, Billinghurst, Sussex RH14 9SJ, UK.

Dyno Particles AS, PO Box 160, N-2001, Lillestrom, Norway.

ECACC PHLS Centre for Applied Microbiology and Research, Porton Down, Salisbury SP4 0JG, UK; in USA see American Type Culture Collection, 12301 Parklawn Drive, Rockville, Maryland 20852.

E–C Apparatus Corporation, 3831 Tyrone Boulevard N, St Petersburg, Florida 33709, USA.

Enzyme Center Inc., 33 Harrison Avenue, Boston, MA 02111, USA.

Eppendorf Gerateban Netheler & Hinz GmbH, PO Box 630324, 2000 Hamburg 63, W. Germany; UK suppliers: Anderman & Co Ltd., London Road, Kingston upon Thames, Surrey KT2 6NH, UK.

ESCO (Rubber) Ltd., Clockhouse Lane, Feltham, Middlesex TW14 8QS, UK.

Falcon, see Becton, Dickinson and Co.; UK Suppliers: Marathon, Scientific Supplies.

Flow Laboratories Ltd., Harefield Road, Rickmansworth, Herts WD3 IP2, UK.

Gallenkamp & Co. Ltd., Belton Road West, Loughborough LE11 0TR, UK.

Genetic Research Instrumentation Ltd., Station Road, Takeley, Bishop's Stortford, Herts CM22 6SG, UK.

Gibco Ltd., PO Box 35, Washington Road, Paisley, Scotland PA3 4EP, UK.

Gilson France SA, BP No 45-95400, Villiers le Bel, France; UK suppliers: Anachem Ltd., Charles Street, Luton, Beds LU2 0EB, UK.

Hanimex (UK) Ltd., Faraday Road, Dorcan, Swindon, Wilts SN3 5HW, UK.

C.A. Hendley Ltd., Oakwood Hill Industrial Estate, Loughton, Essex IG10 3TZ, UK.

Hopkin & Williams, Freshwater Road, Chadwell Heath, Essex, UK.

ICI, Imperial Chemical Industries Ltd., Neuman Street, Northwich, Cheshire, UK.

Ilacon Ltd., Gilbert House, River Walk, Tonbridge, Kent TN9 1DT, UK.

Ilford Ltd., PO Box 21, Mobberley, Knutsford, Cheshire WA16 7HA, UK.

Inotech, Northumbria Biologicals Ltd., South Nelson Industrial Estate, Cramlington, Northumbria NE23 9HL, UK.

Isco, 4700 Superior, Lincoln, Nebraska 68504, USA; UK Suppliers: Life Science Laboratories, Sarum Road, Luton LU3 2RA, UK.

Janssen Pharmaceutical Ltd., Grove, Wantage, Oxon OX12 0DG, UK.

Jencons Scientific Ltd., Stanbridge Road, Leighton Buzzard, Beds LU7 8UA, UK.

Kabi AB, Stockholm, Sweden.

E. Leitz Inst. Ltd., 48 Park Street, Luton, Beds, LU1 3DP, UK; D-6330, Wetzlar, W. Germany.

LKB Instruments Ltd., 232 Addington Road, S. Croydon CR2 8YD, UK; LKB-Produkter AB, Box 305, S-161 26 Bromma, Sweden.

Lorne Diagnostics Ltd., Unit 11, Cratfield Road, Bury St Edmunds, Suffolk IP32 7DF, UK.

Luckham Ltd, Burgess Hill, Sussex RH15 9QN, UK.

Marathon Laboratory Supplies, 820A Harrow Road, London NW10 5JU, UK.

Miles Laboratories Ltd, Stoke Court, Stoke Poges, Slough SL2 4LY, UK.

Millipore (UK) Ltd, 11–15 Peterborough Road, Harrow, Middlesex HA1 2YH, UK; Millipore Corp, Freehold, NJ 07728, USA.

Mini-instruments Ltd, Burnham-on-Crouch, Essex CM0 8RN, UK.

Monoclonal Antibodies Inc, 28 Crown Road, Wheatley, Oxon OX9 1NB, UK; 2319 Charleston Road, Mountain View, CA 94043, USA.

MSE Scientific Instruments, Manor Royal, Crawley, Sussex RH10 2QQ, UK.

National Diagnostics, Unit 3, Chamberlain Road, Aylesbury, Bucks HP19 3DY, UK; 198 Route 206 South, Somerville, NJ 08876, USA.

NEN, New England Nuclear, Wedgewood Way, Stevenage, Herts SG1 4GN, UK; NEN Corp, Boston, Mass, USA.

Nordic Immunological Laboratories, PO Box 544, Maidenhead, Berks SL6 1PW, UK; PO Box 22, Tilburg, The Netherlands.

Nuclear Enterprises Ltd, Bath Road, Beenham, Reading RG7 SPR, UK.

Nunc A/S, DK-4000 Roskilde, Denmark; UK suppliers: Gibco.

Nycomed (UK) Ltd, 2111 Coventry Road, Birmingham B26 3EA, UK; Nycomed AS Diagnostics, PO Box 4284, Torshov, 0401 Oslo 4, Norway; US distributors: Accurate Chemical and Scientific Corp., 300 Shames Drive, Westbury, NY 11590, USA.

Packard Instrument Ltd, 13–17 Church Road, Caversham, Berks, UK.

Perstorp Biolytica, S-22570, Lund, Sweden; in USA see Pierce.

Pharmacia Ltd, Midsummer Boulevard, Milton Keynes MK9 3HP, UK; Pharmacia Biotechnology AB, S-751 82 Uppsala, Sweden; Pharmacia Inc, 800 Centennial Avenue, Piscataway, NJ 08854, USA.

Pierce (UK) Ltd, 36 Clifton Road, Cambridge CB1 4ZR, UK; Pierce Chemical Company, Box 117, Rockford, Illinois, 61105, USA.

Polysciences Ltd, 24 Low Farm Place, Moulton Park, Northampton NN3 1HY, UK; Polysciences Inc, Paul Valley Industrial Park, Warrington, PA 18976, USA.

Porvair Ltd, Estuary Road, King's Lynn, Norfolk PE30 2HS, UK.

Raven Scientific Ltd, PO Box 2, Haverhill, Suffolk CB9 0ES, UK.

Raymond Lamb, 6 Sunbeam Road, London NW10 6JL, UK.

Sartorius GmbH, PO Box 19, 3400 Göttingen, W. Germany; Sartorius Instruments Ltd, 18 Avenue Road, Belmont, SM2 6JD, UK.

Schleicher and Schull GmbH, Postfach 4, D-3354 Dassel, W. Germany; UK distributors; Anderman and Co. Ltd, London Road, Kingston-upon-Thames, Surrey KT2 6NH, UK.

Schuco Scientific Ltd, Halliwick Court Place, Woodhouse Road, London N12, UK.

Scientific Supplies, Vine Hill, London EC1R 5EB, UK.

Sera-Lab Ltd, Crawley Down, Sussex RH10 4FF, UK.

Serotec, Station Road, Blackthorn, Bicester, Oxon OX6 0TP, UK.

Seward Laboratory, Norse Road, Bedford MK41 0QG, UK.

Shandon Southern Products Ltd, 91–96 Chadwick Road, Astmoor Industrial Estate, Runcorn, Cheshire WA7 1PR, UK.

Sigma London Chemical Company Ltd, Fancy Road, Poole, Dorset BH17 7NH; Sigma Chemical Co, PO Box 14508, St. Louis, MO 63178, USA.

Silverson Machines Ltd, Waterside, Chesham, Bucks HP5 1PQ, UK.

Spectra-Physics Ltd, 17 Brick Knoll Park, St. Albans, Herts AL1 5UF, UK.

Sterilin Ltd, Teddington, Middlesex TW11 8QZ, UK.

TCS, Tissue Culture Services, 10 Henry Road, Slough, Berks, UK.

Travenol Laboratories Ltd, Caxton Way, Thetford, Norfolk, UK; Deerfield, Illinois 60015, USA.

Unipath Ltd, Norse Road, Bedford MK41 0QG, UK.

Uniscience Ltd, 12–14 St Ann's Crescent, Wandsworth, London SW18 2LS, UK.

Vector Laboratories Inc, 16 Wulfric Square, Bretton, Peterborough PE3 8BR, UK; 1429 Rollins Road, Burlingame CA 94010, USA.

Wellcome Foundation Ltd, Temple Hill, Dartford DA1 5AH, UK.

Whatman Ltd, Springfield Mill, Maidstone, Kent ME14 2LE, UK; 9 Bridewell Place, Clifton, NJ 07014, USA.

Worthington — see Lorne; Millipore.

Wright Scientific — distributed by Amicon.

Zeiss, Carl Ltd, PO Box 78, Woodfield Road, Welwyn Garden City, Herts HL7 1LU, UK; 7082 Oberkochen, W. Germany.

References

ALTERMAN L., BIRD C., CALLUS M., FORD A. & THORPE R. (1987) The use of monoclonal antibodies raised against a human IgE myeloma paraprotein for the study of allergen extracts and sera from allergic patients. *Clin. Exp. Immunol.* **67**, 617.

ALWINE J.C., KEMP D.J. & STARK G.R. (1977) Method for detection of specific RNAs in agarose gels by transfer to diazobenzyloxymethyl-paper and hybridization with DNA probes, *Proc. Nat. Acad. Sci. USA* **76**, 4350.

AXELSEN N.H. (1983) Handbook of immunoprecipitation-in-gel techniques. *Scand. J. Immunol.* **17**, suppl. 10.

BEALE D. & VAN DORT T. (1982) A comparison of the proteolectic fragmentation of immunoglobulin M from several different mammalian species. *Comp. Biochem. Physiol.* **71B**, 475.

BELEW M., JUNTTI N., LARSSON A. & PORATH J. (1987) A one-step purification method for monoclonal antibodies based on salt-promoted adsorption chromatography on a "thiophilic" adsorbent. *J. Immunol. Meth.* In press.

BIDLACK J.M. & MABIE P.C. (1986) Preparation of Fab fragments from a mouse monoclonal IgM. *J. Immunol. Meth.* **91**, 157.

BIRD C., CALLUS M., TRICKETT L. & THORPE R. (1986) Immunochemical character-ization of a new platelet specific monoclonal antibody and its use to demonstrate the cytoskeletal association of the platelet glycoprotein IIb–IIIa complex. *Bioscience Rep.* **6**, 323.

BOLTON A.E. & HUNTER W.M. (1973) The labelling of proteins to high specific radioactivities by conjugation to a ^{125}I-containing acylating agent. *Biochem. J.* **133**, 529.

BONNER W.M. & LASKEY R.A. (1974) A film detection method for tritium-labelled proteins and nucleic acids in polyacrylamide gels. *Eur. J. Biochem.* **46**, 83.

BRADFORD M.M. (1976) A rapid and sensitive method for the quantitation of microgram quantities of protein. *Anal. Biochem.* **72**, 248.

BURRIDGE K. (1978) Direct identification of specific glycoproteins and antigens in SDS gels. *Meth. Enzymol.* **50**, 54.

CHARD T. (1986) An introduction to radioimmunoassay and related techniques. In *Laboratory Techniques in Biochemistry and Molecular Biology*, Eds. T.S. Work & E. Work, Vol. 6, Part 2, 3e. Elsevier/North Holland, Amsterdam.

CHUA N-H & BLOMBERG F. (1979) Immunochemical studies of thylakoid membrane polypeptides from spinach and *Chlamydomonas reinhardtii. J. Biol. Chem.* **254**, 215.

CLEVELAND D.W., FISCHER S.G., KIRSCHNER M.W. & LAEMMLI U.K. (1977) Peptide mapping by limited proteolysis in sodium dodecyl sulphate and analysis by gel electrophoresis. *J. Biol. Chem.* **252**, 1102.

CLEZARDIN P., McGREGOR J.L., MANACH M., BOUKERCHE H. & DECHAVANNE M. (1985) One-step procedure for the rapid isolation of mouse monoclonal antibodies and their antigen binding fragments by fast protein liquid chromatography on a mono Q anion-exchange column. *J. Chromatog.* **319**, 67.

CONNELL G.E. & PORTER R.R. (1971) A new enzymic fragment (Facb) of rabbit immunoglobulin G. *Biochem J.* **124**, 53P.

CRUMPTON M.J. & SNARY D. (1977) Isolation and structure of human histocompatibility (HLA) antigens. In *Contemporary Topics in Molecular Immunology*, Eds. R.R. Porter & G.L. Ada, Vol. 6, pp. 53–82. Plenum Press.

CUATRECASAS P. (1970) Protein purification by affinity chromatography. *J. Biol. Chem.* **245**, 3059.

DAVIS B.J. (1964) Disc electrophoresis II. Method and application to human serum proteins. *Ann. N.Y. Acad. Sci USA* **121**, 404.

DEAN P.D.G., JOHNSON W.S. & MIDDLE F.A. (1985) *Affinity chromatography: a practical approach.* IRL Press, Oxford.

DIXON M. (1953) Nomogram for ammonium sulphate solutions. *Biochem J.* **54**, 457.

DREXLER G., EICHINGER A., WOLF C. & SIEGHART W. (1986) A rapid and simple method for efficient coating of microtiter plates using low amounts of antigen in the presence of detergent. *J. Immunol. Meth.* **95**, 117.

EVANS W.H. (1978) Preparation and characterisation of mammalian plasma membranes. In *Laboratory Techniques in Biochemistry and Molecular Biology*, Eds. T.S. Work & E. Work, Vol. 7, Part 1. Elsevier/North Holland, Amsterdam.

EY P.L., PROWSE S.J. & JENKIN C.R. (1978) Isolation of pure IgG1, IgG2a and IgG2b immunoglobulins from mouse serum using Protein A-Sepharose. *Immunochemistry* **15**, 429.

FASMAN G.D. (1976) *Handbook of Biochemistry and Molecular Biology*, Vol. II, 3e. Chemical Rubber Company.

FLEISCHMAN J.B., PORTER R.R. & PRESS E.M. (1963) The arrangement of the peptide chains in γ-globulin. *Biochem J.* **88**, 220.

FRAKER P.J. & SPECK J.C. (1978) Protein and cell membrane iodinations with a sparingly soluble chloroamide. *Biochem. Biophys. Res. Commun.* **80**, 849.

GAHMBERG C.G. (1976) External labelling of human erythrocyte glycoproteins. *J. Biol. Chem.* **251**, 510.

GAHMBERG C.G. & ANDERSSON L.C. (1977) Selective radioactive labelling of cell surface sialoglycoproteins by periodate-tritiated borohydride. *J. Biol. Chem.* **252**, 5888.

GHETIE V., MOTA G. & SJÖQUIST J. (1978) Separation of cells by affinity chromatography on Sp-A Sepharose 6MB. *J. Immunol. Meth.* **21**, 133.

GLOVER J.S., SALTER D.N. & SHEPHERD B.P. (1967) A study of some factors that influence the iodination of ox insulin. *Biochem. J.* **103**. 120.

GORDON A.H. & LOUIS L.N. (1967) Preparative acrylamide electrophoresis: a single gel system. *Anal. Biochem.* **21**, 190.

GREAVES M.F. & BROWN G. (1974) Purification of human T and B lymphocytes. *J. Immunol.* **112**, 420.

GREENWOOD F.C., HUNTER W.M. & GLOVER J.S. (1963) The preparation of ^{131}I-labelled human growth hormone of high specific radioactivity. *Biochem. J.* **89**, 114.

HAYES C.E. & GOLDSTEIN I.J. (1975) Radioiodination of sulfhydryl-sensitive proteins. *Anal. Biochem.* **67**, 580.

HELENIUS A. & SIMONS K. (1975) Solubilization of membranes by detergents. *Biochem. Biophys. Acta.* **415**, 29.

HELENIUS A., McCASLIN D.R., FRIES E. & TANFORD C. (1979) Properties of detergents. *Meth. Enzymology* **56**, 734.

HERBERT W.J. & KRISTENSEN F. (1986) In *Handbook of Experimental Immunology*, Eds. D.M. Weir, L.A. Herzenberg, C. Blackwell & L.A. Herzenberg, 4e, Section 133. Blackwell Scientific Publications, Oxford.

HEREMANS J.F. (1974) Immunoglobin A. In *The Antigens*, Ed. M. Sela, Vol. II, p. 365. Academic Press, New York.

HOWARD I.K., SAGE H.J., STEIN M.D., YOUNG N.M., LEON M.A. & DYCKES D.F. (1971) Studies on a phytohaemagglutinin from the lentil. *J. Biol. Chem.* **246**, 1590.

HUBBARD A.L. & COHN Z.A. (1976) Specific labels for cell surfaces. In *Biochemical Analysis of Membranes*, Ed. A.H. Maddy, pp. 427–501. Chapman & Hall, London.

INBAR D., HOCHMAN J. & GIVOL D. (1972) Localization of antibody combining sites within the variable portions of heavy and light chains. *Proc. Natl. Acad. Sci. USA* **69**, 2659.

297

JAFFE B.M.E. & BEHRMAN H.R. (Eds) (1974) *Methods of Hormone Radioimmunoassay.* Academic Press, New York.

JENSENIUS J.C., ANDERSON I., HAU J., CRONE M. & KOCH C. (1981) Eggs: conveniently packaged antibodies. *J. Immunol. Meth.* **46**, 63.

JENSENIUS J.C., SIERSTED H.C. & JOHNSTONE A.P. (1982) Quantification of human immunoglobulins by semiautomatic PEG precipitation radioimmunoassays. *J. Immunol. Meth.* **56**, 19.

JOHNSTONE A.P. & MOLE L.E. (1977) The subunit and polypeptide chain structure of rabbit secretory immunoglobulin A. *Biochem. J.* **167**, 245.

KESSLER S.W. (1975) Rapid isolation of antigens from cells with a Staphylococcal Protein A-antibody adsorbent. *J. Immunol.* **115**, 1617.

KÖHLER G. & MILSTEIN C. (1975) Continuous cultures of fused cells secreting antibody of predefined specificity. *Nature* **256**, 495.

KOSHLAND M.E. (1975) Structure and function of J chain. *Adv. Immunol.* **20**, 41.

LAEMMLI U.K. (1970) Cleavage of structural proteins during the assembly of the head of bacteriophage T4. *Nature* **227**, 680.

LAMOYI E. & NISONOFF A. (1983) Preparation of F(ab')$_2$ fragments from mouse IgG of various subclasses. *J. Immunol. Meth.* **56**, 235.

LASKEY R.A. & MILLS A.D. (1975) Quantitative film detection of ^{3}H and ^{14}C in polyacrylamide gels by fluorography. *Eur. J. Biochem.* **56**, 335.

LASKEY R.A. & MILLS A.D. (1977) Enhanced autoradiographic detection of ^{32}P and ^{125}I using intensifying screens and hypersensitized film. *FEBS Lett.* **82**, 314.

LEA T., SMELAND E., FUNDERUD S., VARTDAL F., DAVIES C., BEISKE K. & UGELSTAD J. (1986) Characterization of human mononuclear cells after positive selection with immunomagnetic particles. *Scand. J. Immunol.* **23**, 509.

LING N.R. & KAY J.E. (1975). *Lymphocyte Stimulation.* 2e. North Holland/American Elsevier, New York.

LOWE C.R. (1979) An introduction to affinity chromatography. In *Laboratory Techniques in Biochemistry and Molecular Biology,* Eds. T.S. Work & R.H. Burdon, Vol. 7, Part 2. Elsevier/North Holland, Amsterdam.

LOWRY O.H., ROSEBROUGH N.J., FARR L. & RANDALL R.J. (1951) Protein measurement with the folin phenol reagent. *J. Biol. Chem.* **193**, 265.

MOLE L.E., GEIER M.D. & KOSHLAND M.E. (1975) The isolation and characterization of the V_H domain from rabbit heavy chains of different *a* locus allotype. *J. Immunol.* **114**, 1442.

MÖLLER G. (Ed.) (1978) Immunoglobulin E. *Immunological Reviews,* Vol. 41, Munksgaard, Copenhagen.

MOSTOV K.E., FRIEDLANDLER M. & BLOBEL G. (1984) The receptor for transepithelial transport of IgA and IgM contains multiple immunoglobulin-like domains. *Nature* **308**, 37.

NEOH S.H., GORDON C., POTTER A. & ZOLA H. (1986) The purification of mouse monoclonal antibodies from ascitic fluid. *J. Immunol. Meth.* **91**, 231.

NISONOFF A., HOPPER J.E. & SPRING S.B. (1975) *The Antibody Molecule.* Academic Press, New York.

NUSTAD K., JOHANSEN L., UGELSTAD J., ELLINGSEN T. & BERGE A. (1984) Hydrophilic monodisperse particles as solid-phase material in immunoassays. *Eur. Surg. Res.* **16**, **suppl. 2**, 80.

O'FARRELL P.H. (1975) High resolution two-dimensional electrophoresis of proteins. *J. Biol. Chem.* **250**, 4007.

ORNSTEIN L. (1964) Disc electrophoresis I. Background and theory. *Ann N.Y. Acad. Sci. USA.* **121**, 321.

OUCHTERLONY O. & NILSSON L.Ä. (1986) Immunodiffusion and immunoelectrophoresis. In *Handbook of Experimental Immunology,* Eds. D.M. Weir, L.A. Herzenberg, C. Blackwell & L.A. Herzenberg, 4e, Section 32. Blackwell Scientific Publications, Oxford.

PARHAM P. (1986) Preparation and purification of active fragments from mouse monoclonal antibodies. In *Handbook of Experimental Immunology,* Eds. D.M. Weir, L.A.

Herzenberg, C. Blackwell & L.A. Herzenberg, 4e, Vol. 1, Section 14. Blackwell Scientific Publications, Oxford.

PETERSON G.L. (1979) Review of the Folin phenol protein quantitation method. *Anal. Biochem.* **100**, 210.

PLAUT A.G. & TOMASI T.B. (1970) Immunoglobulin M: Pentameric Fc$_\mu$ fragments released by trypsin at higher temperatures. *Proc. Natl. Acad. Sci. USA* **65**, 318.

PLAUT A.G., GENCO R.J. & TOMASI T.B. (1974) Isolation of an enzyme from *Streptococcus sanguis* which specifically cleaves IgA. *J. Immunol.* **113**, 289.

PORTER R.R. (1959) The hydrolysis of rabbit γ-globulin and antibodies by crystalline papain. *Biochem. J.* **73**, 119.

REIS K.J., HANSEN H.F. & BJORCK L. (1986) Extraction and characterization of IgG Fc receptors from Group C and Group G streptococci. *Molec. Immunol.* **23**, 425.

RICHMAN D.D., CLEVELAND P.H., OXMAN M.N. & JOHNSON K.M. (1982) The binding of staphylococcal Protein A by the sera of different animal species. *J. Immunol.* **128**, 2300.

ROGERS A.W. (1979) *Techniques in Autoradiography*, 3e. Elsevier, Amsterdam.

ROITT I. (1987) *Essential Immunology*, 6e. Blackwell Scientific Publications, Oxford.

SCHREINER G.F. & UNANUE E.R. (1976) Membrane and cytoplasmic changes in B lymphocytes induced by ligand-surface immunoglobulin interaction. *Adv. Immunol.* **24**, 37.

SCHREMPF-DECKER G.E., BARON D. & WERNET P. (1980) *Helix pomatia* agglutin affinity chromatography. *J. Immunol. Meth.* **32**, 285.

SEARS D.A., REED C.F. & HELMKAMP R.W. (1971) A radioactive label for the erythrocyte membrane. *Biochem. Biophys. Acta* **233**, 716.

SHARON N. (1983) Lectin receptors as lymphocyte surface markers. *Adv. Immunol.* **34**, 213.

SHARON J. & GIVOL D. (1976) Preparation of Fv fragment from the mouse myeloma XRPC-25 immunoglobulin possessing anti-DNP activity. *Biochem.* **15**, 1591.

SINGER S.J. & NICHOLSON G.L. (1972) The fluid mosaic model of the structure of cell membranes. *Science* **175**, 720.

SPIEGELBERG H.L. (1977) The structure and biology of human IgD. *Immunol. Rev.* **37**, 3.

STERNBERGER L.A. (1986) *Immunocytochemistry*, 3e. John Wiley and Sons, New York, Chichester, Brisbane and Toronto.

SUNDERLAND C.A., McMASTER W.R. & WILLIAMS A.F. (1979) Purification with monoclonal antibody of a predominant leukocyte-common antigen and glycoprotein from rat thymocytes. *Eur. J. Immunol.* **9**, 155.

TAYLOR R.B., DUFFUS P.H., RAFF M.C. & DE PETRIS S. (1971) Redistribution and pinocytosis of lymphocyte surface immunoglobulin molecules induced by anti-immunoglobulin. *Nature New Biol.* **233**, 225.

TEALE J.D. (1978) Radioimmunoassay. In *Scientific Foundations of Clinical Biochemistry*, Eds. D.L. Williams, R.F. Nunn & V. Marks, Vol I, pp. 299–322. Heinemann, London.

TOWBIN H. & GORDON J. (1984) Immunoblotting and dot immunobinding — current status and outlook. *J. Immunol. Meth.* **73**, 313.

TOWBIN H., STAEHELIN T. & GORDON J. (1979) Electrophoretic transfer of proteins from polyacrylamide gels to nitrocellulose sheets: procedure and some applications. *Proc. Natl. Acad. Sci. USA.* **76**, 4350.

WEDRYCHOWSKI A., OLINSKI R. & HNILICA L.S. (1986) Modified method of silver staining of proteins in polyacrylamide gels. *Anal. Biochem.* **159**, 323.

WILLIAMS A.F. (1977) Differentiation antigens of the lymphocyte cell surface. In *Contemporary Topics in Molecular Immunology*, Eds. R.R. Porter & G.L. Ada, Vol. 6, pp. 83–116. Plenum Press, New York.

WINTERBOURNE D.J. (1986) Cell growth determined by a dye-binding protein assay. *Biochem. Soc. Trans.* **14**, 1179.

WRAY W., BOULIKAS T., WRAY V.P. & HANCOCK R. (1981) Silver staining of proteins in polyacrylamide gels. *Anal. Biochem.* **118**, 197.

299

Index

303

IRMA (immunoradiometric
assay) 254–7
Isoelectric focusing
analytical 172–6
preparative 203–5
two-dimensional 176–80
Isoelectric point (pI) 172
Isopaque-Ficoll 94 *et seq.*

J

J chain 2, 56, 65, 66, 68, 69, 73,
77, 79

K

Kappa (κ) chain 48, 50, 250

L

Labelling proteins
enzymic 258, 276
fluorescent 264
radioactive 115 *et seq.*
Lactoperoxidase 117, 122
Lambda (λ) chain 48, 50, 85, 250
Lectins 198, 224–9, 231, 232,
268
Lens culinaris (lentil) lectin 2, 224,
226, 228
Light chains, immunoglobulin 2,
48, 50, 55, 56, 57, 66, 68, 73,
77, 84, 85, 250
Limiting dilution cloning 40
Lipids 105, 106, 124–30
Liquid scintillation counting 20–
24, 155
Lowry protein estimation 3
Lymph node 97–9
Lymphocytes 86
B and T 97, 100–3
counting 88–91
fractionation 100–5, 231–3,
263
fusion to form hybridomas 35
in fluorescence
microscopy 262–75
in radioimmunoassay 244
isolation 94–100
radiolabelling 113, 117, 121,
123, 124–7
solubilization 105–12
storage 86–8, 91
surface stripping 92

see also B lymphocytes, T
lymphocytes, Histo-
compatibility antigens and
Immunoglobulin, cell surface

M

Magnetic beads 232
Mancini (single
immunodiffusion) 135
Membranes 105–12
Micelle, detergent 105, 106
Molecular weight
determination 5, 6, 9, 160,
163, 164, 168
Monoclonal antibodies 35 *et seq.*
class and subclass
determination 43
isolation 52–4, 67, 68, 167,
218, 220
fragmentation 63–5, 72
human 45–7
production 35–47
screening for secretion of 241,
243–5, 261, 271, 272
Mu (μ) chain 2, 56, 66, 68
Myeloma 65, 72, 83, 85

N

NANA (N-acetylneuraminic acid;
sialic acid) 125, 127, 225,
226, 227
Neuraminidase 127
Nitrocellulose sheets 187, 191–5
Nonidet P40 107, 108, 109, 110,
111, 137, 225, 235
Non-ionic detergents 105–11
Nylon fibre 100–1
Nylon membranes 187, 191–2

O

Ouchterlony (double
immunodiffusion) 133–5,
136, 199

P

PAP (peroxidase-
antiperoxidase) 278–82
Papain 57, 59, 63–5, 66, 70, 73,
81, 84, 85, 182